Publication #12

ANCIENT TALES OF KAMCHATKA

Edited by
Alexander B. Dolitsky

Translated by
Henry N. Michael

Published by
Alaska-Siberia Research Center
P.O. Box 34871
Juneau, Alaska 99803
www.aksrc.org

First Edition

Cover illustration: fragment of ivory carving by Maya Gemauge; Chukchi legend "Two Wise Reindeer," published in *Novaya zhizn drevnikh legend Chukotki* (New Life of Ancient Legends of Chukotka), T. Mitlyanskaya and I. Karakhan (1987). Magadan.

Back illustration: fragment of ivory carving by Maya gemauge; Chukchi legend "Two Wise Reindeer," published in *Novaya zhizn drevnikh legend Chukotki* (New Life of Ancient Legends of Chukotka), T. Mitlyanskaya and I. Karakhan (1987). Magadan.

Printed and bound by the McNaughton & Gunn, Inc., Saline, Michigan, USA.

Paperback edition (April 2002) ISBN # 0-9653891-4-6
Key words: Koryaks, Kereks, Itelmens, Kamchatka, Legends, Tales

The paper in this book meets the guidelines for permanence and durability of the Committee on Production Guidelines for Book Longevity of the Council on Library Resources.

CONTENTS

III

PREFACE

This volume is a translation from Russian into English of ninety-five tales of the Kereks, Koryaks and Itelmens. Dr. Henry N. Michael translated the stories into English from *Fairy Tales and Myths of the People of Chukotka and Kamchatka* (*Skazki i Mify Narodov Chukotki i Kamchatki*). The Russian edition was compiled by G. Menovshchikov and edited by E. Meletinsky (1974). Altogether Menovshchikov and Meletinsky's Russian edition consists of 206 Asiatic Eskimo, Chukchi, Kerek, Koryak, and Itelmen (Kamchadal)[1] stories. Dolitsky and Michael's (1997) English edition began with the Chukchi stories and was followed by Dolitsky and Michael's (2000) Siberian Yupik stories. This volume of Kerek, Koryak and Itelmen tales is a pioneering translation of the Paleoasiatics'[2] (natives of the Chukchi and Kamchatka Peninsulas) folklore from Russian into English. It consists of the transliteration table, ethnographic information on the Kereks, Koryaks and Itelmens, introduction, ninety-five stories, glossary, and bibliography.

This book endeavors to relate not only the major genre and subject matter of Kerek, Koryak and Itelmen narrative folklore, but also the specific aspects of the folklore of each people of the Chukotka-Kamchatka regions. The factual material presented in this collection will be interesting to those fond of oral folk creations, as well as to specialists interested in comparative-typological research in anthropology.

The compiler of this volume was faced with the task of acquainting the reader only with examples of oral narrative traditions of the aboriginal peoples of Chukotka and Kamchatka. Therefore, the genre of songs to be danced to, individual entertaining songs and improvised songs for plays were not included. This also applies to the specific genre of shamanistic exorcisms present mainly among the Chukchi and Asiatic Eskimos and also to riddles existing only among the Koryaks.

For their useful comments and constructive suggestions, I would like to express my thanks to Robert Price, former Vice-President of the Bristol Bay Native Corporation; Kristen Tromble, Research Analyst, Alaska Department of Health and Social Services; Wallace Olson, Professor Emeritus of Anthropology, University of Alaska Southeast; Dr. Michael Bachem, Professor of German, Miami University, Oxford, Ohio, and especially to Dr. Henry N. Michael, Senior Fellow of the University Museum of the University of Pennsylvania, the translator and associate editor of this volume.

Alexander B. Dolitsky
Director
Alaska-Siberia Research Center
Juneau, Alaska

---

[1]The current self-designation Kamchadal is derived from an early Russian term for a native of Kamchatka, an ethnographic group of Russians of mixed Russian and Itelmen origin. Few relatively pure Itelmen survive today. Although the Kamchadals speak Russian and consider themselves part Russian, they maintain many Itelmen cultural elements. They live on the Kamchatka Peninsula (see Figures 1, 2). [Editor].

[2]Paleoasiatic is the term coined by S. Schrenck (Shrenk), a Russian ethnographer in the mid-19th century. Under this term he grouped, on the basis of languages, several Siberian peoples, among whom were the Yukaghirs, Koryaks, Chukchi, Asiatic Eskimos, Kereks, Itelmens, Kets, Nivkhi and Ainus (see Figures 1, 2). Today, the term Paleoasiatic is used with great caution. It is mostly avoided by North American scholars. [Editor].

TRANSLITERATION TABLE

The system of transliteration adopted in this work is that of the United States Board of Geographic Names with slight modifications for technical reasons. Instead of *e*, we use *ye* at the beginning of names, after vowels and after the soft sign (ь), or *yo* (*ё*) where e is accented as *ё*. The soft sign (ь) and hard sign (ъ) have no sound value but they soften or harden the sound of the letter in front of them. A hard sign (ъ) is transliterated when in the middle of a word and disregarded when final.

Russian Letters | Transliteration

Russian Letters		Transliteration	
А	а	a	(as in star, car, **A**rkansas)
Б	б	b	(as in **b**oots, **B**ill, **B**ritain)
В	в	v	(as in **v**oice, **V**irginia)
Г	г	g	(as in **g**o, **g**ood, Michi**g**an)
Д	д	d	(as in **d**o, roa**d**, **D**akota)
Е	е	ye	(as in met, **ye**s)
Ё	ё	yo	(as in **yo**nder, **Y**ork)
Ж	ж	zh	(as in pleasure)
З	з	z	(as in **z**oo, is, Kansas)
И	и	i	(as in sh**i**p, m**ee**t, **I**llinois)
Й	й	y	(as in ma**y**, bo**y**, Carolina)
К	к	k	(as in **c**at, **k**ind, **K**entu**ck**y)
Л	л	l	(as in be**l**t, **l**ion, F**l**orida)
М	м	m	(as in a**m**use, **m**other, **M**exico)
Н	н	n	(as in **n**ow, **n**oose, **N**ebraska)
О	о	o	(as in p**o**rt, p**o**t, **O**klahoma)
П	п	p	(as in **p**ure, **p**oor, **P**ortland)
Р	р	r	(as in **r**iver, t**r**ee, A**r**izona)
С	с	s	(as in **s**wim, **SOS**, **S**outh)
Т	т	t	(as in **t**ool, **t**iger, **T**exas)
У	у	u	(as in l**u**nar, b**oo**k, L**u**bbock)
Ф	ф	f	(as in **f**ood, **f**unny, Cali**f**ornia)
Х	х	kh	(as in **h**oop or **h**appy)
Ц	ц	ts	(as in i**ts**, quar**tz**, wal**tz**)
Ч	ч	ch	(as in **ch**eap, **ch**ain, **ch**eese)
Ш	ш	sh	(as in fi**sh**, **sh**eep, **sh**rimp)
Щ	щ	shch	(as in bor**shch**)
Ъ	ъ	"	(hard sign; no equivalence)
Ы	ы	y	(as in rip)
Ь	ь	'	(soft sign; no equivalence)
Э	э	e	(as in about, best, paper)
Ю	ю	yu	(as in assume, **y**ou, **Y**ukon)
Я	я	ya	(as in **y**ard, **y**ak, Californi**a**)

INTRODUCTION

Ethnogenesis[3] and historiography of Paleoasiatic folklore

The folklore of the aboriginal peoples of the Chukchi and Kamchatka Peninsulas (see Figures 1, 2) preserves much valuable information for the study of the remote past of the Asiatic Eskimos, Chukchi, Kereks, Koryaks, and Itelmens (Paleoasiatics). Indeed, these peoples' oral narratives are both a literary and an ethnohistoric source. The oral narratives of peoples with no written language do not yield precise data on historical events during various epochs and periods; these oral traditions reflect ancient notions, customs, beliefs, and particulars of their economy that are directly tied to the productive and spiritual life of the people during various stages of their history.

A number of legends and tales were derived from the ancient myths of a hunter-gatherer, egalitarian society. Many of these legends and tales evolved during the break-up of the egalitarian society and later were continued in other social organizations such as reindeer herding and sea-mammal hunting (Vdovin 1948). Under these conditions, many elements of spiritual culture (Vdovin 1961), Eskimo-Chukchi bilingualism (Menovshchikov 1970), and ethnic assimilation between the Coastal Chukchi, Eskimos, Kereks, Koryaks and Itelmens were inevitable. There formed a distinctive chain of major tale cycles such as the legends about the raven, the orphan, the woman (creator of people and animals), conjugal unions of people and animals, and myths about other worlds. This chain of relationship of oral narratives among Paleoasiatics may be expressed as follows:

Asiatic Eskimos ↔ Chukchi ↔ Kereks ↔ Koryaks ↔ Itelmens

This outline does not indicate that the chain is restrictive. The folklore of each people in contact with one another at various times interacted with the folklore of other neighboring peoples of related or unrelated languages. Up to the 1930s, Asiatic Eskimos, aside from the Chukchi, had regular contacts with Alaskan Eskimos, and the latter with Canadian Eskimos and northern Indians. The Chukchi, aside from the Eskimos and Koryaks, mingled with the Kereks, Yukaghirs, Yakuts, and Evens. The Koryaks, aside from the Chukchi and Itelmens, were in contact with the Kereks and Evens.

In translating the texts from Kerek, Koryak and Itelmen languages into Russian, the translators sought to preserve the specific traits of the language without violating its grammatical and stylistic norms. Such factors as the time of the recording, the skill, age, and literacy of the narrator, and the genre of the work strongly influenced the formal expression and content of the text. Examples of the oral narratives of the Kereks, Koryaks and Itelmens recorded from illiterate narrators at the beginning of the 20th century are told among these peoples in a different style today.

In the early 20th century, the collection of oral traditions of the peoples of Chukotka and Kamchatka had already caught the attention of such important investigators of their cultures and languages as Bogoras and Jochelson. They collected and published a considerable number of texts of the folklore of the Chukchi, Asiatic Eskimos, Koryaks, and Itelmens.

During the Soviet period [1917-1991], a large collection of texts in the native languages of these peoples was recorded by Skorik, Belikov, Tynetegyn, Inenlikey, and Yatgyrgyn (Chukchi folklore); Rubtsova and Menovshchikov (Asiatic Eskimo folklore); Stebnitsky, Barannikov, Zhukov, Nutevi, Vdovin, Bogdanova,

---

[3]Ethnogenesis is a widely used term by Russian social scientists that simply means a historical continuity or transformation of one cultural tradition into another. The search for ethnogenetic relationships was a central problem of Soviet social scientists and ethnographers, and it deals directly with the determination of common cultural features and their relationship and similarity through time and space.

Figure 1. The Russian Far Eastern Administrative Regions

Zhukova (Koryak folklore); Orlova, Volodin, Starkova (Itelmen folklore); and Leontev (Kerek folklore). A part of the collected materials was published in the native languages with a word for word translation, the bulk of it in Russian translation only. A considerable number of the texts are in the personal archives of the collectors.

For a more or less complete characterization of the genre and subject matter of the folklore of the Paleoasiatics of Chukotka and Kamchatka, there was essentially no new textual material, particularly for Koryak and Itelmen folklore. Publications, done at various times in special issues for local needs or for specialists-linguists, were not available to a broader circle of folklorists and general public. This gap was filled by recordings done by Soviet linguists and ethnographers, and also by the translation into Russian of a number of Itelmen texts of Jochelson, which were fully published in 1961 by D. Worth (Kamchadal Texts).

The inclusion in this collection of a part of the Itelmen texts recorded by Jochelson was necessary because of the paucity of new material that would characterize the Itelmen raven cycle. Besides extensive texts of Itelmen folklore, Jochelson collected and, in 1905, published in English 130 Koryak tales in which the mythological base of the Koryak raven cycle is reflected.

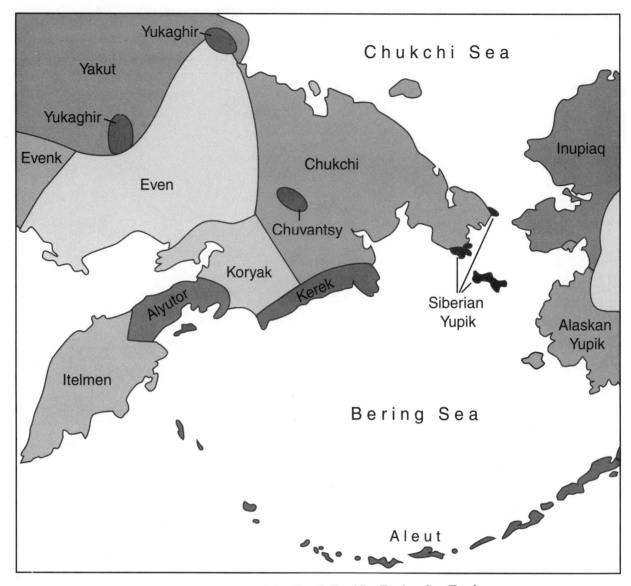

Figure 2. Cultures of the North Pacific–Bering Sea Region

Typology and classification of Paleoasiatic folklore

The problems of the classification of Paleoasiatic folklore have been only partially resolved. Bogoras and Jochelson were among first collectors, translators and interpreters of the genres, subject matter, and relationship of this folklore with the folklore of other peoples of the Russian Far East and North America, (see Figures 1, 2). In Soviet times [1917-1991], the research of Nikiforov and Propp dealt with the separate questions regarding structure, origin, and the lifeways in some Chukchi tales. On the basis of the Koryak folklore, a provocative philosophical investigation started in the beginning of the 1930s by the well-known Soviet ethnographer and linguist Stebnitsky. Stebnitsky distinguished three basic genres of the oral artistic traditions of the Koryaks: (1) mythological folklore, (2) historical folklore, and (3) economic folklore. He also pointed out the folkloristic base of the young artistic literature founded by the first Koryak writers.

According to Stebnitsky (1941: 106-107), mythological folklore is very rich and varied but, with all its variety, it represents a single cycle of myths about the Raven-Creator, common to all the Paleoasiatic peoples of the Chukotka and Kamchatka group, that is, the Chukchi, Koryaks, Itelmens, Kereks and

Asiatic Eskimos. Economic folklore is considerably poorer. It contains primarily stories about the master and the worker—the rich reindeer herder and the reindeer worker hired to handle the reindeer. The historical folklore contains descriptions of inter-tribal wars. In the legends of the Chavchuvens (Koryak reindeer herders), the wars of the Koryaks with the Chukchi are primarily described. In the descriptions of the Apukintsy and Alyutors (the northeastern groups of settled Koryaks), wars with the Chukchi are also described. In addition to wars with the Chukchi, Apukintsy and Alyutors also described inter-tribal wars between settled and nomadic reindeer Koryak herders.

Stebnitsky assigns myths, legends and tales about animals to mythological folklore (Stebnitsky 1941: 142), as well as Koryak and Itelmen tales about the raven Kutkh and Kutkynneku (Stebinitsky 1941: 147). Further, Stebnitsky asserts that the mythological folklore of the Koryaks contains a clear description of the types of spiritual beliefs and the material culture of the ancient Koryaks, as well as types of dwellings and fortifications.

Problems pertinent to the classification of the genres of Itelmen and Kerek folklore were resolved only in part in a comparative-typological approach but were not specifically put in place. Until recent times [1974], the folklore and language of the very small number of Kereks remained altogether uninvestigated. A specific investigation of the history and language of the Kereks was undertaken only after World War II (Skorik 1968: 310-333). In the middle of the 1950s, Skorik managed to record three texts (nos. 1, 4, 6 in this edition). In 1969, Iunevut recorded several texts of which one is presented in this collection (no. 5 of this edition), and in 1971, Leontev recorded and translated eight texts (nos. 2, 3, 7, 8, 9, 10, 11, 12 of this edition). Since the beginning of the 20th century, the language and spiritual culture of the Kereks was subjected to an intensive assimilation by the Chukchi. This process of assimilation has been particularly rapid in the past 40-50 years [from the 1920s to the 1970s] and as a result the Kereks, with the exception of several families, lost their native tongue and began to speak Chukchi.

The basic genres of the oral narratives of the Paleoasiatics of Chukotka and Kamchatka can be classified as: (1) mythical or cosmogonic stories; and (2) magical-heroic tales with the following subdivisions: (a) magical-heroic tales about the fantastic adventures of the heroes in different worlds and their struggles with evil forces; (b) tales about the *kele* and *kala* [Chukchi and Koryak], *nynvity* [Koryak] and *tungaki* [Eskimo]—all of these are evil spirits and werewolves; (c) tales about friendly and conjugal ties of people and animals; (d) tales about the rebellious daughter; (e) tales about an orphan; (f) tales about shamans; (g) heroic legends; (h) historical stories; (i) tales about animals; (j) economic tales (stories); (k) plots and exorcisms; (l) songs; and (m) riddles (found only among the Koryaks).

Mythological narratives, as the earliest form of oral traditions that directly reflect ancient mythological beliefs of the Paleoasiatics about the origin of the world, of people, animals and heavenly bodies, were universally disseminated in the folklore of the Chukotka-Kamchatka region. Bogoras first noted the cosmogonic myths for the Chukchi who called them *tottomvatken pynylte*, that is, "...the beginning of the creation of things" (Bogoras 1900: IV).

The fantastic forms, the mythical heroes in the folklore of the Paleoasiatics, are expressions of the actual economic and spiritual life of the originators of the early myths. Among the Paleoasiatics, as well as among other peoples in the early phases of historical development, the knowledge of natural phenomena was implemented through instinctive artistic reworking of their ideas about the realities surrounding them.

Since prehistoric times, the existing contacts between the native peoples of the Chukotka-Kamchatka region and the similar adaptation to the northern environment has led to a mutual adoption of the core elements of culture, including oral traditions. Among the Paleoasiatics, the principal heroes of mythical stories have much in common; the cultural heroes of mythical narratives appear as birds, animals, people,

IX

and mythical rulers of the upper world, sea, wind, and sun. The most important role in the universe is allotted to the all-powerful raven, whom the peoples' fantasy endowed with magical properties, which allowed him to create all of dry land.

The raven motif

Bogoras (1900: VII) noted that myths about the Raven-Creator of the world were widespread not only in Chukchi folklore, but also among the North American Indians. Myths about the incredible Raven-Creator were particularly widespread among the Chukchi, Koryaks and Itelmens. The same kind of myth existed among Asiatic, American and Greenlandic Eskimos. It is possible that mythical stories and tales about the raven were widespread and extended to all peoples of northeastern Asia and North America.

In a comparison of the ancient subject of various tale genres, it is quite evident that certain tales about the mythical raven Kutkh in Itelmen folklore reached, through Koryak and Chukchi folklore, to the Asiatic Eskimos. This was at a time when tales about the raven among the Greenlandic Eskimos could have originated independently of other peoples during the period of the proto-Eskimo origin.

The similar conditions of the material, subsistence and spiritual life of these multilingual tribes of the region appear to be the vital factor in influencing the development of similar genres. Evidently, these genres developed at the same time and were exposed to interaction and adaptation by Paleoasiatics. The remote antiquity of the Eskimo-Aleut culture on the crossroads of the Old and New Worlds is supported by not only the affinity of languages and folklore but also by the more abundant data resulting from archaeological and ethnographic researches. The myths and tales of the Eskimos about the raven are just as ancient as those of the Chukchi, Koryaks, Itelmens, and northern Indians. But a particular formation of cycles of these myths found its distinctive and inimitable development in the Itelmen-Koryak region. From there it spread, in part, to the Chukchi and Eskimo folklore. In some cases, a notable cycle with the raven personage of Kutkh or Kutkynneku coexisted with more archaic stories about the Raven-Creator.

A comparative analysis of cosmogonic stories and tales about the raven indicates that the center in which the raven cycle is most widespread is not Chukotka, but Kamchatka. Particularly, in Koryak and Itelmen folklore there originated and developed quite unique stories and tales about the raven Kutkh or Kutkynneku embodying the traits of a cultural hero. The hero was the creator of the universe and the personage in magical-mythical and animal tales whose heroic posture is lowered to a comical one in which the wise creator turns into a fool, cheat, and glutton. This fusion of myth and tale is characteristic of the oral traditions of the majority of native peoples of Northern Asia and northwestern America.

The raven Kutkh of Itelmen tales appears to be the ancestor of the Koryak Kutkynneku (Kuykynnyaku), Chukchi Kurkyl, Kerek Kukki, and Eskimo Koshkli. A linguistic analysis points out that all of these appellations come from the Itelmen word *kutkh*, the lexical semantics of which are unknown. The greatest frequency of myths and tales with the name of Kutkh, particularly in Itelmen folklore, suggest that the earliest center of diffusion for the same type in subject matter and topical treatment of the raven cycle about Kutkh could be the Itelmen region. The use of the name Kutkh, prominent in Itelmen folklore, is less frequent among the Koryaks and Kereks and becomes altogether insignificant among the Chukchi and Asiatic Eskimos. However, this does not exclude the strong influence of the Itelmen raven cycle with its hero Kutkh. The Koryaks, Chukchi and Asiatic Eskimos developed in parallel this type of folklore, but with a nameless raven hero. This explains the variety of some of the plots as well as the presence in the beliefs of these peoples of the cult of a raven-ancestor. The movement of this folkloristic cycle from southern Kamchatka to the north up to the Bering Strait was marked by a gradual loss of a number of plots or by their local mutations. Nevertheless, at the same time, the narratives and tales about the nameless raven spread all over the Asian and American North.

The mythical hero of Itelmen tales, together with the "cultural" acts of the creator of the universe, freely perpetrates a number of mischievous pranks and tricks. He is a creator, trickster, and simpleton—all at the same time. Therefore, his acts, useful for humans and animals, are consistently violated by improper acts in regard to his surroundings. It is quite evident that in the Itelmen tales about Kutkh, as well as the Koryak ones about Kutkynneku, there is a distinct reflection of the processes of disintegration of the egalitarian society in connection with the development of proprietal inequality.

The majority of present-day [1974] Itelmen tales about Kutkh and his family are no longer mythical stories in a straightforward sense, but magical-mythical and animal tales in which the role of the hero-creator can be barely traced. As a rule, the mythical heroes-creators do not have ancestors. They are first to appear in a fantastic world [universe] and they create the earth, stars, oceans, rivers, mountains, animals, and man. Such is the Chukotka-Kamchatka Raven-Creator who does not have parents.

The Raven-Creator motif

The Raven-Creator, having created life around him, himself becomes a common participant. But nothing is told in the Chukotka-Kamchatka myths about his origin although other personages of the raven cycle have a genealogy. In the first case, they are descendants of animals; in the second, they result from a conjugal union of humans and animals; in the third, from a phenomenon and natural objects; and in the fourth, at the wish of the raven. Thus, Miti, the wife of the raven in one of the Koryak versions, turns out to be the daughter of a magpie (no. 23 of this edition; Menovshchikov 1974, no. 134). In other versions, noted by Jochelson, she is the daughter of white whales [belugas], the daughter or wife of the crab, the master of the sea, the daughter of the master of the night, the daughter of thunder, and so on (Jochelson 1904: 17-22; Bogoras 1900: VII-VIII).

In the tale "The Egg Maidens" (no. 64 of this edition; Menovshchikov 1974, no. 175), Kutkh creates his daughters from birds' eggs, and in tale no. 70 of this edition (Menovshchikov 1974, no. 181), "Sinanevt and the Little Bear," he "commands" Miti to give birth to a bear cub, and so on. The older children of the raven and Miti, Ememkut and Sinanevt, take part in the entire "raven" cycle. In the Itelmen cycle of the other children of the raven and Miti, the sons may be called the bear cubs Sisilkhana, Kotkhonamtalkhana, and the daughters Sirim, Amzarakchan, Nyaa or Naa, Mrorot, Anaraklnavt or Eltalkhan. In the various dialects of the Koryak language we encounter the same names with some phono-morphological differences, as well as new names of the personages [participants] in that cycle. The younger children of Kutkh most often enter into marriages with animals that reincarnate into people, reflecting the totemic concepts of the Itelmens before class differentiation.

The conjugal union of Kutkh and Miti is permanent. The oldest son of Kutkh, Ememkut, does not observe the unity of the family. In various situations he enters into marriage with different women. Thus, in different tales his wives are Iyanamltsyakh, Maroklnavt, Sinanevt, Valen-Sinanevt, and the maiden of the woods Eltalnen. Notwithstanding that Ememkut inherits the raven characteristics of his father; in the tales he appears as a man and, in the majority of cases, his wives are ordinary women. The marriage bonds of Kutkh's daughters are also not permanent. Both men and animals become their husbands. Thus in various situations Sinanevt marries Chelkutkh, Ememkut (not Kutkh's son but his son-in-law), a pink salmon (gorbuscha), a hunter, and so on. The same happens to her sisters.

Characteristically, the grandchildren of Kutkh, the children of Ememkut, Sinanevt and their brothers and sisters, do not get their own names [are not named] and are not endowed with wonder-working properties. The basic characteristics of the pedigreed hero of the raven cycle of Koryak folklore, Kutkynneku (Kuykynneyaku), concur with those of the tales of the Itelmen folklore cycle although their adaptation is impoverished. Kutkynneku's family consists of his wife Miti (Mity), sons Ememkut (Amamkut),

XI

Kotganu, Kigigysynyaku, and Sisisyn (Chichisen), and daughters Tinnenevvut (Tynianavit), Rera (Rira), Uala, and Khaysyaneru.

In the Koryak cycle we find the names of Ememkut's daughters—Inianavyt and Klyukenevyt. The invariable actors of the Koryak cycle remain as Kutkynneku, Miti and their older children Ememkut and Tynianavyt (in Itelmen: Sinanevt). Ememkut is the basic positive character of the magico-mythical tales of Itelmen-Koryak folklore. He is the direct heir of the early cultural deeds of his father from whom he adopted the best traits: the ability to transform himself into a raven, and the ability to perform magical deeds to help neighbors. In transforming himself into a raven, he extends the cosmogonic mission of close interaction between man and animal. Tales in which Ememkut performs improper acts appear to be rare exceptions and apparently represent later developments. Stories about Kutkynneku and Ememkut, in part, penetrate into Chukchi folklore and from it to the folklore of Asiatic Eskimos. Thus, the Itelmen and Koryak cycles clearly reflect the dual concepts of the Paleoasiatics of Kamchatka about the mythical ancestors of man.

The other hero-creators

The other hero-creators in the mythical tales of the peoples of Chukotka and Kamchatka are a "creating" woman, usually a young girl, and various rulers of the sea and the upper world. The basic beliefs of the Paleoasiatics of a given region include images of mythical ancestors who, among various peoples and also among various territorial groups of one people, could be quite different heroes-creators—animals, birds, and human-like rulers of the sea and upper world. The raven is not the only and very early or very late creator of the universe of the Paleoasiatics. Parallel with him there existed other "creators" among whom the most widespread is the "creating" woman.

Among the Asiatic Eskimos and the Chukchi such a creator comes from the village of Mamrokhpak. After refusing to marry at the command of her father, she goes away into the tundra, acquires miraculous powers and creates shore-dwelling and nomadizing peoples, as well as reindeer and sea mammals. Myths about a strong woman refusing to marry on command and wishing to select a husband are widespread over the northern regions of Asia and America. Consequently, a whole cycle of magical tales developed that reflect not only the vestigial expressions of "world-making" but also motifs for the social organization of pre-class society. This cycle includes the Chukchi legends of the "creating" woman Kytty, and the Eskimo, Chukchi and Koryak legends about a woman or young girl organizing her life at her own discretion, about orphans fighting their cruel village-dwellers or uncles, and women-warriors. These legends reflect such important social features as familial and marital relations, the decay of the traditions of egalitarian societies of the division of the products of communal labor, the appearance of property differentiation, and the isolation of families.

The magical-mythical tales

The magical-mythical tales of the Paleoasiatics represent an artistic transformation of mythical legends. In these, the principal actors are not the heroes-creators but "creations" of earlier human and other participants in tale events and their magical helpers. The heroes of these tales fight with their antagonists—harmful "spirits," giants, shamans, oppressors—and invariably emerge as victors.

In the folklore of the Paleoasiatics of Chukotka and Kamchatka, it is very difficult to draw a distinction between mythical stories explaining the origin of the universe, earth, mankind or animals, and the magico-mythical tales in which the moral-ethical base is tightly interwoven with elements of cosmogony. Often the motifs about hero-creators are contaminated with the motifs of the adventures of the hero in the magical tale. The mythical elements in the magical tales of the Paleoasiatics find their expression in the steadfastly preserved motifs about the dependence of humans on the manifestations and objects of nature that surround them, that spiritualize and endow human life with their traits.

Animals, birds, insects, and fish are endowed with anthropomorphic traits, as are the wind, sun, moon, northern lights, and thunder. In the magical-mythical tales of the Paleoasiatics, the cosmogonic, animistic, and totemic beliefs are particularly clearly expressed. They are the constituent elements of the world view of a people in an egalitarian society. The artistic strength and world view of the tale had an enormous influence on the upbringing of members of each society. On the whole they gave useful and stable moral and ethical norms of behavior to a people, actively influencing the realities surrounding them. The people believed in the tale and thus it was a school of life, not merely an artistic reflection.

Thus, the tales and stories of the aborigines of Chukotka and Kamchatka characteristically represented not only the transformation of animals, birds, and insects into people but also the spiritualization [animation] of articles and natural phenomena. For instance, in a number of magico-mythical tales of the Eskimos, Chukchi and Koryaks describe the interaction of natural forces when the wind and sun compete to create better living conditions for mankind, and thunder together with wind and rain destroy a mountain to free fox cubs held by the mountain.

The mythical legends and magical-mythical tales about giant eagles are found mainly in the folklore of Asiatic and Alaskan Eskimos but also among the Chukchi. These genres are not present in the folklore of the Koryaks and Itelmens. There are mythical legends about giant eagles who could carry two whales at the same time and could swallow them as if they were small fish. These legends originated and developed principally in the Chukchi Peninsula, Alaska, and Canada, where, until recent times, there existed the great Canadian eagle. In the peoples' fantasies these great birds were personified in the legends and tales and served as prototypes of the mythical giant eagles appearing in the folklore as hunters of northern wild deer or sea mammals. A characteristic content of the stories about eagles is the search for food. The realistic life of the aboriginal population along the Bering seacoast is directly reflected in the legends and tales about giant eagles. Securing food in the Arctic was challenging and time consuming.

The zooanthropomorphic rendering of animals is not only distinctive for the animal tale but, in equal measure, for the magical-mythical tale. This relates particularly to the Eskimo-Chukchi tales where the characters, aside from man, are polar bears and giant eagles, sea swallows, wolves, spiders and beetles, foxes and ravens, which often change into human beings, speak a human language and lead a human kind of existence. In the Itelmen-Koryak cycle of tales about Kutkh-Kutkynneku, the personification of animals and birds, particularly the raven, bear, and fox, is also widespread.

The principal heroes of the magical-mythical tale are people who have gotten into a complicated life situation. The helpers and advisors to the human hero appear as wise men endowed with the gift of foresight, and also as animals and miraculous objects. Such shamanistic helpers of man could be the fox, swallow, mouse, wolf, ermine, loon, brown bear, spider, white-tailed deer, raven, and sea mammals such as the walrus, bearded seal, ringed seal, and whale. The giant eagle and the polar bear hold a special role in the magical-mythical tales. They could be either a totemic protector of man or his direct enemy. Personages such as the swallow, loon, spider, fox and white-tailed deer, most often play the role of a totemic protector. At the same time they fulfill the most archaic functions of the hero-creator.

The invariable antagonists of man in the animal world are crabs, worms, and beetles. The beetle, in the form of a small, black-clothed old woman, becomes a harmful being and brings bad luck to people. In this sense the beetle is the opposite of the spider who brings miraculous help to the human hero when he is in trouble. As a rule, the fox and the spider, in helping and protecting man appear as a small woman (Dolitsky and Michael 2000, nos. 15, 39; Menovshchikov 1974, nos. 15, 39).

In the folklore of the peoples inhabiting the Chukchi and Kamchatka Peninsulas, the sword, charcoal, a stone, flint, [carpet]-beater, flying boat (kayak, skin-boat), arrow, knife, skis, a staff, oar, box, sack, torch, candle, drum, gloves, hat, deer skin garment, the entryway to a semisubterranean hut, fly agaric, berries, and a dead head (skull) appear as miraculous objects. Spiritualized objects and natural phenomena in the tales, particularly in Eskimo tales, are represented by the sun, moon, northern lights or splashes of summer lightning, and thunder (Dolitsky and Michael 2000, nos. 1, 2, 3; Menovshchikov 1974, nos. 1, 2, 3).

The rulers of the upper world, the sea, the universe (or weather), fire, and light appear as human-like creatures. These "rulers," particularly sky dwellers, appear as protectors of the hero, but also as his antagonists. In the genre of magical-mythical tales of the Paleoasiatics of the Chukchi and Kamchatka Peninsulas a specific place is held by the harmful "spirits" which are called by the Chukchi and Koryaks *kele* or *nynvit*, and by the Eskimos *tungak* or *tugnygak*—the latter being dialectic differences.

The fantastic reflection of the harsh struggle of the Paleoasiatics during their early social formation with the harsh natural surroundings of the north, their day-to-day work and existence, is the pivotal trend of the magical-mythical tale. Elements of family life, traditional ways of hunting the northern wild deer and sea mammals, gathering, and other subsistence activity of the Paleoasiatics is preserved in their collective traditions through the prism of the artistic reworking of reality. Different from mythical (cosmogonic) legends, the magical-mythical tales detach themselves from the initial mythological base and become artistic reflections of the struggle of man with the inhospitable and unknown forces of nature. The artistic fancies were taken by the people of that epoch as the truth of life, the guiding principles to the active influence upon the surrounding world. The belief in the tale is directly tied to the world outlook of notions about cosmogony, animism, and magic that are so clearly reflected in the folklore of the Paleoasiatics.

In his struggle with hostile forces, man invariably displays initiative, resourcefulness, and mental and physical superiority over the hindrance of his enemies. A considerable number of these tales has been included in this collection; the hero enters into single combat with *kele, tungaks* and *nynvits* who interfere with his life and often the life of the entire community.

The magical-mythical tales about the struggle of man with malevolent "spirits" were particularly widespread among the Eskimos and Chukchi. There are very few such tales among the Koryaks and none among the Itelmens. A characteristic peculiarity of the tales in which *kele, nynvit,* and *tungak* are present is that the name of the human hero is rarely mentioned. Instead, the hero is reffered to as reindeer herder, person, man, little old man, young girl, orphan, younger son, shaman, or various other identities. Only in separate tales, in which the evil spirits appear, does the principal hero have a proper name. For example, Yynuve in the tale "The Herder Yynuve" (Dolitsky and Michael 1997, no. 13; Menovshchikov 1974, no. 68), Kykvat in "Shaman Kykvat" (Dolitsky and Michael 1997, no. 22; Menovshchikov 1974, no. 77), and Akhakhanavrak in the tale with the same title (Menovshchikov 1974, no. 29; Dolitsky and Michael 2000, no. 29).

In these archaic tales man enters into a struggle with hostile forces. He defeats them either with the help of animal protectors, various "masters," sorcerers and magical articles or because of magical invocations on his own strength and resourcefulness. Despite the resourcefulness of the *kele* and *tungak*, their ability to transform into people, or to save themselves from the pursuing hero by submerging themselves into the earth crust, they cannot escape human punishment. The pursuit of the *kele* is depicted as a matter of course. The hero catches up with the *kele*, and thrusts a harpoon into him as into a walrus. The wounded *kele* disappears into the earth, but with a float tied to the harpoon with a long thong the hero finds the enemy and finishes him. In the Chukchi tale "The Shaman Kykvat" (Dolitsky and Michael 1997, no. 22), the shaman Kykvat cunningly subdues a man-eating *kele*. Kykvat's fellow-villagers firmly tie up the *kele* and hold his jaws open with a stick. Throughout the summer the people of Neten village pour slop into the *kele*'s mouth. Afterwards Kykvat demands a promise from the defeated and humbled monster. The latter gives his word not to bother people and to go away forever. The plot of this archaic tale has an obvious satirical trend. The struggle of man with the *kele* and other monsters takes place against an ironic background and with a mocking attitude of the hero toward his ancient enemies.

The magical-heroic tales

The magical-heroic tales of the Paleoasiatics belong to a special sub-section of magical-mythical tales. Their differentiating trait is the accomplishment by the hero of fantastic activities for the sake of protecting the members of his tribe, the members of his family or himself from enemies who appear as various fantastic creatures. The hero of these tales undertakes journeys to places beyond the sea and to fantastic worlds, and combats singly or approaches in a friendly way giants, monsters, and elements of nature. He endeavors to aid, with proper forces or magical means, people who have fallen on bad times or to protect himself from enemies. In his combat with enemy forces the hero uses miraculous helpers and wonder-working objects. The hyperbolism and fantasy of the magical tale is interwoven with the realistic conditions in which the hero lives. The realistic developments are related in this type of tale through the medium of fantastic transformations and actions of the hero.

Tales about friendly and conjugal ties of people and animals

Among the magico-mythical tales of the Paleoasiatics of considerable significance are the tales about man's friendly, congeneric, and conjugal unions with animals. To the same cycle belong the tales about hostile clashes of man and animals, be they beasts, birds, or insects. The human being, the hero of the tales, is never named. Of the 35 tales (Dolitsky and Michael 1997, 2000, and this edition) with human and animal beings (excluding the cycle about Kutkh-Kutkynneku), there are only two in which the hero has a proper name derived from the existing semantically disclosing basic content of the tale. For instance, Kayahsigvik or Kayachnyy—"a man in a kayak," and Kaynyvalyu—"bear's ears." In tales of this type, the motifs about ancient totemic beliefs of the primordial hunter and his unceasing contact with the living [real] world are clearly expressed. In these tales, the hunting skills of the primordial hunter in securing food are tied to his ancient mythological and animistic beliefs.

In a number of tales of this genre, a person, male or female, enters into an amorous or conjugal union with an animal. As a result of such unions, children are born who have a human mind and strength. Sometimes the children are born as animals (Menovshchikov 1974, no. 19; Dolitsky and Michael 2000, no. 19), sometimes as humans with animal ears (no. 28 of this edition; Menovshchikov 1974, no. 139). A whale-born of a woman drives to his human kinsfolk other whales for them to kill (Dolitsky and Michael 2000, nos. 56 and 58), and a man with bear's ears-born of a bear kills his mother and then defeats the mysterious giants carrying a grove of birch trees, a volcano with cedar trees, and a wet tundra.

The helpers and protectors of man—wolves, loons, swallows, spiders, foxes, white-tailed deer, and sea mammals—are furnished with magical powers, which the hero utilizes to reach his goals. Giant eagles appear as antagonists of man. After a hunting flight, usually for whales or northern wild deer, they take off their clothing of feathers and transform into giant people. Brown bears and polar bears appear in various situations as antagonists or helpers of people with whom they often enter into amorous or conjugal relationships.

Tales about shamans

In the Koryak tale "Ammalyo" (Menovshchikov 1974, no. 141; no. 30 of this edition), the heroine obtains shamanistic powers, casts a spell on the whining *nynvits* who had captured her, and runs away. Such unmotivated [unreasoned] possession of magical powers by the heroine or hero is usual in the tales of the Paleoasiatics. Apparently this characteristic reflects their pre-shamanistic mythological beliefs. In a number of Koryak tales women hold the role of shaman. In the tale "The Five Sisters" (no. 31 of this edition; Menovshchikov 1974, no. 142), the shamaness turns into a people-eating *kele*. In the tale "The Shamaness Kytna," (no. 32 of this edition; Menovshchikov 1974, no. 143) the heroine, turned into a wolf, sends back her daughter abducted by a pack of wolves. The origin of similar themes is also tied to early mythological beliefs.

Narratives about shamans are not direct reflections of the professional shamanism of the Paleoasiatics of the Chukchi and Kamchatka Peninsulas. Shamanistic legends and exorcisms [incantations] used for ritualistic purposes originated and developed in the medium of an egalitarian world view based on an irrational and fantastic reflection of the consciousness of people about objects, and the world of reality. Shamanistic legends and rituals, having entered as separate component parts into the magical tale, were subjected to the artistic comprehension of the people and became one of the constituent parts of their oral traditions. Meletinsky (1963: 79) observed that: "In the people's tale is also reflected the growth of self-consciousness in the individual, the hero of the tale is made more active and the distinctive cult of the hero is brought to life. This process took place independent of shamanism and also in principle to counterbalance it; in the tales it is shown that not only the shamans but also ordinary hunters and herders could possess exceptional abilities. To be sure, these very abilities were thought of as a union of physical and magical powers."

Economic and domestic tales

During the times of starvation, the state of the helpless orphans, old people, widows, and indigent solitary hunters among the coastal dwellers became particularly insufferable. This predicament occurred when the sea mammals did not arrive or bad weather raged because of a protracted winter. During such periods, the disaster affected the entire population, and people deprived of food became "deprived mouths." During periods of hunger, some of the villagers would mercilessly put orphans out from their houses, and the "orphaned" families found themselves without food. The hunting of sea mammals in the ice-covered reaches of the Bering Sea and Arctic Ocean was a constant risk. Hunters were often carried to the open sea on ice floes that had detached themselves from the fast shore ice and the "orphaned" families found themselves without food. All of these social and economic conflicts in the condition of the orphan found expression in the magical-heroic tales of the Paleoasiatics.

With the arrival of uneven property holdings and the break-up of the earlier established democratic custom of sharing the results of the hunt evenly by all of members of the coastal community regardless of their part in the economy, it was, before all, members of families who had lost their provider-hunter who were either displaced or suffered most. These were the orphaned children, old people, widows, cripples, and unlucky solitary hunters. All were economically dependent on those who had previously secured a lion's share of the catch—*umilyki* (strong men, "the rulers of the land") or owners of large *baydaras*.

An analogous process of social differentiation is found also among the nomadizing population. As a result of the Chukchi-Koryak wars for the control of the reindeer herds, most of the animals become concentrated in the hands of individual enterprising reindeer herders. Those neighbors or kin who did not have reindeer or had only a few became economically dependent on the owners of large herds. In fact the owner of the herd of reindeer became the head of the camp and the people who were dependent on him became the herders (Bogoras 1931, no. 12; Belikov 1960: 289; Vdovin 1965).

Nevertheless, the decay of relations in the egalitarian communities took place very slowly and at the time of the Russian Socialist Revolution of 1917 clear-cut class division had not taken place. Traditional customs and living conditions of the neighborhood community continued until the 1930s (Vdovin 1950, 1965; Sergeyev 1955). In terms of the coexistence of ancient democratic norms in the community and of new public [social] attitudes, the ideological, moral and ethical orientation of the miraculous heroic tale became more apparent.

In the development of new kinds of oral traditions of the coastal dwellers and the nomadizing population of the Chukchi Peninsula, including the cycle of tales concerning the orphan, the principal influence was the difference in the economies of sea hunting and animal herding. New relations developed between the coastal dwellers and the reindeer herders. With the depletion of the northern wild deer, the coastal people became dependent on the reindeer herders because they could not do without deer hides. These were necessary for clothing and bedding. Besides, during periods of hunger, with no sea mammals in sight, the coastal dwellers had to approach the herders for reindeer meat. On the other hand, with the growth of the herds it was necessary to use all means available to pasture the herds in the far reaches of the tundra. With the steady specialization of the economy and the concentration of all human effort on the pasturing of the reindeer, the herders felt the need for the raw materials of the sea hunt—the bearded seal, ringed seal, and walrus hides for thongs, soles of footwear, sled runners, runners of whale bones (the upper jaw), rendered seal fat for lighting and warming dwellings, and various domestic objects made by the coastal people. The peaceful, natural exchange between the two groups was sometimes disrupted and replaced by armed conflict between the groups or separate [extended] families in the groups.

Domestic tales (or domestic narratives) tell of particularly memorable and typical events that occurred earlier in various situations and that were incorporated in the oral traditions of the people. A particularity of this genre of oral narratives is the reflection of the domestic and social aspects of life, inter-tribal relations, battles of the hero with trickster enemies, violators, and oppressors. Bragging, conceit, laziness, and stupidity are ridiculed in this tale. The hero of the domestic tale is not helped by magic-wielding helpers, but by brains, justice, resourcefulness, and superiority in strength and deftness.

Domestic tales originated during various historical times but predominantly during the period of the break-up of the egalitarian society's relationships and the appearance of uneven property holdings; they reflect the contrast of the strong and weak, the rich and poor. These tales often have a story telling [fable] aspect: the narrator, with a good-natured irony, exposes and ridicules the stupidity, sluggishness, and impracticality of his characters as they try to surmount the difficulties of life.

Tales about an orphan
The ancient tales about the orphan describe the adventures of the heroes in another world, and their combats with evil forces. For instance, in the Eskimo and Chukchi tales about the orphan we discover notions of cosmogonic images about nature, worldviews, and collaboration and blood relationship of man and animal. The separate subject matter of the tales about the orphan represents the direct use of the subject matter of animal tales (Menovshchikov 1974, nos. 36, 37; Dolitsky and Michael 2000, nos. 36, 37).

The early tales about the orphan still preserve the benevolent attitude of relatives and neighbors toward orphans. This testifies to the continued observance, at the time of the initial social differentiation of old customs, of the [former] equity of all members of the community. For instance, the Eskimo tale begins with these words: "There lived a young girl and boy—brother and sister. The sister was named Taykynaun, the brother—Taykygyrgyn. They lived in the village of Nutkan. Many people lived there. They helped the orphans, brought them meat so they would not be hungry" (Menovshchikov 1969: 124-129). However, orphans in a similar situation where the entire community does not help them as before endeavor to extricate themselves from the lower position so they can obtain their food independently. Their resourcefulness, diligence, and magical animal helpers—the ermine and owl—enable them to prevail over their neighbors.

There are few tales about the orphan in Koryak folklore and collectors have not noted any at all in Itelmen folklore. This points to Paleo-Eskimo folklore as the possible source of this type of oral tradition since similar subject matter has been noted in the early mythical narratives of various territorial groups of Eskimos in Alaska, Canada, and Greenland.

Heroic legends

In the folklore of the Paleoasiatics of Chukotka and Kamchatka the genre of heroic tales stands out. This alone developed, as did the tales about the orphan, during the period of decay of egalitarian social relations and the establishment of social differentiation. The heroes of these tales are strong and brave people, warriors and hunters, young men and women, fighting their offenders or captors whom they defeat without fail. The essential idea of the heroic tales is expressed in such topics as the struggle with the newly arrived strangers, the *tannity*, fights between different strong men (*bogatyrs*), the peaceful resolution of conflicts, and the appeal for peace among tribes. The moral and ethical essence of heroic tales is expressed in the personal exemplary behavior of the hero, in the establishment of justice, and in the punishment of offenders. In stories of this type there are detailed descriptions of the military and physical training of the warrior and hunter, and of the duels of heroes of the warring sides. Also described are scenes of fighting with bow and arrow or spears and slings, the pursuit and annihilation of the opponent, and the capture of prisoners and property stock. Unlike mythical stories in the magico-mythical and magico-heroic tales, the hero is an ordinary man endowed with physical strength and a keen wit. He is the protector of his family hearth. The struggle between the hero and his enemies takes place without the help of magical helpers. The magical beginning serves only to endow the hero with hyperbolic strength with the help of which (but without the presence of magical helpers) he defeats the superior forces of the enemy. The principal thrust of the subject matter of heroic tales has a solid historical base.

Belikov substantiated the necessity of isolating in Chukchi folklore a special genre of heroic stories that had originated and developed on the basis of the people's memory of oral narratives about inter-tribal wars between Chukchi and Koryaks over the capture and concentration of reindeer herds during the 17th and 18th centuries. He noted that "...the inter-tribal wars hastened the consolidation of the Chukchi people, and resulted in the necessity and ideo-poetic perception [realization] of that unity [consolidation]" (Belikov 1965: 154-169; see also Stebnitsky 1941). Additionally, the Koryaks who opposed the Chukchi also experienced such a consolidation. Consequently, at the same time, a similar development of heroic tales among the Koryaks occurred.

The glorification of the Herculean strength, deftness and courage of the hero, his victorious combat with the enemies of the tribe, community, or family, absolute devotion to his people, the emphasis of the social meaning of the hero's battles, the exact rendering of the details of the dwelling, clothing, and armament, the tireless physical pursuit of the hero of power and deftness, the colorful description of the duels of the hero with enemy *bogatyrs* or entire detachments of the enemy, the removal from the actions of the hero of miraculous helpers and the dominance, when telling about him, of truthful elements over fantastic ones—these are the principal elements in heroic tales.

While the hero of magical-heroic tales is nameless, the principal personages of heroic stories have their own names. The lexical semantics of these names often reflect a personal quality or physical trait of the hero. For instance, Kunlelyu—*Odnoukhiy* (One-eared), Lyavtylevalyn—*Kachayushchiy golovoy* (Shaking One's Head), or Umilgu from the Eskimo *umilyk* (Strong Man).

Heroic stories are found in the folklore of the majority of the native peoples of Chukotka and Kamchatka but they were particularly widespread among the Chukchi and Koryaks. The bases of the heroic stories of these two peoples were realistic historical events—the fighting of the Chukchi and Koryaks over the control of reindeer herds. Siding with the Chukchi reindeer herders were the Coastal Chukchi, and the

Asiatic Eskimos with the Koryaks and Yukaghirs. The subject of clashes between the *tannity* (foreigners) and local inhabitants apparently originated at the same time and independently with each warring side. But together with the stories of fighting to control the herds, the Chukchi and Koryaks also told stories of fighting between separate communities, extended families and individual *bogatyrs* (Belikov 1960: 286-289, 1965; Menovshchikov 1969: 16-17).

Heroic stories with a different subject matter spread among peoples who lived far away from each other. For instance, the closing episode of the Eskimo story "*Yakuni*" (Menovshchikov 1958: 156-158) is the same as the closing episode of the Kerek story "The Boy with the Bow and Arrow" (no. 1 of this edition; Menovshchikov 1974, no. 112). In both stories the small son of herders, lost when the enemy killed his parents, kills the *bogatyr* of the enemy. In the Eskimo tale, the vanquished *bogatyr* is a bearded white man Yakuni. According to Bogoras, the Chukchi had given this name to the leader of the Cossack detachment, Major Pavlutskiy, who fought to enslave them and was killed in a clash in 1747 (Bogoras 1900: 93). The episode of the boy falling from the sled coincides with that of the Eskimo story "*Naydenysh*," (The Foundling; Menovshchikov 1969: 218-221) and the Kerek "The Boy with the Bow and Arrow" (no. 1 of this edition; Menovshchikov 1974, no. 112). Stories about heroes who defend the honor of their community or family also reflect the motif of blood revenge. To this category belong, for instance, the Eskimo story "The Revenge" (Menovshchikov 1974, no. 41; Dolitsky and Michael 2000, no. 41), and the Koryak story "The Revenge of Rynnynalpylyn" (no. 39 of this edition; Menovshchikov 1974, no. 150).

It is quite likely that the heroic narratives and domestic [economic] stories about reindeer-herding people originated among the nomadizing Chukchi and were later adopted and creatively reworked by the Asiatic Eskimos who spoke the Chukchi language. While in the majority of Chukchi heroic narratives relating to the fighting with the foreigners, Koryaks are described as cruel oppressors and violators, in the Koryak narratives of the same type such oppressors and violators are the alien Chukchi. In this respect the Koryak stories A Narrative about "Those Who Lived Before" (no. 36 of this edition; Menovshchikov 1974, no. 147), and "The Settled and the Nomadic Reindeer Herders" (no. 38 of this edition; Menovshchikov 1974, no. 149) are revealing.

In the folklore, there is no indication that the Itelmens took part in the Koryak-Chukchi wars. In the cycle of stories about the Itelmen *bogatyr* Tylvale, there is only mention of the protection of tribal and familial traditions from the incursions and disturbance of the Koryaks. At that, the protection is not carried out collectively but by a single hero in whom the strength and unity of all people is symbolically embodied.

Texts nos. 48 to 53 of this edition (Menovshchikov 1974, nos 159 to 164), represent a cycle of heroic stories about the *bogatyr* [strong man] of Itelmen folklore, Tyvale. He is presented as a preserver of traditions and a protector of his people from treacherous foreigners. The pathos stories about Tylvale reach epochal elation. The artistic and stylistic means of narration, the hyperbole and the particular respectful treatment of the hero, differentiate the language of this genre from the language of the economic dialogue that is characteristic to the cycle of stories about Kutkh. The stories about Tylvale were recorded and told by various people at various times but the majority of them preserve the unity of the subject matter.

All stories about Tylvale distinctly correlate the depiction of the clashes with a specific geographic location. Each of the storytellers "settles" Tylvale in a locality near himself. In the stories about Tylvale, there are no magical transformations but the hyperbole often reaches fantastic dimensions. Tylvale is an ordinary man with extraordinary strength. The principal subject matter of the stories about Tylvale is the revenge of the hero on his sister who had betrayed the principles of his family and people, and she conspired with the foreign Koryaks to dispose of her brother Tylvale. In his role as an avenger of there is direct influence on the basic subject matter of the Koryak story "The Revenge of Rynnynnalpylyn" (no. 39 of this edition; Menovshchikov 1974, no. 150), in which the narrative about blood revenge is locked into a ready-made frame.

The heroic narratives, which in the folklore of the Paleoasiatics reflect a separate stage of their historical development, extend the tradition of the magical-heroic tale in a number of structural (morphological) signs and subject matter. Thus, for instance, in the Chukchi heroic narrative "Kunlelyu" (Menovshchikov 1974, no. 85; Dolitsky and Michael 1997, no. 30), which is an excellent one in an artistic and compositional sense, the realistic battle of two tribes—the Chukchi and Koryaks—for the control of reindeer herds is depicted in a fanciful way, interwoven with elements of the magical-heroic tale. This includes the adventures of the hero, killed in a hand-to-hand fight with the enemy, in the country of his deceased ancestors, and his miraculous revival. The beginnings of such narratives can be traced to the ancient mythical tales. The inserted element of the fantastic journeys of the principal hero is merely a distinctive historical event, although its roots are in the magical-mythical tale. However, the magical element in this narrative is episodic and its basic content reflects the realistic struggle and way-of-life of reindeer herders. In the narrative Kunlelyu, the Chukchi *bogatyrs* achieve full victory over the Koryak enemies who had earlier taken their herds away. The realistic rendition of the journey to a foreign land, the overcoming of natural obstacles, the description of duels, the return of the herd, the punishment of the offenders, the capture of women, and other military and domestic details add up to a striking ethnographic portrayal of the way-of-life of the Chukchi and Koryaks in the remote past.

The heroine of this epic narrative, Kytgy, the sister of Kunlelyu, is pictured as a freedom-loving and independent woman who struggled for peace between the tribes, and with it the glorification of the Herculean strength of her brothers—Kunlelyu and Reyipgev, who lead the fight against violence and injustice. At the same time Kytgy displays anxiety for preserving the tribe. She goes to various villages, marries and produces children. Then she leaves them to be brought up by their fathers. Kytgy's struggle for the peaceful coexistence of the various tribes, and the increase and well being of humankind, has a social meaning to it. It is quite probable that the depiction of Kytgy reflects to the mythological motifs about the "creating" woman and surviving elements of maternal descent (Menovshchikov 1974, no. 89; Dolitsky and Michael 1997, no. 34).

In content and composition close to the heroic narratives are the historical legends, which deal with specific historical occurrences or separate episodes. They also reflect the life of the Paleoasiatics of Chukotka and Kamchatka during the various historical periods of their lives. These stories differ from the heroic narratives by containing, instead of epic depictions of battles of individual heroes with foreign or local enemies, a description of specific events without concentrating on the acts of a single hero. They tell about "authentic" facts of a battle with a preponderant enemy in which there is no place for hyperbolism, fantasy and glorification of feats of individual heroes. A characteristic feature of historical stories is often the appearance of mass heroism of the people in their fight with the enemy. At the base of such stories are past actions not burdened with epical or fantastic elements. Such stories include, for instance, the Eskimo *Viyutku-predvoditel,* "Viyutku, the Leader," in which, under the leadership of one Viyutku and his brothers, a large detachment of warriors is organized from among the multitude of inhabitants of Chukchi and Eskimo settlements. This detachment is called upon to prevent the army of newcomer *tannity* (apparently the Koryaks and their satellites, the Yukaghirs) from entering the land of the Chukchi (Menovshchikov 1958: 151-155). In the narrative, a detailed ethnographic description of the training and organization of the soldiers is given. These include the slingers, soldiers with bow and arrow, and spear bearers. The traditional beginning of the clash, that is, the duel of two soldiers, is depicted, as well as the traditional ending—the sparing of one or two captives and the sharing of loot.

Tales about animals

Tales about animals were widespread among Paleoasiatics. The differentiating feature of tales of this genre were tied with the cosmogonic, totemic, and animistic concepts of the Asiatic Eskimos, Chukchi, Koryaks, Kereks, and Itelmens in the early epoch of their egalitarian communal system. This kind of oral tradition developed in the same time, as did the mythical legends and magical-mythical tales. Elements of the latter are revealed in the tales about animals. In these, as in tales of other genres, are reflected generalizations of world-view beliefs of the peoples of Chukotka and Kamchatka, as well as accumulations of vital knowledge of life so necessary for the practical activities of the ancient hunters of this region.

The personification of animals and surrounding environment in the tales of Paleoasiatics had direct and vivid ties with the primitive hunting of animals. Because of the harsh climate of the remote North, hunting was their principal occupation and the sole means of survival. Being the principal source of life over the various stages of their historical development, animals inevitably were endowed with totemic and animistic properties. The worldview and the artistic fantasy of the Paleoasiatics were particularly tied in with the animal world.

The differentiating feature of a number of magical-mythical tales about the harmful *kele, nynvit,* and *tungak* was the man's fear of the unknown and mysterious forces of nature. But the tales about animals often reflect friendly relations with animals. Animals, who were the object of the hunt, were not enemies of man. The hunter did not overkill the animals he subsisted on; he took the game rationally, and by doing so endowed them with spiritual, human qualities, which he himself possessed. This is an example of a direct connection between mythological legends involving animal personages with tales about animals.

Having created the fantastic legends about animals and other creators of the world, man begins to believe in their reality, their protective forces. With the development of human society, the myth, artistically reworked and enriched, develops into a magical tale in which moral and ethical norms of early man are reflected. From the magical-mythical tale develops the tale about animals, which becomes the same, and often even more powerful, "school of life" of the hunter then the magical-mythical tale. The animal tales of the Chukchi, Asiatic Eskimos, Koryaks and Itelmens glorify the work experience of the people, the economy, pastimes, and the hunter's deftness and resourcefulness in bagging animals. Contrarily, stupidity, clumsiness, and physical infirmity are ridiculed as dangers for the hunter (Belikov 1969: 123).

The animal tales of the aborigines of Chukotka and Kamchatka, preserved and developed from the mythical stories, do not significantly differ from them. In many of the tales, the actors appear at the same time as people or animals, but in a number of cases it is difficult to discern who is the principal one. This is particularly the case of Itelmen-Koryak tales with several contaminated topics in which people and animals work in close cooperation. This becomes evident most clearly when we analyze the remarkable and, until now, little known cycle of tales about the raven-hero Kutkh-Kutkynneku. He is a raven and man at the same time. In some cases he is in close contact with animals (nos. 15, 16, 62 of this edition; Menovshchikov 1974, nos. 126, 127, 173), in others with people (Menovshchikov 1974, no. 176; no. 65 of this edition). In many of the tales of the raven cycle, the hero acts with the mediation of mythical helpers—animals. Such tales belong more to the genre of magico-mythical ones than to animal tales. Thus, for instance, the hero of the cycle of Itelmen tales about Kutkh, and particularly Kutkh himself, his wife Miti, and their children Ememkut, Sinanevt and others, despite being birds—Kutkh is a mythical raven, Miti is a magpie's daughter—appear in the form of people, most often in the animal surroundings. Kutkh himself, when it is necessary, transforms into a raven, but for a short time only in order to fulfill his magical mission. The ability to transform into a raven was inherited from his parents by their older son Ememkut. Only Miti remains a woman in all of the tales although she was born of a magpie. In the meantime, the daughters of Kutkh and Miti enter into conjugal unions with both human and animal beings. When absent from the family, Kutkh usually finds himself in the animal surroundings.

In a number of other tales only human beings surround Kutkh. These are usually the domestic tales. In "Kutkh and Miti" (no. 59 of this edition; Menovshchikov 1974, no. 170), and "How Kutkh and Miti Picked Nuts" (no. 60 of this edition; Menovshchikov 1974, no. 171), the men Kutkh and Ememkut, having absented themselves from the women, transform themselves into ravens. Thus these are not animal tales any more but magical ones in which the principal actor is the same Kutkh.

In the Koryak tales about Kutkynneku (Kuykynnyaku) and Ememkut, which extend the Itelmem cycle about the raven Kutkh, the image of the raven-hero is also not clearly expressed. Thus, in "The Travels of Kuykynnyaku" (no. 14 of this edition; Menovshchikov 1974, no. 125), it is impossible to discern the outward appearance of the hero: Is he man or raven? A ringed seal accompanies Kuykynnyaku and leads him into the ocean deep to the whale people, then to the walrus people, and to the seal people. The different kinds of sea animals are rendered as separate human communities. In gratitude for being hosted Kuykynnyaku gives his daughter Tinianavut in marriage to the bearded seal people. In the Itelmen tale "Kutkh and the Crab" (Menovshchikov 1974, no. 174; no. 63 of this edition), Kutkh descends to the underwater kingdom of sea people and for quenching his thirst gives them his daughters in marriage. In this tale, the ideas of mythical contacts and blood ties between man and animals are survived and preserved. The mythological basis of the tales about Kutkh-Kutkynneku in Itelmen-Koryak folklore is obvious. At the same time the direct association of many of the tales of this particular cycle with this genre make it difficult because of the changes and later developments they had undergone in the course of their formation.

A significant characteristic of the animal tale is the complete absence of magico-mythical deeds of the heroes. Here the participants of the events lead the usual kind of hunter's life often imitating people in their activities. They have tools for working, obtain and prepare food, sew clothing, build dwellings, enter into marriages, and fight their enemies. In animal tales, as a rule, the creatures that prevail have physical infirmities or are small in size, but have brains and are clever and deft (Belikov 1969: 125-126). In "Akannykay" (Menovshchikov 1974, no. 107; Dolitsky and Michael 1997, no. 52), the wolf eats a doe but leaves her fawn to grow up so he can eat it when it matures. The fawn, training himself to jump on cliffs and rocks, becomes a strong [mature] deer and defeats the wolf. In the Kerek tale "The Fox and the Raven" (Menovshchikov 1974, no. 115; no. 4 of this edition), the animals have a full set of articles needed for living and hunting. They live like humans do. The fox tries to trick the raven but the raven exposes and humbles her. There is a considerable number of these ancient animal tales in this collection.

The children's teasing tales about the bullhead and the deer, about the bull-calf and fox, and a number of others hold a special place among the tales about animals. In these tales characters tease each other with ditties containing offensive words. Among the tales with animals and magical-mythical characters are those with toponymic content, and with etiologic or cosmogonic subject matters and conclusions.

Ancient tales as an archaeological, historic and ethnographic source

The personification of the animal world in the oral traditions of the Paleoasiatics interacts in an intimate and direct way with their graphic and singing-dancing arts. The Chukchi and Eskimo folk dance and ditty [short song] improvisations, which were used until recently [1974] on festive occasions, are dedicated to the successful whale or walrus hunt, and among the Reindeer Chukchi, to the autumn slaughter of reindeer. The cosmogonic beliefs of the ancient hunters about the world of the tale of raven, swallow, and other animals are also reflected in these works of art. In the dances of the raven, swallow and gull, which depict the results of the hunting process, the thorough knowledge of the habits and anatomy of animals is evident.

In the petroglyphs of the Chukotka Peninsula, first discovered in these northern latitudes by geologists and archaeologists in 1965-1967, the hand of an early artist depicted impressive figures of the hunt for the northern wild deer and sea mammals (Dikov 1969: 214-229). On the rocky spurs of Pegtymel cliff are carved figures of northern wild deer, wolf, and dog, a hunter in a kayak thrusting a spear into a swimming deer, and scenes of hunting a whale (Dikov 1971). All of these are witness to highly developed early graphic arts that also reflect the life of the indigenous people of the region. Next to these truthful renditions of the surrounding world, the ancient artist also engraved mythical occurrences that are obviously reflections of the artistic and fantastic images of the Paleoasiatic hunter.

To such images belong the renditions of dancing women with very large mushroom caps on their heads. These petroglyphs of jolly women-mushrooms have a direct parallel with the contents of the Itelmen tale "Chelkutkh and Maidens-Mushrooms" (no. 78 of this edition; Menovshchikov 1974, no. 189). In it, the jolly forest girl-mushrooms entice the hero and carry him away. In their world he forgets about his wife and children. Winter comes and with it hunger. Chelkutkh walks out of the forest to his wife and children and the mushrooms that had captured him wither in the forest.

The Koryaks and Chukchi used toadstool mushrooms to induce a stupor, and attributed them with souls. As indicated by Bogoras, toadstool mushrooms appear to drunk people in a strange, human-like form. The personification by the Paleoasiatics of phenomena and articles of the world surrounding them likewise applied to toadstool mushrooms, the use of which entered man into an abnormal psychic condition. These images have found their expression most abundantly in the myths, tales, and stories of all the aborigines of Chukotka and Kamchatka.

Introduction by
Gregory A. Menovshchikov

Translated by
Henry N. Michael
Senior Fellow
Museum Applied Science Center for Archaeology
University of Pennsylvania, Philadelphia, Pennsylvania

Edited and adapted by
Alexander B. Dolitsky
Director
Alaska-Siberia Research Center
Juneau, Alaska

TALES AND LEGENDS OF THE KEREKS

ETHNOGRAPHIC INFORMATION

Kereks is the self-appellation of a small group of people living in the valley of the Mayno-Pyigino River in Beringovsky *rayon* of the Chukotka National *Okrug,* Kamchatka Peninsula (see Figures 1, 2). In 1959 they numbered about one hundred people (Menovshchikov 1974: 598), and in 1994 Kereks' population has increased to about four hundred but with only three speakers of the Kerek language (Chaussonnet 1995: 109). In the early 1970s, the Kereks lived in several settlements with separate families mixed with the Chukchi and Russians and therefore they were subjected to intensive assimilation by the latter. The Kerek language is related to the Chukchi and Koryak languages. Elements of the Siberian Yupik language are also found in the Kerek vocabulary. All Kereks freely use the Chukchi language. Their native language is at the point of disappearance. By the early 1970s the Kereks were absorbed by the peoples surrounding them. There is no reliable information about the remote past of the Kereks or about their spiritual and material culture. The present-day material and spiritual culture of the Kereks appears to have much in common with that of the Chukchi.

The Soviet Paleoasiatic specialist P. Skorik (1957, 1968) was the first to do a short scientific description of the Kerek language. He did so on the basis of materials collected by him in 1954-56. He also recorded several texts in the Kerek language, which are presented in this publication. In 1969, V. Iunevut recorded several texts of which one is presented in this edition, and V. Leontev recorded and translated another eight Kerek texts in 1971.

1. The Child with Bow and Arrow

Narrated in 1954 by an inhabitant of Khatyrka village in Anadyr *rayon*, Tevlalkot, age 24. Recorded and translated into Russian by P. Skorik. Published in Voskoboynikov and Menovshchikov 1959, p. 449. The theme of this heroic story has appeared often in the folklore of the Chukchi and the Asiatic Eskimos. It describes a bearded strongman and oppressor Yakuni who is blinded by arrows shot by a Chukchi (or Eskimo) child. This version reflects a Kerek adaptation, particularly in the beginning of the story, where the reindeer-herding Kereks are killed by the enemy or taken captive and turned into herdsmen, and their herds taken by the enemy. As in Chukchi heroic stories here also are reflected the inter-tribal struggles for the control of the reindeer herds. The story is told in an epic, animated style but elements of fantasy are absent. In their narratives about the 18th century clashes between the Chukchi and the Russians, or the Chukchi, Asiatic Eskimos and Yukagirs applied the name Yakuni or Yakunin to a Major Pavlutsky who commanded a detachment of Russian Cossacks[1] and who was killed by the Chukchi on March 21, 1747 (see Bogoras 1900, p. 93, add. 1 to no. 15).

They say that this happened long ago, very long ago. At that time there were as yet many Kereks. The Kereks were reindeer herders. Then enemies began to appear in Kerek country. They suddenly swept by on fast reindeer, killed off the men, took the women and children with them, and drove their reindeer off. The Kerek women had to do various domestic chores and the children had to pasture the herds.

And so it happened one day. A Kerek, his wife and little son were traveling in a harnessed sled. The child was two years old. The father was armed with a bow and arrow. And the child also had a bow. As soon as the child began to walk his father made him a small bow so he could practice shooting arrows.

And so they traveled together—the man with his wife and small son. Suddenly his wife exclaimed:

—Oy, what's that over there?

The man glanced back. Not far back of them it seemed like the wind was making the snow whirl. Then a harnessed sled appeared. It was beginning to overtake them fast.

The man guessed that it must be the enemy. He drove the reindeer faster. The sled was jumping over the hardened snow. And the father and mother did not notice that their son had dropped out of sight. But the bright child hid himself behind the runners and he got his small bow.

The enemy was in pursuit; he did not see the child. Then he decided to steer his sled closer to the harness. The boy got ready. He shot an arrow. It struck the enemy directly in his eye. The enemy yelled in pain. He covered the eye with his hand. And the boy shot an arrow again and struck the enemy's other eye.

The enemy was blind; he wheeled around. He threw his hands out. He wanted to catch the boy. The enemy failed many times. He stopped altogether. Finally he sat on the runner and asked:

—Who are you? You've defeated me! I can't see; I'm blind.

—I've defeated you, —said the boy.

The enemy was astonished when he realized that a child had defeated him. He lowered his head, thought for a while. Then he said:

If you, a child, defeated me, a strongman, an oppressor, then kill me. Where will I go, a blind man! Everybody will laugh at me because a child defeated me.

The child said this:

—I'm still small and am afraid that I'm not strong enough to kill you.

The enemy begged him:

---

[1]Cossacks were free Russian peasants who were commonly recruited by the tsar's government to serve in the army. Russian Cossacks also were among the first explorers of Siberia, the Russian Far East and North America in the 17th and 18th centuries. Aboriginal people of the Russian Far North and North America have used this word to describe a white man.

—Give me a spear!

The child gave him a spear. The enemy pointed the spear to his chest and then asked the child to set the other end against the runner. The child did so. The enemy told him:

—Take my reindeer! You've defeated me. They'll be your booty. Now drive to your parents!

And he killed himself. And the child sat on the sled and soon caught up with his parents.

2. The One Possessing an Iron Hook

Narrated in 1970 by a Kerek of Maynypilgino village in Beringovsky *rayon*. Kerek M. Etynkeu, age 67, was hardly literate and spoke Russian with difficulty. Recorded and translated into Russian by V. Leontev together with a Kerek woman E. Khatkano, also an inhabitant of Maynypilgino village in Beringovsky *rayon*, age 70. The subject of *kele* bursting (in Kerek *kala*) after drinking too much water has been interpreted variously in the folklore of the peoples of Chukotka and Kamchatka. Compare in this collection the Itelmen text no. 68 *Kutkh is Sewing*, and the Eskimo tale *Pyat devushek i Mayyrakhpak*, "Five Girls and Mayyrakhpak," published in *Eskimoskiye skazki i legendy*, Menovshchikov 1969, p. 53, and the Chukchi text no. 164 in Bogoras 1900.

Grandmother fell asleep, but before she did, she tied the man-eating *kele* to the floor. In our way, in Kerek, they call the man-eater *kala*.[2] He was always tethered. Two sisters lived with grandmother. All of a sudden the *kala* said to the younger sister:

—Sister, oh sister, grandma is asleep, will you untie me?

The younger sister replied:

—No, I'll not untie you. Grandma said that you'd roam wherever you please. You know that you're bad and dumb. So stay tied up.

Then the *kala* turned to the other sister:

—Little sister, untie me!

The younger sister having more sense than the older told her:

—We shouldn't untie him.

Again the *kala* begged of the older sister:

—Untie me! Let me loose!

The older sister listened to him and untied the *kala*. As soon as she untied him the *kala* grabbed an iron hook and went toward the *zemlyankas* where the Kereks lived. He arrived there, uncovered the smoke hole and saw that there were only women in the *valkara*[3]—all the men had gone hunting.

The *kala* yelled into the smoke hole:

—Hey there, are you asleep?!

Two old women answered from there:

—No, we're not sleeping.

—Then what is making that noise, as if small children were screaming?

—That's not children, —one of the old women replied, —probably my chest hurts because of the coming bad weather.

—Then now I will fish with the hook! —the *kala* cried out.

—And what do you want to catch?

—Young ducks.[4]

—There are no young ducks now; in the summer they roost on the cliffs. There are no ducks here, we, people live here.

—Well, not in vain have I come?!

—All right, have it your way, —they replied from the *valkara*. —Only, why be violent? Fish with the hook!

—All right, look, I'm beginning now!

—Well, then begin! Whom do you want to catch?

---

[2]*Kala* — spirit-werewolves with evil powers in Kerek folklore.

[3]*Valkara* — the term may indicate a special location within a *zemlyanka* for women's domestic activities, or it may be another word for a *zemlyanka* in the local dialect [Editor].

[4]During the spring and summer the Kereks prepared for their winter-food birds taken in bird colonies, mainly murres. They prepared them in a special way, drying them over the fire and hanging them from the beams.

The *kala* lowered the hook into the *zemlyanka* and tossing it around started to sing:

—Today, today, there'll be food! Today, today, there'll be food! Even tomorrow, even tomorrow, there'll be food! Even tomorrow, even tomorrow, there'll be food! Whom, whom will I catch? Whom will I hook? Now where are you, you young ducks?

—There are no young ducks now, we told you.

—Then I'll come to you.

—No, don't come in. Fish from where you are and we'll get you some young ducks.

In the meantime one of the women dug a hole in the wall to escape through it.

—Now look, I'm starting to fish with the hook again! —cried out the *kala.*

—Go ahead!

—Whom, whom will I catch? Today and tomorrow there'll be food! —the *kala* sang.

Suddenly he hooked something. And it seemed to be a *kerker.*[5] He pulled it up and without looking started to tear it apart. Outdoors there was a wind and all of the grass flew into his eyes. The women had filled the overalls with dried grass and placed it on the hook.

—Oh-oh! —The *kala* began to yell. —They've heaped rubbish on me! What is this? What is it filled with? A duck? No, it's not a duck! It's not anything!

The *kala* threw the stuffed overalls into the *zemlyanka.*

—Take it for yourself. I don't need it. It's not a duck.

While the *kala* was busy with the overalls, the women crawled through the hole in the wall and ran off.

—Now, wait a little, I'm coming to you!

The *kala* went into the *zemlyanka* and nobody was there. Only a little dog on a leash sat there. He asked her:

—Where are the people?

But the dog said nothing. She knew that this was not a person but a *kala*, and the dog scratched the *kala's* eyes.

—Oh-oh-oh-oh! —yelled the *kala.* —My eyes are a mess. What are you tearing at?

He did not recognize that the dog had scratched his eyes.

The *kala* became infuriated and began to run all over the *zemlyanka*. He dragged out the cushions and tore them apart. He roamed about in the *zemlyanka* for a long time.

In the meantime the women ran up to the *Tinnaya babushka*, the Old Woman of the Sea,[6] and they said to her:

—Ah, the *kala* is chasing after us; he wants to catch us. Help us run away from him!

—Oh-oh, how he scared you, how he scared! Now then we shall see. The Old Woman of the Sea stretched her legs to the other side of the sea and said:

—Carry the children straight over my legs and run yourself.

The women got over to the other side of the sea.

The *kala* calmed down and became himself. He, the one with the iron hook, started thinking: "O-ho, they must have left through here, —he guessed, seeing the hole in the wall. —It was they, the woman, who at that time were screaming."

He followed the footprints of the women. He ran up to the Old Woman of the Sea. The old woman was washing her overalls, muddy from the rubbish heap, in the sea.

The *kala* asked her:

—What are you washing, old woman? Why?

—Don't you see, I'm washing my clothes.

—Oh, are those really clothes? You're trying to fool me. Our old women wore only iron coverings, —he took the muddy clothing and threw it into the sea. —That's not clothing, it is not.

---

[5]*Kerker* — a woman's fur overalls.

[6]The Old Woman of the Sea — the mythical mistress of the sea among the Kereks.

—What do you mean it's not clothing? My life is such, I live in the sea and I wear such clothing. Didn't you see the women? Their footprints led to here. Where did they go?

The Old Woman of the Sea replied to the one with the iron hook:

—They drank up the sea and went to the other side.

—And what about me? Can't I drink up the sea?

—You can, you know they did it!

—Well, all right, I'll try!

—The *kala* begin to drink the seawater, but the sea did not diminish a bit. He drank and drank, he became heavy and he burst. It was no match for the *kala*; he burst like a bubble.

The Old Woman of the Sea threw the dead *kala* in the sea and said:

—Let his iron body turn into various useful things; you know he was the *kala* with the iron hook. Let his head become a teapot, his feet and hands muskets, and his brain become beads. Let his body give benefit to people.

And so it happened.

In this tale there were also two friends—the first one Itchym[7] and the other Itchym. The other Itchym was the namesake of the first.

The first Itchym went to the other Itchym and said to him:

—Come, Itchym, my friend, let's go to the seashore.

—First I'll go and ask grandma, —replied Itchym, the friend.

He went and asked grandma:

—Itchym wants me to go with him to the seashore

—Who?

—Yes, Itchym.

—Oh, it's not man's business to go to the seashore. That concerns women only.

—So, you're not allowing me to go?

—I'm not allowing it. Don't go! Tell Itchym to go to the seashore by himself. Tell him that grandma did not allow you to go.

Itchym the friend went to Itchym and said to him:

—Go by yourself! Grandma won't let me go.

—Well, all right, I'll go by myself. I'll find many useful things by the seashore.

—What can I do, she won't let me go. If I go, she'll scold me. You go there by yourself.

—So what; I think I'll go.

Itchym went to the seashore. He walked along the beach and soon he found a clasp knife, a teapot, and what more, he saw muskets and beads. What wasn't there that he did not get from the one with the iron hook! Itchym collected many different goods; he had found all sorts of riches. Whatever he wanted, he found. Itchym went home carrying a heavy load. He arrived at the place of his sisters: one they called Ilynau[8] the other Kayklyukanau.[9] Itchym called out to his sisters:

—Sisters, Ilynau, Kaykltukanau! Come out; relieve me of my burden!

The sisters came out and questioned their younger brother:

—What is this? Why does your load clatter like iron?

Itchym answered his sisters:

—You know I was told that if I went to the seashore I would find riches there. I invited Itchym, my friend, to come along but he didn't. So I became rich all by myself. And there're still many goods left there. Let's go there again. The only thing we have to do is to give the clasp knife to our first cousin Auppali, the son of Kukki. Let's go, we'll carry out many things.

—Well, all right, let's go, —the sisters agreed.

---

[7]Itchym is the mythical relative of the raven Kukki.

[8]Ilynau, a relative of the raven Kukki created by him from the lungs of a whale.

[9]Kayklyukanau, the sister of Ilynau, the other female relative of the raven Kukki created by him from a berry.

They went to the seashore. Again they came home with a big load. Their first cousin said to them:

—Give to your cousin one of the teapots. Where do these riches come from?

—Well, we've found them at the seashore, —Itchym answered.

In the meantime Itchym, the friend, went to neighbor Itchym, who had invited him to go to the seashore. Itchym, the friend, said:

—Oh, it's true; my namesake has become rich. Not for nothing did you say that you'd find useful things.

—Grandma didn't let you go, Itchym said, and he turned to his sisters:

—Give to my namesake, my friend Itchym, the clasp knife.

The sisters gave him the clasp knife. Itchym, the friend, was happy, went home, showed it to his grandma and said:

—Itchym has really become rich. Not for nothing did he say that he'd find riches. And you didn't let me go.

— How many times did I tell you, —said his grandmother angrily, —that the sea doesn't cast ashore such things. It only casts ashore food.

—All right, I'll be quiet now.

Itchym, the friend, again came to his neighbor.

—Aha, you've come again, —Itchym greeted him.

—Yes!

—Well, don't be angry. You know I invited you to go there. It's you that didn't go. Let's be friendly again, —Itchym told him.

Then a certain Ynnulnakut also said:

—Those were nice things he found for his sisters. They liked the beads best of all.

This will do; that's the story. I've finished.

3. The Hare

Narrated in 1970 by an inhabitant of Maynypilgino village in Beringovsky *rayon*, the Kerek M. Etynkeu, age 67, who was hardly literate and spoke Russian with difficulty. Recorded and translated into Russian by V. Leontev together with a Kerek woman E. Khatkano, also an inhabitant of Maynypilgino village in Beringovsky *rayon*, age 70. This tale reflects the early myth of the Paleoasiatics about a resurrection of an animal, which is prey. This represents an act of mutual assistance of man and animal.

The hare told his grandma and sisters:

—Grandma, will you give me the thong for carrying a load! I'm going to strip bark from the trees.

Grandma was afraid to let her grandson go:

—Don't go after bark, your liver will ache!

—No, my liver will not hurt! Better give me the thong; you're delaying me!

—I'll not give it to you! Your gut will hurt.

—My gut will not hurt. Better give me the thong; I'm going after bark!

—No, you're not going after bark. Your liver will hurt.

—It won't!

—Your gut, your kidneys will hurt.

—My gut will not hurt, —insisted the hare. —What are you talking about, grandma? Now, sister, you give me the thong.

His sister gave the thong to her younger brother. He went out. The hare saw the dwelling of a *kala*; he went toward it and began to strip the bark off the logs. He was stripping the bark and saying to himself: "This one I'll give to grandma. It's a little bitter but really good for her teeth." He stripped a second piece of bark: "This one I'll give to sister Lylachak. It's sweetish and strong."

The hare was stripping the bark and putting it in a heap so that he could better tie it into a bundle.

—This one I'll give to my older sister, —exclaimed the hare, —it's a bit dry but bitter!

The dwelling of the *kala* was close to the sea. The very young ringed seal [*nerpa*] Upapil surfaced and began to tease the hare:

—You're cleaning the *zemlyanka* of the *kala*!

—It's none of your business! Go away, playmate! —the hare couldn't contain himself.

But Upapil wanted to quarrel with the hare; the seal came out of the water and sang:

—You're cleaning the *zemlyanka* of the *kala*!

The hare could not contain himself:

—The ice floe is clean and when you lie on it you leave it dirty. So!

—No, my droppings are thick and fatty but yours are dry and hard, like white pebbles.

—You yourself are fat and heavy and so are your droppings.

— And you are scraggy, very scraggy!

—Wait a bit, and I'll also be fat. Then you'll not be able to compare me with yourself.

—You'll never be like me!

—You'll see. It's not your business; go away!

Why are you teasing me, —Upapil took offense, —now I'll call for my grandfather, he'll kill you.

—Go ahead, Go ahead, Go ahead!

—All right! Wait a bit; I'll go tell my grandpa.

—I'm not afraid, I'm not afraid, I'm not afraid! —the hare yelled.

And he prepared himself: what if the bearded seal [*lakhtak*] suddenly appearres. He took the scraper with which he peeled off the bark and held it in readiness.

Upapil dove into the water and swam away.

—Grandpa, grandpa! The hare is hurting my feelings, he's teasing me, —Upapil complained.

The grandfather, the bearded seal, swam toward the shore. Ice had already formed at the shore. He surfaced at the edge of the ice and asked the hare:

—Why are you teasing my granddaughter?

—Serves her right, serves her right! —the hare cried out. —Swim to the shore. I can't come to you on the water. Come to the shore, here, to a dry place and we'll talk about it.

The grandfather, the bearded seal, plunged and plunged through the thin ice and finally crawled onto the shore. The hare raised the scraper and killed him.

—Oh, oh, why did you kill my grandpa?! —cried Upapil.

—I did not kill him. Look, he's flapping his flippers for you. Come, swim to the shore!

—No, I saw you hit him. Now I'll go to grandma and tell her, —and Upapil dove into the deep.

—Grandma, grandma, wake up, —cried Upapil. —Our grandpa is no more. The hare killed him.

—Apa-pa-pa! —Grandma woke up with her teeth chattering. —No wonder my back is stiff, a friend has left in my dreams.

Upapil again swam away, surfaced and called out to the hare:

—Wait a while; now grandma is swimming to you! She will kill you too!

—I'm not afraid, I'm not afraid, I'm not afraid! —the hare called out.

—Don't be so brave! You're simply yelling!

—I'm not afraid, I'm not afraid, I'm not afraid! —yelled the hare.

And he readied the scraper ready to meet the grandma, the bearded seal.

The grandmother, the bearded seal, surfaced at the edge of the ice.

—Come out here; look your husband wants you, —the hare said to her. —You know I can't swim in the water. Come here, to the shore.

The grandmother, the bearded seal, swam near the shore, surfacing frequently.

—It can't be that we'll meet on the water, —the hare did not budge. —And yes, would you not kill me in the water?

The grandmother-seal made a decision and crawled onto the shore. As soon as she crawled out the hare killed her with the scraper.

Oh-oh, now you've killed my grandma! —cried Upapil.

The hare turned his back on Upapil and began to dress the carcasses. He had killed two seals. He refreshed himself, and made himself a bundle: "Well, now I'll go home. It's a rich take!"

His two sisters and grandmother were waiting in the house.

—Grandma! —the sisters called out. —Your grandson, the hare, is coming.

—Ah, let him come, we'll wait for him in the *zemlyanka*.

—Why is he coming so quietly? —the sisters were wondering.

You know they did not see what he was carrying. They went into the *zemlyanka*.

—Sisters, little sisters, come out, meet me! Take my load! Your little brother, the hare, has come home.

The sisters came out and wondered:

—And where is the bark?

They tried to lift what the hare had brought. They couldn't; it was too heavy for them. The older sister said:

—No, this is not bark. Bark is light.

—Well, all right, bring it here quickly! —the grandmother called out; she was also curious to know.

—We can't carry it in.

—Very well, I'll carry it myself.

The hare carried the bag into the *zemlyanka*.

—Ah, hare, you finally came back! —grandma greeted him.

—Yes, I did come back.

—Where is the bark?

—Now untie that bundle. There's no bark here!

—What is it? It's very soft, —wondered grandma.

—Untie it quickly!

9

The hare couldn't wait and untied it himself.

—I've brought seal meat and pieces of blubber.

—Where did you find that carrion?

—That's not carrion. I've killed two seals. Let's eat and then we'll go after the rest of the meat.

—Oh, I'll prepare the food right away! —said grandma happily.

In the neighborhood there lived a fox.

—Imynna, —she said to her daughter, —will you give me the braided rope?!

—Where are you going? —Imynna asked.

—I'm going to the seashore to look around. Maybe something got thrown on the shore.

—Very well, go ahead! I doubt that you'll find anything.

—We'll see!

At that time the hares came to the place where the meat was left. They had not yet prepared the load to be carried away when they saw the fox running toward them.

—Oho, look, —said the hare, —our auntie, the fox, is running here. And how did she learn so soon that I've killed two seals?! No doubt somebody whispered in her ear.

The fox ran up to them.

—Oho, my nephew, you've really killed a seal! —the fox was amazed.

—Yes, I really did. And you're here at the right time. Did somebody tell you that your nephew had killed animals?

—No, no! I simply decided to wander along the shore a bit. The wind was blowing from the sea and brought in a pleasant smell.

And foxes have an excellent sense of smell.

—Very well then; you take as much as you need, —said the hare.

—With pleasure! Only how much can I take?

—As much as you can carry. You know, you're strong.

The fox took as much meat that she could carry and tied it together with the braided rope.

—Well, let's go, —the hare said. —Even if there is some meat left. We can't take it all. And we're going to be breathing heavily on the path.

The hares went home. The fox also ran home.

Lymnoynytkym, the younger son of the fox was strolling near the *zemlyanka*. Suddenly he saw the fox running.

—Mom is coming over there, —he said. —Imynna, I'm going to run over there and meet her.

Lymnoynytkym ran to meet his mother.

—Oh, mom, what are you carrying so much?

—Well, it's seal meat

—How did you kill the seal?

—I didn't, the hare did. We better get home fast. Tomorrow all three of us will go and take the rest of the meat.

But the next day the hares got up at daybreak. They quickly ran after the remaining meat. They were worried; they knew the fox was smart. No doubt the fox, with all her children, would go after the meat. Then, to be sure, nothing would be left for them. But the hares were not stupid. All three went to the shore. They ran, they hurried, so that the fox would not overtake them.

And, truly, the fox also started out in the morning. She walked and behind her, in her footsteps, walked Imynna, and the last one was Lymnoynytkyn, plodding along.

—Oh, you've come! —the hare greeted them.

—Yes, we have!

—Then take these remaining pieces. We've already loaded up.

The fox and her children went back. The fox in the front, behind her Imynna and last, the plodding Lymnoynytkyn. Lymnoynytkyn was still small and weak; he carried nothing.

The hare and his sisters also started for their dwelling.

And the grandmother hare was impatient to see the take. Often she came out of the *zemlyanka* to look and see if the hares were coming. Finally she saw them. "I must hurry a little and cook a meal" — she decided.

Her children arrived.

—Here, grandma, take the load!

—Oh, so you finally came, —said grandma.

—Yes, we have come.

—And where is the fox?

—She with her children also went after the meat. This time I didn't tell her: "Take as much as you want." She only took what was left.

—It's nice that even our aunt got enough; you've hosted them with blubber, —grandma said happily.

In the morning the hares awakened and grandma said to them:

—Well, we've had enough of our fill. We'll have to show our friends our gratitude. Prepare gifts for them—wild deer meat, crowberries, and small root plants. It's time to go to friends' homes, granddaughter Upapil misses us; she is waiting. Go and take the gifts to them!

The hares went to the seashore taking with them all of the bones of the seals together with the gifts. They buried the bones on the shore and left the gifts there. And they returned home right away.

Suddenly the granddaughter Upapil saw that grandpa and grandma were coming. She was happy. Her father was already home. He had scolded his daughter because she allowed grandpa and grandma to be killed. And just then grandma with grandpa came home. They brought gifts.

—Look here with what the hares are hosting us—there are berries, root plants, and wild deer meat.

—Oho, not in vain did you, grandmother, go after those gifts, —said the father of Upapil.

And grandfather even brought a toy made of a stem of wild rye, a long blade of wild rye.

4. The Fox and the Raven

Narrated in 1956 by an inhabitant of Maynypilgino village in Beringovsky *rayon*, Nutau, age 62. Recorded and translated into Russian by P. Skorik. Published in Voskoboynikov and Menovshchikov 1959, p. 447.

The fox was too lazy to look for food; she lived poorly, she was starving. One day she told her daughter:

—I'm going to fool the raven; I'll tell thim that I married and now live well.

Her daughter said:

—It's not necessary to fool him. It would be better to ask, in a nice way, for food.

The fox did not listen. She took an old wet fish net, stuffed it in a pouch, and tied the pouch. She went to the raven. The raven heard that someone was coming and he told his family:

—Go out and see who's coming.

They went out. The fox was already in the entryway. It was dark there. The fox said:

—My husband and I have come.

The fox had told a lie. And the raven believed her, and in surprise said:

—How do you like that! My first cousin got married. Well, show us your husband.

The fox said:

—My husband can't stand light. His forefathers lived in darkness, and he likes darkness. Otherwise he would be blind[ed] and would see nothing. He can't come into light.

The raven said:

—Well, all right, blow out the oil lamps and let's go in.

They entered. The raven asked:

—What will you have to eat?

The fox answered:

—We have a lot of food. Eat by yourselves!

The wife of the raven went in the storeroom after food and the fox very quietly slipped in after her and began to fill the pouch with food. She filled it fully, tied it, and carried it out to the entryway and put it there in a corner.

And the raven was still amazed:

—What do you know; my first cousin got married! Finally she got married!

And all the time the fox was bragging:

—Yes, my husband has many reindeer since very long ago. He has two large herds.

Then she asked if there were any eggs available. She said that her husband liked eggs very much. In exchange she offered reindeer hides. She said:

—Here in the pouch are the hides. Feel them!

The raven felt the pouch. Indeed there was something soft in it, something like reindeer hides. He was happy: "There're riches here. There'll be enough for clothing for all." He told her to put the pouch on the *polog*.[10]

The wife of the raven said to the fox:

—We have a son and you have a daughter. Maybe we should propose a marriage.

The fox thought a little and said:

—If your son wants to marry I think we should propose it.

So they talked and drank tea. The fox finished drinking and said, as if she were talking to her husband:

---

[10]*Polog* — a sleeping platform inside a dwelling [a semi-subterranean house, a *yaranga*]. It consists of deer hides stretched over a wooden frame.

—Let's go home now. The reindeer could become frightened and run off; or worse, they could be driven away.

(She made all of this up. She does not have a husband; she came alone).

Then she took leave of the hosts and went out. In the entryway she grabbed the pouch with the food. She hoisted it onto her back; she could hardly carry it home. Laughing, she said to her daughter:

—Look at this; you see I did fool the raven. He thought that I was really married. And he took the old fish net for reindeer hides.

Again her daughter said to her:

—Why fool him? It would be better to ask him in a nice way.

The fox replied angrily:

—Don't teach me; do you want me to be left without food!

The daughter fell silent and her mother had a snack of the eggs and began to cook the meat.

In the meantime the raven was happy that he obtained the reindeer hides so easily. Suddenly something dripped from the roof onto the bed.

His wife exclaimed:

—What is this?

The raven said:

—No doubt the fox got the hides wet on the road.

At that time their son came in. They told him about the hides. The son asked them:

—Now, show me your riches!

His mother got the pouch and untied it. She pulled out the net. She was amazed:

—Look, there's nothing here! Only an old, wet net!

The raven became angry and he ordered:

—Hang the net with the pouch on the storeroom door. No doubt the fox will again come here today. Let her go by herself for food to the storeroom. Slip a cramp iron into the pouch and tie it. It'll be like a trap.

And sure enough after some time the fox came again. The daughter of the raven told her mother:

—Look, the cheat came here again.

And the fox again continued her lying:

—I've come again with my husband. We've brought hides. Very nice hides, already dressed.

The raven's wife pretended to be sick. She said:

—Ah, today I've suddenly gotten a headache; I cannot walk. So you've come again?

The fox said:

—Yes, we have, but not for long. We're in a hurry. See you again!

And she herself went to the storeroom and slipped the cramp iron in the pouch. She tied the cramp iron in the pouch. The fox tugged at the cramp iron. She wanted to run off but became enmeshed in the net. She cried out:

—Oy, what are you doing to me?

And the raven said:

—We're not doing anything to you. You've done wrong to yourself. Why have you fooled us? Why, instead of hides did you give us an old net? Why did you go in a storeroom not your own?

The fox cried and begged to be untied. They did not untie her. They laughed at her and called her a cheat and a thief. Finally the fox ripped the old net and jumped to the path. And the pouch was tied over the cramp iron. So she came running home with the pouch.

She told her older daughter:

—Quickly, untie the pouch.

The daughter replied:

—I'm not going to untie it. Why did you cheat the daughter of Kukki?

The younger daughter untied it all.

And so the raven taught the fox a lesson for her cheating and stealing.

That is all.

5. The Pranks of the Fox

Narrated in 1969 at the fishing lake Kuet, by an inhabitant of Maynypilgino village in Beringovsky *rayon*, the Kerek M. Etynkeu, age 67, who was hardly literate and spoke Russian with difficulty. Recorded by V. Iunevut; translated into Russian by P. Skorik together with a Kerek woman E. Khatkano, also an inhabitant of Maynypilgino village in Beringovsky *rayon*, age 70.

One day the mice were sliding down a hill and yelling:

—Pa-a-a! We're having fun!

They were sliding down the roof of a *yaranga*[11] in which a woman *kala* lived.

They slid down again:

Pa-a-a! We're having fun!

And in the *yaranga* the woman *kala* was sewing. Her husband had gone to the tundra to hunt.

And the mice were sliding down anew:

—Pa-a-a! We're having fun!

Then the old *kala* said to herself:

—What is blocking the light? No doubt it's my nose and lips.

She cut them off with a knife:

—Iki-i-i!

Then she ate them. The same way our parents in their time ate the nose and lips of a wild deer.

But then the mice again slid down:

—Pa-a-a! We're having fun!

Again the old *kala* said:

—Well, what is blocking the light? No doubt my cheek. And she cut it off:

—Iki-i-i!

She was very voracious. She ate the cheek. The same way our parents cut off the ears of wild deer and ate them.

Then the mice slid down again:

—Pa-a-a! We're having fun!

The old *kala* said:

—What is it that's blocking the light? Probably my other cheek.

Again she cut it off:

—Iki-i-i!

She ate it, too.

And the mice again slid down:

—Pa-a-a! We're having fun!

The old *kala* cried out:

—All right, I'll go out! What could be blocking the light all the time?

She went out, her face covered with blood. The mice saw her. They became frightened. They ran away. The old *kala* enticed them:

—So, it turned out to be you! Let's go; let's slide together!

The mice returned. They slid down with the old *kala*. She grasped them and stuffed them into a large pouch. She hung them on the highest cross-beam of the *yaranga*. Then she went to get some firewood.

Not too far away there lived a fox with her daughter.

---

[11]*Yaranga* — a Chukchi word for a dwelling in form of a tent with a frame of poles covered with reindeer hides among the nomads or with walrus hides among the coastal dwellers. The *yarangas* of the coastal dwellers had a complex frame of beams, girders and thin poles.

The fox said to her daughter:

—Imynna, where is my braided rope for bundles?

—Where are you going? —asked her daughter.

—Oh, I'll go and wander a bit.

The fox left. She walked. Suddenly she heard a sound as if someone was crying. She went in the direction of the crying. She saw the mice. She exclaimed:

—Oh, oh! Who hung you up so high?

Then she asked:

—What is that pouch mumbling about?

The mice asked her in earnest:

—Please, say this: "Tilt down, I'll fill you with mouse fat."

The fox said to the pouch:

—Now, tilt down, I'll fill you with mouse fat.

The pouch tilted and the fox let the mice out. But the very smallest of them had died. The fox filled the pouch with crowberries, and put the little dead mouse back in it.

The fox told the mice:

—Now go home and tell your parents to move on to the upper world. And let them leave in their old dwelling, a carcass of a ram.

The mice started for home. They were crying. They came home.

Their parents asked them:

—Where are you coming from?

—From over there. We were sliding down the hillside. And the old *kala* stuffed us in a pouch and hung it way up in the *yaranga*. It was our good luck that the fox came. She freed us. The fox told us to move to the upper world and to leave a carcass of a ram in this place.

Indeed the mice moved to the upper world.

The fox started for home. She walked by the old mouse dwelling. She saw there the carcass of the ram and also ram's guts with fat. She went home. Her daughter Imynna asked her:

—Where did you come from?

—From over there. There the old *kala* stuffed the mice in a pouch and hung it up high. I set them free. The mice went home. I told them to move on to the upper world. And you go to their old dwelling. You'll find there a ram's carcass and guts with fat.

The daughters went there. They brought back everything. The fox told her daughter Imynna:

—Prepare the alder-tree bark.

Imynna asked:

—Why do you suddenly need the bark of the alder?

Her mother said:

—For this, when the old *kala* comes here I'll get sick.

Imynna asked:

—Why didn't you leave the mice there and let the old *kala* eat them? Why did you let them out?

And the old *kala* returned home with the firewood. She started looking for the mice. But they were no longer there. She found the dead mouse only. She was about to eat it but then she changed her mind. She grabbed a skeleton of a man and she wanted to burn it. He bared his teeth jeering at her. She hurled him away.

—Why are you taunting me? Why did you die then? —she yelled at the skeleton.

Then she started to question the perforated stone:

—Where are the mice? Maybe the raven carried them away?

The stone answered:

—No, not he.

Again the old *kala* said:

—But to where did the mice go? No doubt to the black raven Itchimankay?

The stone answered again:

15

—No, it's not so!

—Then, for sure, it must be the silver fox?

—Aka-a! —and the stone stuck to her forehead.[12]

The old *kala* went after the fox.

At the time the son of the fox, Lymnoynytkyn, was outdoors. He saw the old *kala* and said to his mother:

—Mom! Look over there; our auntie is coming!

The fox told her daughter Imynna:

—When the old *kala* comes here, tell her that your mother is sick. And now give me the bark of the alder.

Imynna gave her the crushed [pounded] bark. The fox sat on it.

—The old *kala* approached. Lymnoynytkyn, the son of the fox, met her with joy:

—Aka-a-a! Auntie!

And there and then he bit his tongue and fingers. He began to cry. He went home.

The old *kala* entered. She was happy. Suddenly she stumbled on a stone. She fell. The fox laughed. Imynna said to her:

—Come on in, aunt, you'll have some food!

The old *kala* entered the *yaranga*. And the fox was laughing:

—Igi! Igi! Igi! I'm hurting. My husband didn't take me with him because he rode to the fiery Tannits.[13]

The old *kala* asked:

—How come you're laughing at me?

—No, no, I'm not laughing at you. I want to ask something of you. Help me to get better.

She took the alder hash and said:

—Here's my illness. Take it to Olynayytkin Mountain. But if you pour it out nearby, I'll die.

The old *kala* said:

—Very well then, since you are so helpless.

The old *kala* left. And the fox asked her daughter:

—Imynna! Where is my *kerker*?

Her daughter asked her politely:

—Why do you suddenly need clothing?

—I'm going to go and push the old *kala* over the precipice.

In the meantime the old *kala* came to the rocky precipice.

The fox sneaked up to her and pushed her into the abyss.

The old *kala* broke her legs.

—Aka-a-a! —the fox laughed a bit and left.

She walked and walked and suddenly the strait appeared before her. And on the strait among the ice floes eiders were swimming.

The fox spoke to them:

—Yky-y, yky-yky-yky! My uncle is again riding in a boat in his white *kamleyka* [parka]. Uncle, take me with you. The eiders said:

—If hit by a wave, the boat will disappear.

The fox replied:

—How bad you are! I should really bite your noses off!

And sea gulls were swimming there. The fox was happy again:

---

[12]Apparently, guessing was done by holding a perforated stone to the forehead. When the stone did not fall, the answer was regarded as affirmative.

[13]The Russian Cossacks were called the fiery Tannits ["strangers"] by the local natives when they first encountered them using firearms.

—And there is my uncle in his white *kamleyka*. I'll jump to him on the ice floe.

The sea gulls answered her:

—Why not? Jump!

The fox jumped to a big sea gull sitting on an ice floe and sat next to him.

The sea gull told her:

—Wait a bit. Let me fit you with wings.

And she really fitted her with wings. Then she said:

—Well, let us start. But when the sun starts coming out, do not sneeze. You could fall down

The sun started to come up. The fox sneezed and fell into the sea.

—Yka-a! Yka-a!

The sea gulls laughed. And there was a log floating in the sea. The fox clambered on it. The log was washed ashore. The fox jumped to the ground. She told herself: "I should rest in the ditch!"

But then she took out her eyes. She told them:

—You, my eyes, guard me. If somebody shows up, wake me.

And the old *kala* hauled herself out of the abyss and started for home. She saw the fox sleeping at the path. And the fox's eyes also saw the *kala*. They began to wake up the fox but the fox did not awaken. Then the old *kala* thought of something. She filled one of her fur stockings with water and poured it on the fox. The fox awakened and was surprised:

—Aka-a-a! They poured water on me again. How disobedient you are, eyes! Didn't I tell you to waken me? I'm going to eat you!

And she ate the eyes. Eye-less she walked at random. She found redberries. She tried to put them in place of her eyes. The ground became red, but nothing was to be seen. They did not fit. She ate them. She found cranberries. Again she tried to put them in her eye sockets. They also did not fit. She ate them. Then she found some ice. She shattered it with a stone and put two round pieces in her eye sockets in place of her eyes. She cried with joy.

—Oho, how clear they are! How well I can see!

So she went on. She came to a stopping place and saw somebody's bow and arrow. And she saw further a sleeping bear. She shot an arrow directly into his buttock.

The bear awakened and cried out:

—Iki-i-i! Something has stung me.

The fox said:

—Oh! Oh! Why are you crying, my nephew?

—So it's you who is killing me!

—No, it's not so, I'm not the one. Your father was struck like that when he was in the tundra. And my mother cured him. Let me heat some small stones!

She actually heated some stones. She started to give them to him one by one. She said:

—Put them in your mouth! Swallow them!

The bear answered:

—Oh-oh-oh! I'm already getting better.

The fox told him:

—Just like this my mother healed and cured your father.

And the bear's innards were just seething.

The fox told him:

—Wait, I'll bring some snow; it'll quench your thirst.

She went to the top of the hill. She looked down from there.

But the bear was already dying. He had turned and dug up the ground all around him. He yelled:

—Fox where are you? I'm going to crush you!

Then the bear became quiet. The fox came to him and first, threw a stone at him. She was holding a piece of snow. She enticed him:

—My little nephew!

The bear did not respond. He had died. She was full of joy. She skinned him. She finished and started for home. She came home and asked of her daughter:

Imynna! Serve the hare meat!

Her daughter told her:

—Well, come on in, you'll have your meal.

Her mother went in, ate, and fell asleep right then.

In the morning she woke up and exclaimed:

—Oy! Go right away after the bear meat. Don't even leave the bones.

Her children asked her:

—With what did you kill the bear?

—Well, in the enemy's place there were arrows and a bow. I shot the bear with an arrow directly into his buttock. He awakened and said: "You've struck me." I answered: "My nephew, what's wrong with you?" The bear asked: "Did you shoot that?" I said: "No, not I. But I will cure you." I heated stones,and he ate them and died.

Her daughters went and soon returned. The fox cried out:

—O-o-o! They arrived! Imynna, cook it fast. Let your sisters eat.

The fox threaded all of the little bones into a plaited rope. And she went to the forest. She saw a wolf sleeping. She tied the bunch of bones to the tail of the fox and yelled out:

—Oy, oy! The ones with the big tusks are after you!

The wolf jumped up and flung himself toward the forest. But the bones got entangled in a bush. The tail was torn off.

The wolf ran to his grandma complaining:

—Look! My fluffy tail is no more! It was torn off. I was sleeping in the forest. And the fox woke me up.

The wolf decided to find the fox. He sought her for a long time. Then he came to the stone pillars.[14] He saw the fox there. He said:

—Why did you steal my fluffy tail?

The fox replied:

—Oy! I didn't do it! I'm a peaceful fox; I live not far from here.

All the same the wolf gave her a good licking. He came home and said:

—Grandma! Sew on my new fluffy tail.

And his grandma replied:

—Very well, I'll sew it on. But it's not fluffy anymore. It's flat, all tangled up.

—Well, so what. Let it be that way, —the wolf said, grieving.

In the meantime the fox crawled to the place where the wolf's tail was caught. She took it and went home crawling. She came home and said to her daughter:

—Imynna! Take this fluffy tail, cut it in pieces, and sew it to your and your sister's tails. From now on let all foxes have bushy tails.

Well, and the wolf's grandma also sewed on the tail. But it was not fluffy; it was flat and tangled.

But the wolf was happy with even such a tail. He said to his grandma:

—I'm going to bring some deer meat to our auntie, the fox.

He went off. He arrived at the fox's. The fox's daughter Imynna went out and exclaimed:

—Oh-oh-oh! My brother has come!

—Yes, I've come! Here take the deer meat. You know I've given your mother a good licking. So let her have this tasty morsel!

In answer Imynna said:

—Well, the hell with her! Why didn't you finish her off? She always plays dirty tricks. She can't live in any other way.

---

[14]The stone pillars are remnants of weathered rocks that have various fantastic forms, sometimes human-like forms. In the mythology of the Kereks, as well as of the Chukchi, they are petrified people.

The wolf stood there for a while and then said:

—Very well then, I'll go home.

He left.

And that's the way it was. Before the fox had a thin tail and the wolf a bushy one. Now the wolf has a flat, thin tail and the fox a fluffy one. The end of the fox's tail is white, but that of the arctic fox is black. These are the sewn on pieces of the wolf's tail.

The old people still say that, earlier, sea water was clean and fresh. But since the time when the fox fell from the ice floe into the water, it became turbid and salty. That is all.

6. How the Fox Proposed Marriage

Narrated in 1956 by an inhabitant of Maynypilgino village, Beringovsky *rayon*, Nutau, age 62. Recorded and translated into Russian by P. Skorik. Published in Voskoboynikov and Menoshchikov 1959, p. 445.

The fox heard that the roaming wolf Ankakumikaytyn intended to propose marriage to his neighbor, the dog. And the girl-dog lived with her brothers and her younger sister.

The fox sewed for herself a man's parka, breeches, boots and a cap. Then one day, when the brothers were not home, she went to the sisters as a guest. She arrived and they began to drink tea. The fox said to the older sister:

—I have two herds of reindeer, I want to propose marriage to you, —deceivingly.

And the young girl thought that here actually was a suitor and she said happily:

—Oy, you've again come to propose marriage!

She thought that this was the reindeer herder Ankakumikaytyn. The fox had bewitched her. The young girl hosted the fox with fat deer meat, brains, and blood-pudding. She offered the best pieces. And the fox sat there with her cap on. She was afraid to take her cap off because they could recognize her. She said:

—I'm a rich man; I don't have to take my cap off.

Suddenly barking was heard from afar. The young girls rejoiced. The older one said:

—These are my brothers returning from the hunt.

The fox was frightened. She wanted to run away. Then she thought a bit and said:

—Oy-oy! They will break up my herds!

She ran out of the house, clambered up the mountain and got some big stones ready. When the brothers came by, she cast the stones below and killed the brothers. The sisters did not see that she had killed them. The fox returned to the *yaranga*, drank a little of the tea and in the evening went home. She made off with all the supplies.

The sisters waited for their brothers for a long time. They did not come. They woke up in the morning, looked around—and there were no supplies. They went to the mountain and saw their brothers. They cried. The older one said:

—Who has brought us such misery?

The younger one thought for a while and said:

—No doubt it was the fox.

The older one objected:

—Why accuse her unjustly? You know that the fox did not come to see us.

—At one time the cap on Ankakumikaytyn's head shifted a bit and it seemed to me that it could be the fox.

The older one became angry. And the younger one said:

—Let's go to Ankakumikaytyn and find out. In any case our brothers are gone and we're left with no food at all.

The sisters went. Crying they told Ankakumikaytyn all about it. Ankakumikaytyn was surprised. It turned out that he did not go anywhere yesterday. He was in his storehouse all the time. Then they all guessed that it was the fox. They decided to take revenge. They went to the *yaranga* of the sisters.

The next day they saw the fox coming again, dressed as Ankakumikaytyn. But the real Ankakumikaytyn hid himself. Again the fox drank tea and ate everything that was tasty. The older sister was hosting her. But the younger one went quietly to the entryway and secured the door with a boulder. And the real Ankakumikaytyn was there. They grabbed the fox and tied her up.

Ankakumikaytyn asked:

—What will we do with the thief, with the robber?

The older one said:

—I don't know.

But the younger one said:

—We'll put her in a bag and carry her to the tundra.

And so they did. In the tundra they put the bag on a hummock. Frightened, the fox fainted. The younger sister gathered a bit of dry grass and bush stems and fastened them on the fox. The older one said:

—We ought to take her out of the bag and untie her.

The younger one did not agree:

—We should not! Let her sit in the bag tied up!

They quarreled for a long time. All the same, the older sister took the fox out of the bag and untied her. The younger again put the dry grass and twiglets on the fox. She loaded stones on her. She made a sort of oven around the fox with one opening. She set it on fire. The fox regained consciousness. She howled. Nobody heard her. Only when passers-by came about they would see something enveloped in flames run by. It seems that the fox jumped out of the oven, although the clothing worn by her to deceive, burned. So she was scorched in the tundra and she ran away. From that time on red foxes appeared.

And the sisters together with Ankakumikaytyn buried the brothers. All of them started living together. The older one married Ankakumikaytyn. The younger one took care of their children. When she grew up, she herself married. That is all.

7. The Trickster Fox

Narrated in 1970 by an inhabitant of Maynypilgino village, Beringovsky *rayon*, Keshginto, age 67. He was illiterate, did not speak Russian but spoke very well in the Kerek and Chukchi languages. Recorded and translated into Russian by V. Leontev and E. Khatkana. This is the Kerek variant of the widespread subject matter of the tale about the vixen tricking the dumb wolf. Elsewhere, instead of the fox and wolf, the personages of such tales are the arctic fox and the bear, the vixen and the bear. (Compare with the Eskimo tale no. 50 in Dolitsky and Michael 2000).

The fox met the bear.

—Oh-oh, my nephew, I'm glad to see you!

—I'm glad too.

They walked together to the edge of a high cliff.

—Let's sleep a little in the full sun, —the fox said.

—Very well, —agreed the bear.

And the cliff was high and sheer.

—Don't lie down at the edge, —the fox said to the bear, —you could roll over and fall down.

He lay farther away from the edge.

They lay down to sleep, the fox at the very edge of the precipice, and the bear next to her. Just as the bear fell asleep, the fox at once moved over to his other side. She said to the sleeping one:

—My nephew, you'll move and you'll bump into me, —and she pushed him slightly toward the edge.

Suddenly she grasped him and pushed him. The bear fell off the cliff.

The fox jumped up and began to lower herself to the foot of the cliff. There she saw that the bear was dead.

The fox had many children. They carried the bear meat home. There was enough food. The fox said to her oldest daughter Imynna:

—Imynna, don't throw the bear's backbones away. I'll collect them and bury them.

And sure enough, the fox collected the backbones and tied them to a rope.

Then the fox made up her mind and went to the tundra again. She went and dragged the backbones tied to the rope after her. Suddenly she saw a wolf sound asleep in the bushes. She tied the backbones to the wolf's tail and she then yelled out:

—Nephew, my nephew, the big-toothed monster is after you! Run quickly! Run into the thick bushes!

The wolf jumped up and in fear threw himself into the bushes. The backbones entwined themselves in the branches ripping off the fluffy white tail of the wolf.

The wolf ran home and cried out:

—Grandma, grandma! I've lost my tail somewhere!

—Where were you running about? How can you lose your own tail? —his grandmother scolded him and she sewed him another tail from remnants of an old hide.

And at that time the fox followed the footsteps of the wolf. She saw a wolf's tail hanging in the bushes. She took it and went home.

—Imynna, here, I've brought a fluffy, white tail of a wolf. From this tail sew on a white end to the tails of all foxes.

Imynna sewed on to the tails of all foxes pieces of the wolf's tail. From that time on, the tail ends of all the foxes were white.

8. Kukki

Narrated in 1970 on the lake Kuet by an inhabitant of Maynypilgino village in Beringovsky *rayon*, E. Kalgichapau, age 54, illiterate. He did not speak Russian. Recorded and translated into Russian by V. Leontev and E. Khatkana. In the tales of the very small group of Kereks, the raven is presented as the creator of everything alive, as well as the land and the mountains. The cycle of tales about the raven also found in nos. 9-12 of this publication.

The very young mice said:

—Come; let's go to the seashore.

They went to the seashore and suddenly they saw a very small motley seal that had been washed ashore by a wave.

One little mouse said:

—Ukh! We've found a very small seal!

An older mouse then said:

—Quiet, or grandpa will again hear it and he will come here.

And Kukki was sitting in the *yaranga* and he said to his wife:

—Miti, I'm going outside to do the necessary.

Kukki went out. Suddenly he heard somebody squeaking like mice. He went to the seashore.

—Over there, over there! Grandpa is coming. I told you he would hear us, —cried out one of the mice. —Be quiet or he'll take the seal from us.

—What did you find? —asked Kukki.

—Nothing, grandpa, nothing at all, —the mice replied.

And unnoticed they had covered the seal with dry seaweed.

—But wasn't there something thrown on the shore? It left a trace there.

—Yes, that must be some rootstock that was thrown on the shore.

Kukki thought for a little while then he suddenly said:

—Come here and lick my head; look for lice.

The smallest of the mice answered:

—Come here grandpa, I'll lick you and find some lice.

But her sisters laughed at her:

—Little sister, who do you think you are? Stop in a shaggy head to look for lice.

What are they saying? —said Kukki, getting angry.

—They're saying it's no good to look for lice in your shaggy head.

—All right then; all of you now grasp my hair and you, the smallest one, hold on at the back of my neck.

The mice grasped his hair, Kukki shook his head and the mice fell in the water; but the smallest one did not.

The little sister cried:

—Ee-ee, why did you shake your head and throw my sisters in the water?!

—Don't worry; they'll get out of the water. You know that they can swim. And now tell me about what you have found. Where is it?

—We've already told you that we've found rootstock.

Kukki did not believe her. He threw back the seaweed and there, under it, was the small seal.

—Why did you hide this from your grandpa? Now see here granddaughter, let's divide it in halves.

And the little mouse was foolish.

—All right, let's divide it, —she agreed.

They divided it and each went their own way. Kukki brought his load home. His son, Auppali, met him and asked:

—Oh-oh, what are you bringing father?

—Well, here it is, a small seal. Tell your mother to do a thanksgiving service.

Auppali ran ahead:

—Father found a small seal. We have to do a thanksgiving service.

—Oh-oh, a small seal? —Miti asked.

—Yes, a small one.

Kukki came in. And Miti sang and danced, thanking the spirits:

—Ku-y-kki ki-i-lled a sse-a-l wi-i-th one fli-i-p-per, wi-i-th one ki-id-ney!

—Well, it was good to catch it! —Kukki said. —Cook it and for the time being take it outside. Take it there and say: "Well, we've all had our fill."

—How come that you've killed the animal and now you don't want to eat? —Miti wondered.

They carried the pot with the seal meat outside, and went to sleep themselves.

And the mice got out of the water and went home. Their grandmother told them:

—Oh-ho, you've come!

—Yes, but grandpa divided the seal in halves and took one.

—When they go to sleep, we'll go after it, —grandma calmed them.

And they did quite so. The mice went all together to Kukki's dwelling. And Kukki was sleeping with his mouth open. They relieved themselves right into his mouth. They pulled the meat out of the pot and ran off.

Kukki woke up and said:

—Miti, will you bring the seal meat? But my mouth smells something like mouse droppings.

His wife went out.

—There's nothing there; the pot is empty.

Kukki became angry:

—All right then, I'm going to go to them! Give me a small pot.

Kukki went. He began to shake the *yaranga* of the mice.

The grandmother mouse said to her younger daughter:

—Look, your sisters will perish; go and tell grandfather this: "Why are you frightening me? You know I am the daughter of Sikulylan, your son."

The little mouse went outside:

—Grandpa, why are you frightening me? Don't shake the *yaranga*; better have a bite of the root plant.

In the meantime the mice urinated on the root plant.

—Come, you'll have a bite!

—And why did you take the seal away?

—No, we did not take it. When we divided it we ate it right there.

—I don't believe you!

—My older sisters perished!

—All right, let's go.

Kukki went in the *yaranga* of the mice.

—Grandpa, listen to me!

Kukki came to his senses:

—Why did I frighten the daughter of my son? Well bring in the pot!

Kukki entered the *yaranga* and it collapsed.

—Oh, oh, what happened to the *yaranga*! —the mice were frightened.

—It was blown down by a gust of wind! Then Kukki built it again.

—Here, eat the root plant! Then the girls will lick you and look for lice, —said the grandmother mouse.

The little girls licked the raven. He fell asleep.

—Entangle his eyelashes.

They did.

—You should awaken, father-in-law! It's getting dark.

—Oh, I must have fallen asleep. No doubt the girls have done my hair. I guess I'll go.

—When you'll be near your *yaranga*, lower your eyelashes, —the grandmother mouse told him as he was leaving.

Kukki began to walk toward his *yaranga*. He lowered his eyelashes [eyes].

—Oh, oh, it's like the earth is burning! —Kukki could see nothing.

He became angry:

—Miti, Miti! —he cried out. —Put the fire out, the earth is burning!

His son Auppali ran to meet him. Kukki wanted to grasp him but then his wife came and tore the eyelashes out.

—How unruly you are! The mice entangled your eyelashes; the earth is not burning.

Oh, that's what they did to me! I'll go again. Give me the small pot!

Kukki went to the mice again. He shook the *yaranga* of the mice. "I'm not going to believe that girl anymore," —he decided.

The grandmother-mouse spoke to her granddaughter:

—Tell him: "Grandpa, why are you frightening me? I am the daughter of Sikulylan."

And the little mouse told that to the raven Kukki.

—I don't believe you! Why did you entangle my eyelashes?

—I didn't do it, my older sisters did. I did not entangle your eyelashes.

—I don't believe you!

—It's true, I didn't, grandpa. Why are you frightening me?

—Ah, you're the daughter of my son! Here's a small pot for you!

Kukki entered the *yaranga* again.

—Oh, the *yaranga* fell down again! —the mice cried out.

—That was the wind gusting, —and the raven righted the *yaranga*.

—Eat some of the root plant grandpa!

Kukki ate some of the root plant.

—Let the little girls lick you again, —the grandmother-mouse told him.

Kukki fell asleep.

—Paint his nose!

The mice painted his nose. The grandmother mouse awakened him:

—Wake up, it's getting dark; it's time to go home.

—Oh, how well I slept! And soundly!

—Well, now go and drink some, —said the grandmother-mouse.

—You're right; after eating root plants, one gets thirsty.

Kukki went to the water and saw his reflection.

—Oh, what a beautiful red nose that woman has! Well, come here; show yourself! Oh, you don't want to! Wait a bit, I'll only go home, wait.

Kukki went home. He brought a white stone, cutting board and [wooden] scraper, and grabbed the *polog* with stanchions. He threw the stone in the water. It gurgled and sank.

—Oho, it pleased her; she accepted the gift!

Kukki threw in the cutting board and scraper. But they were wooden and floated.

—Now I'll go, —he tucked himself under the cover of the *polog* and bent forward.

He fell in the river and it carried him to the seashore.

Miti became worried and said to herself:

—Where did Kukki go? I'll go and look at the seashore.

Miti went to the seashore. She saw a *polog* with stanchions that had been on the shore by the waves. She uncovered the *polog* and there was Kukki.

—You're some jealous woman. Why did you come here? —Kukki said.

—I'm not jealous at all, and I didn't even know that you were in the *polog*.

Kukki said:

—Let's go home, Miti!

—Let's go. All this happened because the mice are taunting you, —Miti said.

And the ravens went home.

9. Kukki and His Wife Miti

Narrated in 1970 by an inhabitant of Maynypilgino village, Beringovsky *rayon*, Keshginto, age 67. He was illiterate, did not speak Russian but spoke very well in the Kerek and Chukchi languages. Recorded and translated into Russian by V. Leontev and E. Khatkana. The tale reflects the recreation of an animal, which had been eaten by the provider of food for the household.

There was nothing to eat; there was hunger. Kukki went to the forest after tree bark.

—You have to go to the forest more often, the children are hungry. We'll have to feed them bark! —Miti called to him when he was leaving.

Kukki went to the forest for bark. Miti mixed it with roe and fed the children but gave very little of it to Kukki.

—There is not enough food, eat the soles of the old boots, —Miti said to him.

Every day Kukki went after the bark. When he returned Miti fed the children, but he had only the old soles.

At one time Kukki came to a pool. From it a pink salmon [*gorbuscha*] was looking out.

—Come here! —the salmon invited him. —Oh, you've lost weight! You're thin!

—There's no food; we're hungry!

—Yes, you are very thin!

Kukki married the salmon.

—Go now and take the fish home, —the salmon said to him.

Kukki took the fish home.

—Here Miti, I've brought food. I've brought many fish.

—Who gave them to you?

—It's like this; I married a salmon.

—And are you going to live with her all the time? Wouldn't it be better if you brought her home?

—Next time I'll bring her home.

—You bring her right now, and make haste!

Kukki went to his wife, the salmon, and said:

—My wife, Miti told me to bring you to her.

—All right, I'll go, —the salmon agreed and she loaded Kukki with boiled fish.

Kukki brought the salmon to his house.

—Here, I've brought you a helpmate; Miti meet her!

—Oh, you've already brought her!

—Yes, I've brought her.

—Now go again to the forest for wood and bark.

Kukki went to the forest.

Miti cut the salmon in pieces and cooked it for the hungry children. They ate the salmon but the spirit of the salmon returned home.

—Oho, you've come back! —Miti greeted Kukki.

—Yes. I've returned. I've brought you wood. And where is your helpmate?

—She's not here.

—Where is she?

—She probably went home.

The next day Kukki went to his wife, the salmon. He saw her again.

—Miti cut me in pieces and cooked me. Don't take me there anymore, —the salmon begged Kukki.

The salmon became thin from the time they cooked her; before that she was plump. Despite all this Kukki brought her home, and he went to the forest; Miti again cooked her. Kukki returned from the forest:

—Miti, take this pack of bark! And where is your helpmate?

—Again, she's not here. No doubt she went home.

—How come that she's always leaving?

Kukki went to the salmon.

—Where are you? —he cried out.

—I'm going to quit going to you; I'm not going to have all of me eaten.

—Very well, it'll be better if you stay home.

And the salmon began to live in the pond again.

10. The Fearful Kukki

Narrated in 1970 by an inhabitant of Maynypilgino village, Beringovsky *rayon*, Keshginto, age 67. He was illiterate, did not speak Russian but spoke very well in the Kerek and Chukchi languages. Recorded and translated into Russian by V. Leontev and E. Khatkana. The subject matter of this tale has something in common with that of the Itelmen tale "The Fight of the Two Kutkhs" (see no. 86 of this edition). In the latter the earth raven Kutkh fights the sea raven Kutkh. Only the beginning of the tale is presented here. Because of the illness of the narrator Keshgynto, V. Leontev could not record the entire story.

Kukki married and began to live with Miti. At that time Kukki was very much afraid of the sun. As soon as the sun rose he fell to the ground in fear. Miti scolded the fearful Kukki. She had to do everything by herself; alone she obtained the food. But then Miti became pregnant and gave birth to two sons. But Kukki, as before, was afraid of the sun and he sat in the dwelling all the time.

Miti often went to the sea. She had a second sea-husband there. From the sea she brought foods of the sea. Miti became pregnant again and gave birth to two sons fathered by her sea-husband. And, as before, Kukki was afraid of the sun. As soon as the sun rose he fell to the ground in fear.

The first two sons were named Sikulylan and Anantakilan. The sons fathered by the sea-husband were also named thus.

Miti became pregnant again and gave birth to two daughters. They were named Sinillymnylnakkut and Anayuptynakkut. Miti wrapped one of them in moss, carried her to the tundra and tossed her away.

The children grew up and began to hunt for wild deer.

—Where do they go? —one day Kukki asked his wife.

—They hunt for wild deer.

Kukki became wiser. At that time all the land was flat; there were no mountains. Kukki disliked the land being flat.

—Well, I'm going to make mountains, —Kukki said one day.

And it happened. When they woke up, the next day they saw that mountains had appeared.

—Now you can hunt deer in the mountains, —he told the children.

And so Miti lived with two husbands. As before, she goes to her sea-husband and from there brings food. In the meantime, the girl that was thrown away by Miti was picked up by other people and nurtured by them to maturity. One day the two Sikulylans came upon the settlement and saw the girl there. She was already fully-grown.

—I am going to court her, —said one of the Sikulylans.

—Why not? It's all right, —the people answered.

Finally Sikulylan married her. He did not know that she was his own sister.

11. The Fox and Kukki

Narrated in 1970 on the lake Kuet by an inhabitant of Maynypilgino village in Beringovsky *rayon*, the Kerek M. Etynkeu, age 67, who was hardly literate and spoke Russian with difficulty. Recorded and translated into Russian by V. Leontev together with a Kerek woman E. Khatkano, also an inhabitant of Maynypilgino village in Beringovsky *rayon*, age 70. This tale about animals contains several topics about the raven Kukki and the clever fox. Separately some of these topics appear quite frequently in Itelmen and Koryak folklore.

The fox came to her daughter and said:

—Imynna, give me the string bag!

—Where are you going?

—I'm going to trick Kukki.

—Quit tricking! Get your food the right way!

—No, I'm going anyway!

Her daughter gave her the string bag and the fox left. It had already become dark but the moon shone brightly. She came to the dwelling of Kukki and began to remove snow from her boots with an antler stick [*vybivalka*]. But she did it in such a way that it seemed that two had arrived.

—Chu-chu-chu-chu! —the fox stamped with her boots.

—Wait a bit, wait a bit, I'll come out right away, —the voice of Kukki was heard from the dwelling.

Kukki wondered why different kinds of noise were heard:

—Hey, who's there?!

—Yes, it's me; I'm here with my brother-in-law! My husband's reindeer are very frightened.

—Drive the reindeer away!

—Oh-oh, don't come out, better stay inside!

—Oh, then I'll go back!

—Wait a bit, wait a bit, my husband is a night owl; he doesn't like light. Put out the oil lamps!

—Oh, I'll go and tell my daughters!

Kukki went into the dwelling and said:

—Ilynau, Chilnakkut, put out the lamps!

Miti, the wife of Kukki, wondered:

—What kind of guest is it that arrived? He doesn't like light. Well, since he requested it, let it be so.

—Hey! —Kukki called out. —Come on, the lamps are out. No doubt your husband has tethered the reindeer?

The fox entered the dwelling.

—Oh, they've arrived! —said the hosts (You know, they thought that two had arrived).

—Yes, we have arrived. Here is my husband. I've married a night owl.

—Well, sit down!

— My husband has taught me to do everything in the dark, —boasted the fox.

—Let's eat a bit! Cook a dish for aunty; let's eat seafood!

They cut cheese and meat into small chunks. But the smart fox put all the food in her bag.

—Oh, we've eaten well! —the fox said.

—You shouldn't go away hungry, just a little more.

—Is there any egg sausage?

—Miti, do we have any egg sausage? —Kukki asked his wife.

Miti went and fetched the egg sausage.

—Wait a bit, I'll prepare the dish myself, —said Kukki trying to please the fox.

And the fox put the sausage also in her bag. Although she was by herself she cunningly chattered and talked in two voices—those of herself and of her husband.

The moon shone through the ice-pane window. Kukki's son, Aupalli, then said to his parents:

—The fox is tricking us; she's talking in different voices.

—What is he whispering about? —the fox was beginning to feel uneasy. —I am showing my appreciation.

—Hold your tongue boy; come to your senses! —Kukki became angry with his son.

—Oh, we've eaten our fill!

—Are you leaving then?

—Yes, we're leaving. My husband's reindeer are very easily frightened, —said the fox in her own voice and then added in a strange voice:

—Yes, yes, the reindeer are easily frightened. They're used to one person only; only one person can drive them. Only I know how to handle them.

—Well, then I won't come with you.

—Yes, yes, don't come out, —said the fox happily, —we'll manage by ourselves.

—As you wish!

The fox went out and as soon as she was by herself she ran home as fast as she could.

Aupalli said:

—Oh, mother. The fox is [lives] by herself. She has no husband named Kymyvaltyn.

—All right. It's not your business, lad.

—Ho, ho, ho! —the fox came home to her daughters.

—Oh, you've come!

—Yes, indeed I've come! Now, you untie the string bag and feed your young brother.

The sisters fed their younger brother Lymnoynytkyn.

—And they gave you egg sausage too! What were the sausages filled with?

—The gut was filled with duck egg yolk. And they also fed me with seafood—dried whale meat and blubber.

The next day the Kukki family awakened. The father said to his son:

—Now you follow the traces and see where they went.

Aupalli followed the traces.

—What happened? —Kukki asked, when he returned.

—I've only seen the traces of one fox, —Aupalli answered.

—It seems that they left the reindeer far away.

And the fox said to her own:

—Tomorrow I'm going again. I'll pull out the winter net from under the ice and freeze it. You follow in my footsteps. We'll all go.

The next day the sky became dark; night arrived. But the moon was shining brightly.

The foxes came to Kukki's dwelling.

—I'll pull out the net from here, —the fox told them stopping at an ice hole, —and while the net is freezing, we'll go to the food storage. As for the hosts—they'll be asleep.

Nobody was there. The foxes worked by themselves. The fox got into the food storage and dragged everything out.

—Carry all you can, —she told her children. —Go home and I'll go behind the net. I'll tell them: "Here is a great gift for you from your brother-in-law."

The children went home. In the meantime the net had frozen, and was clinking with icicles, as if they were of iron. The fox went toward Kukki.

—Chu-chu-chu-chu! —near the dwelling she removed snow from her boots with an antler stick.

—Oh-oh, the fox came again, brother-in-law came again! Wait a bit; I'll come out there!

Kukki came to the outer entrance.

—Hey! Who's there?

—It is we, we, we! Like yesterday we've come again. Your brother-in-law has brought you a great gift.

—Where is he?

30

—Here's a full bag, —and she gave Kukki the frozen net. —Only don't put it anywhere. The iron is cold; it'll sweat and get rusty. Put it somewhere high, on the *polog*.

—Miti, Miti! —Kukki called out. —Look here, brother-in-law has brought us riches! Iron! Put it high up, on the *polog*.

—We're going to come in! —the fox called out.

—Come in, the lamps are already out.

—Oh-oh, they've come again!

—Yes, they've come! They've decided to visit their cousins more often. They've come to eat a bit.

They cut the food into thin pieces and put it on a dish. The fox made noises as if two were eating.

—Are there any egg sausages?

—No, we ate all of them yesterday!

—What a pity. I like them best.

—Now, Miti, hurry! Brother-in-law has walked a lot; let him eat well.

—Father, father, the fox started talking by herself. She was feigning and talking with different voices. She was by herself.

—Oh! The boy again said something. The fox should show her gratitude.

—Well, he's simply that way, he doesn't listen; he's still dumb. If you were just one, you know we'd see it.

—Oh, thank you, we've had our fill. We'll take the gifts.

Itchym, a relative of Kukki, also watched the fox closely. At once he said to Kukki:

—She's only one doing the talking. She's tricking us again.

But Kukki did not hear.

—Maybe you still want to eat a bit. If you want to, say so, —he apparently also guessed at things.

—Just stick your paw in the bag and get food, but we have to get some sleep. We slept very little last night.

—Is there more food?

—Didn't I tell you, go by yourself, stick your paw in the bag and get food.

And in the meantime Miti prepared the string bag.

—How will I get the food?

—Well, come over here and stick your paw in the bag, —Miti said.

—Stick your paw in deeper, deeper!

The fox listened to her and stuck her paw in the bag with the food. And then Miti tightened the strings of the bag together with the paw.

—Oy, oy, oy! What are you doing to me?!

—And why are you playing such tricks?! You don't have a husband, you came by yourself, and yesterday you were also by yourself.

The fox jumped up and ran away. So she ran with the bag on her paw as if she was caught in a trap. So the clever fox made away with the bag.

—Imynna, Imynna, my hand is numb! They tied my hand in a bag as if it were a trap!

—You're always tricking to deceive! Wouldn't it be better to ask for food?

—Heat some water quickly; I'll wash my hand.

When the fox was running away, Kukki called after her:

—If you want to play your tricks go to that rich woman Kontytval!

—Imynna, untie my hand quickly.

—You know I told you yesterday that it's better to ask.

—Yes, you would ask them! There are no such people.

Imynna heated the water and the fox washed her paw.

The next day the Kukki family awakened. Kukki said to his daughters:

—Check up on our supplies. No doubt they stole everything.

The daughters went to the food supplies and returned.

—There's no food whatever; they dragged everything out. Only the bare walls and bones are left, —they told Kukki.

However, the ravens were satisfied that they had rid themselves of the cunning fox.

But the fox could not calm down.

—I'm going to go after food to that rich woman Kontytval, —she said.

—When are you going to go?

—I'll go tomorrow.

—You can't live without tricking. You should get food the right way.

—You'll never get anything the right way or the nice way. There are no such people. Now you go to sleep. Tomorrow when it gets dark, I'll go.

The next day they awakened.

—Now, Imynna, give me the string bag. I'm going to get some food.

—Do it only the right way; don't do anything bad. Kontytval lives with her sister-dogs. Something could happen there. The Kukkis only tied up your hand.

—No, no, I'm going to ask the right way. Well, I'm going.

The fox went to the rich woman Kontytval. As she did at Kukki's, she began to beat off the snow from her boots with the antler stick. She did it so that it appeared that two had arrived.

—Chu-chu-chu-chu! —rattled the fox and stood not far to the side of the door.

—Hey, who's there?

—I! —then she remembered:

—We, we, we!

—Who are you?

—We're here with Kymyvaltyn. I married a rich Chukchi. Our herd will be here soon; he'll slaughter a reindeer for you. Just now the herd is a bit far, at the Pynakyn Mountain. But my husband is a night guest, so won't you put out the oil lamps.

—How will you eat in the dark?

—We've learned, we're used to it. We can take the food from the dish.

—I'll go and tell them to put out the lamps.

They put out the lamps but one of the sister-dogs said:

—Older sister, you know the fox is by herself, there's nobody with her.

—All right, let them come in, —Kontytval did not believe her.

—Well then, have you put out the lamps? We're already coming! —she called out from outside.

She entered. Then the fox said in another voice:

—I'm a night person; I can only be in the dark.

—Yes, yes, sit down here.

They prepared a dish with food, but the fox did not eat it—she put everything in the string bag. She loaded as much as she could carry.

—Are there any egg sausages?

—No, we don't have them. We're just women living together, we don't climb the cliffs to get eggs, we don't make egg sausages. But do eat the food.

They wanted to slice more food, but the fox said quickly:

—Let me do it. You're not used to doing it in the dark, —and she made her way closer to the door.

The fox thought: "I'll slice the food here, near the door, and then I'll suddenly, as if by accident, cut myself."

A sister-dog whispered:

—Older sister! The fox is by herself, there's no husband with her.

—Really, no husband?

—What is she talking about? —the fox had heard her. —I'm not tricking you. Control your sister. The herd is very close.

Kontytval rapped the sister-dog who had talked to her about the fox.

32

—You should rap all your sisters, —added the fox. —The herd is very close. Oh, we've had our fill! We're now going to meet the herd.

—I'll go with you.

—No, no, we'll go by ourselves. My husband's reindeer are very easily frightened. Sit on the *polog*.

The fox jumped outside and ran away.

Kontytval said to her sister-dog:

—If the fox comes again, I'll untie you and you'll chase after her.

The fox came home running and said to her children:

—Tomorrow you'll come with me. We'll get a lot to eat. The woman-dog is very rich. There is a lot of food in her storage rooms. While I entertain her, you'll drag out everything from the storage rooms.

The next day all of the foxes went off to the dogs. The fox showed her children the storage rooms.

—Make haste, —she told her children, —take only as much as you can carry and return home quickly. I'll run slowly to them.

The fox ran up to the dogs' dwelling.

—Chu-chu-chu-chu! —again she started to stamp her boots.

The dogs realized that the fox had come again. One of them said to her older sister:

—Yesterday you promised that you would untie me!

—Wait a little while, —and she called outside:

—Hey, who is there?

—It's us, us, us! Your guests of yesterday! The herd is very close. It'll be here by tomorrow.

—When you shake your boots clean, come in.

—Did you put out the lights?

—Yes, we've put them out, come on in!

"Oh, oh, somehow I'm afraid!" —thought the fox, and she called out:

—Wait a little; my husband is taking his cap off. I'll put it away right now.

Finally the fox entered the dwelling

—Sit down, sit down! Certainly you'll eat something?

—Well, I'll eat something, —the fox agreed, and she really wanted to eat.

Kontytval quietly took her sister-dog aside and whispered to her:

—Don't rush at her while she's on the *polog*, let's listen to what she has to say.

—I would very much like to eat some food, —pleaded the fox.

—The food is here, near the door. And you know, you've tricked us.

—Oy, oy, oy! We've grown up together, from the same plate we've eaten! —the fox became frightened, jumped up and ran off.

The sister-dog ran after her.

—Look here. Don't bite her to death; tear her *kerker* [parka] only, —Kontytval called after her and untied her other sister-dog.

Although the fox ran very fast, the dogs caught up to her.

—Oy, oy, oy! We've grown up at one platter; we warmed ourselves at the same hearth!

—You're a lier! We didn't grow up at one hearth, we're not friends! Why are you grumbling? Now we're going to tear you to pieces!

—Oy, oy, oy! —the fox cried out.

And the dogs grasped her fur parka and tore it to pieces.

—Oy, oy! They've grabbed it!

—Well, let's let her run home to her children! We've frightened her enough, and tore up her parka, —said one of the dogs to the other.

So the fox ran home, her parka all torn up. She ran in and said in a plaintive voice:

—Imynna, throw a piece of wood on the fire.

—What happened?

—When the sisters-dogs were biting, they tore my parka to pieces.

—Serves you right, you thief! Some day they'll kill you!

—I'll never do it again; they'd really kill me. Prepare the *polog*. I'm going to lie down.

The fox calmed down; for the present she did not plan to go anywhere.

The next day the dogs awakened. They went to check the storage rooms. Two of the storage rooms were empty; the children of the fox had emptied them while she was talking with the dogs. At least it was good that they had taken their revenge. Most likely she would not return.

The raven Kukki said to his wife Miti:

—I'm going to go to Kontytval. It's possible that our niece, the fox, had visited her. You know yesterday I told her that the woman-dog had a lot of food, that she was very rich.

Kukki went to the dogs. He was cleaning his boots with an antler stick.

—Oh-oh, uncle must have arrived. He doesn't clean his boots like the fox, —the dogs had guessed.

—Hey, who is it?

—It's me, Kukki, your uncle!

—When you clean your boots, come on in. Do you want the oil lamps put out?

Kukki laughed:

—No, don't put them out. We've already gotten used to light. No doubt the fox was at your place yesterday?

—She was. Then my sister saw that she was alone, without a husband. Even I guessed that the fox was planning to trick us.

—And we have been left without food; the foxes took everything.

—Here they have robbed only two of the storage pits. What are you going to do? Maybe you'll stay for the night?

All right, I'll stay.

The next morning the dogs awakened and their uncle was ready to go home.

—It's getting to be light, I'm going home, —Kukki said.

—How can we host you? —and they gave him dried meat, the meat of a wild deer and meat of a mountain ram.

—Take with you whatever you want!

—Oh-oh, I'll take it, I'll take it! Really, my children may have already returned with a catch.

—If there isn't any food, come to us!

—Well, if there isn't, I will.

Kukki started for home. His son met him:

—Father is coming. It seems he's carrying a lot of food, very much. He's walking very slowly.

Kukki lowered the food from his arms and told his son:

—Take this to your mother, to the house. You see how slowly I walk; it's heavy for me.

The son ran home and said to his mother:

—Father is bringing many presents; it's heavy for him. And here is a present for you. He has wild deer meat and that of a wild ram.

Kukki arrived. He called out:

—Hey, Miti, take this load!

—Oh, oh, you've come?

—Yes, I've come! The fox visited the dogs, she tricked them, but they took revenge on her. But, untie the load and eat!

The ravens fed the children with dried meat, wild deer meat and that of the mountain ram.

And that is all.

I've finished telling the tale. I told everything I remembered, some I have forgotten. Earlier we were told these tales by old people. We've heard them over a long time, so I tell them in parts, but I tell them exactly, not just so. Really, this is all. I've finished.

34

12. Kukki and the Wolf

Narrated in 1970 on the lake Kuet by an inhabitant of Maynypilgino village in Beringovsky *rayon*, the Kerek M. Etynkeu, age 67, who was hardly literate and spoke Russian with difficulty. Recorded and translated into Russian by V. Leontev together with a Kerek woman E. Khatkano, also an inhabitant of Maynypilgino village in Beringovsky *rayon*, age 70. This is the Kerek variant of the tale about the raven and wolf sliding down a mountain. Different from the Chukchi variant ("The Wolf and the Raven," no. 55 in Dolitsky and Michael 1997) and the Eskimo one ("The Raven and the Wolf", in *Eskimoskiye skazki i legendy*, Menovshchikov 1969, p. 23), in the Kerek variant the sliding of personages from the mountain appears to be only the beginning of the adventures of Kukki. In this regard the Kerek tale has much in common with the Koryak text no. 15 of this collection in which other wolves and their mythical helpers endeavor to take revenge on the raven for sinking their brothers in the deep of the ocean.

I'll tell the story about the wolf.

Kukki said to his wife:

—Miti, will you get me the straw sled.

—There's no straw sled, only a braided rope.

Kukki did not believe her; he went to see for himself.

—What are you looking for?

—Well, the sled.

—Where are you going?

—Over there, I'm going to slide down the hill.

Kukki went there. He slid down the hill.

—Oh! How nice; the sky flashes before your eyes! —Kukki cried out in joy.

He slid down the hill again and cried out:

—Oh! How nice; the sky flashes so!

The wolf heard how joyfully Kukki cried out when sliding down the hill. "Where is he crying out from?" —thought the wolf and he went over to Kukki.

—Hey, grandpa. What are you doing?

—Oh, you've frightened me. Where did you come from?

—From over there. I heard you cry out when you were sliding and I thought: "I'll go over and see how grandpa is sliding. Maybe I'll slide along!"

—No, you can't, you'd slide in the water

—No, I won't slide. My paws are long.

—Then slide, since your paws are long.

—And what should I say when I am sliding?

—Yell out: "Oh-oh, how nice; the sky flashes by!"

—Very well, I'll cry out like that.

The wolf slid down the hill. Gurgle, gurgle—he rolled into the sea.

—Oy-oy, grandpa, I fell in the water! Pull me out! —the wolf cried.

—No, I won't pull you out. You know, you have long paws! But I have curved claws; that's why I don't fall in the water.

—Pull me out, grandpa!

—I will not!

—If you don't pull me out my paws will get numb!

—No, I will not pull you out; you are the one with long paws.

—Grandpa, I'll give you a swarm of fleas.[15]

—I don't need fleas.

---

[15]Swarm of fleas (*gachyychin nallulan*) — come in the form of small, quick-running insects, white in color, which establish themselves in raw or moldy hide, wool, or fur.

—Hey grandpa. My paws are getting very numb, —the wolf called out from the water.

—I'm telling you, I'm not going to pull you out! —persisted Kukki.

—I'll give you a herd of mountain sheep.

—My children hunt mountain sheep themselves.

—Then I'll give you wolverines!

—I don't need wolverines. I tell you, my children hunt for many kinds of animals.

—What can I give you? —the wolf asked. —Oh, oh, I know!. I'll give you my long-eared sister in marriage.

—That's fine! Kukki said happily. Hey, brother-in-law, wait a bit, wait a bit, I'll pull you out right away!

Kukki pulled the wolf out.

—Br-r-r! My paws have almost become numb, — the wolf said and he wrung out his clothes.

Kukki helped him.

—Now what? —Kukki asked. —Are you going to give away your sister to me?

—I don't have any sisters.

—Wha-a-t? You've tricked me. Well. I'm not going to slide any more, —Kukki was offended. —Which valley are you going to go in?

—I'm going to go in the Vatvytkavnyn valley. And you?

—And I'm going to the upper reaches of the Antchin River.

Kukki and the wolf went in different directions. They went through the valleys of the rivers, but in their upper reaches the rivers joined. The wolf arrived at the source of the Vatvytkavnyn. Kukki climbed up to the upper reaches of the Antchin River. Then, suddenly he changed into a piece of fatty deer meat.

—Oho! —the wolf was surprised. —My friends must have left some food for me, —and he ate the piece of meat.

And it was Kukki.

The wolf went home, and in his stomach Kukki was stirring.

—Oh, probably my father brought these and hung them here in the food storage, —Kukki thus reasoned in the stomach of the wolf, and he took the guts and threw them out.

—Grandpa, it seems that you're talking out of me.

—I'm not with you, but am in my house. I'm sitting in the food storage room.

—Oy, you've thrown out my guts!

—It's not so, you know I'm at home, —And I've thrown out the kidneys myself. —Pah! —he said. —No doubt Itchym hung his stinking boots here.

—Oy, my kidneys!

—What are you yelping about? I'm here at home, in the food storage room, —and he threw out the lungs. —Pah! Again it must be that Itchym brought this.

—Grandpa, those are my lungs!

—Don't make up things; I'm here in the food storage, — and he threw out the heart. —Pah! This must be the haft of a spear. Why is it hanging here?!

—Grandpa! That's my soul! —Pkhu! [Puff!], —and the wolf died.

—Oy, oy, I killed the wolf! —Kukki cried out and jumped out.

Kukki went home. His son Auppali saw him and said to his mother:

—Father is returning from sliding.

—So what, let him come, —his mother replied.

Kukki became angry and called out:

—Auppali, tell mother that she has to do a thanksgiving rite.

—All right, —Auppali said and went in the *zemlyanka*.

—Mother, father was dragging something and he said that you should do a thanksgiving rite.

—Well! But you go and see what he's dragging, —and she started doing the rite.

She sang out:

—Ku-u-kki ki-i-ll-ed a wo-o-l-ff with-out gu-u-ts! Ky-a, ky-a, ky-a!

Kukki came in the *zemlyanka*.

—That's enough of singing; I've already come in.

—Let the daughters skin the catch!

—No, it's not necessary to skin it! Let it stay whole!

Mother-in-law[16] entered and met her father [Kukki]:

—Here's what to do—carry the wolf to the storage room and stand watch there; busy yourself with sewing.

The ravens fell asleep. Kukki went into a deep sleep.

In the meantime the brothers of the wolf followed his footsteps.

The next day Kukki was sitting at the door of the *zemlyanka* repairing a net. His younger son Auppali came out.

—Go out more often, and look around, —Kukki said to him.

—Father, look, two wolves are walking there, —Auppali said to him.

—Oh, oh, wait a bit; I'll make some blubber balls.[17] You'll go to the place where they will pass. Make as if you were playing and leave the balls there, —Kukki said to his son.

The brother-wolves came by and saw the balls:

—Oh-oh, the little boy Auppali must have played here and dropped the balls, —they figured, and ate them on the spot.

They came to the *zemlyanka*. Kukki was repairing a net near the door.

—Oh, you've come!

—Yes, grandpa. But there's something wrong with us. We're reeling; everything goes dark before our eyes.

—Maybe you've eaten something?

And there and then the wolves died.

—Oh, again I've killed two wolves, —Kukki rejoiced and carried them to the food storage of his daughter:

—Here, I've brought more; guard them.

At that time a young wolf was asking his old parents:

—There used to be many cubs here and now I'm the only one left.

The little wolf was called Vechovtyn. (And Kukki was a great shaman-sorcerer).

His parents went to sleep and Vechovtyn followed the scent of his brothers.

Kukki was again sitting at the door, repairing a net. Auppali came out of the *zemlyanka* often.

—Come out more often and look around, —Kukki said to him.

Auppali went out and saw the little wolf coming.

—Look father, a little wolf is coming to us.

—That must be Vechovtyn, —Kukki said. —He must know all about it. Take the blubber balls and throw them on his path.

Auppali took the balls, threw them on the path for the little wolf, and returned to the *zemlyanka*.

The little wolf was running after the scent when he suddenly came across the blubber balls. "Oh, what is this?" —he thought a little and then took them with him.

—Oh, you've arrived! —Kukki greeted him.

---

[16]According to the beliefs of the Kereks, when a daughter was born it was reckoned that the grandmother, that is, the mother of the woman giving birth, had returned. When a son was born it was reckoned that the father of the woman giving birth had returned. In this tale the older daughter of Kukki, Chinillymnylnakkut, was called *naumat,* that is "mother-in-law," if she was referred to or spoken about by Kukki, the father, and *ylla*, that is, "mother" when she was approached or spoken about by Miti, the wife of Kukki.

[17]Blubber balls were used in hunting animals—wolves, bears and foxes. Into the ball of blubber were inserted semicircular blades of balleen with their points sharpened. The balls were frozen and thrown on paths used by the animals. The animal swallowed the ball; the baleen blase straightened out and with its sharp points killed the animal.

—Yes! Have my brothers not come here? —Vechovtyn asked.

—No, they were not here. Don't you see, we're the only ones here, —Kukki answered him.

Then Vechovtyn showed them the blubber ball clutched in his fist and asked:

—Grandpa, what is this?

—Oh, you! —Kukki became frightened, plunged onto the *polog* and crawled under the fur covers.

—What are you doing?! —Miti called after him. —You could have frightened me. What's up?

—The little wolf came, showed me the blubber ball and asked: "What is this?"

—Well, what are you hiding from? You've played pranks, now go to him, —Miti upbraided him.

Vechovtyn entered the *zemlyanka*.

—Oh, you've arrived! —Kukki's wife greeted him.

—Yes, I have. Grandma, what is this? —and Vechovtyn showed her the ball.

—I don't know, it's not known to me. Confound it! —Grandma spat and thought to herself: "You'll not fool the daughter of Akalchiki."[18]

Then she said:

—Get out of there Kukki; what are you afraid of? You know you're a man. I am a woman and I don't back off.

—No, no, I will not come out. I want to sleep.

—Well, then sleep! —Miti said angrily.

It had already gotten dark. Vechovtyn said:

—It's time that I go home.

—Well, all right, go then, —Miti replied.

—But don't spy on me.

Vechovtyn went to the food storage in which Kukki's daughter Chinillymnylnakkut guarded the dead wolves, and cried out:

—Hey, are my brothers here?

—Yes, they are.

Vechovtyn woke up his brothers and said to them:

—What should we do with that brother? We know he doesn't have any innards. We'll leave him here. And you follow us, —he addressed Chinillymnylnakkut.

And so the daughter of Kukki went to the wolf's people. Vechovtyn brought her along and said to his parents:

—Here, mother, come and meet her!

The parents came out:

—Oh, you've arrived! Tell us right away. Where did you find your brothers?

—It's like this: grandpa killed those two at once, and because of that I've carried his daughter away.

Chinillymnylnakkut was afraid; this was the first time she was among wolves.

—Oh-oh, a woman has come!

—Yes!

—Come on in!

—Yes, I will, —and Chinillymnylnakkut entered the dwelling of the wolves.

And she stayed there. The wolves fell asleep.

Miti went to look at the storage room. Her daughter wasn't there and the wolves were gone. Only the wolf without innards lay there.

—Oh, what a wretch that Kukki is! He let them steal his daughter! —Miti became indignant and returned to the *zemlyanka*.

—Kukki! Kukki! —she cried out.

---

[18]Akalchiki was the mythical father of Miti.

38

—Ah-ha!

—Our daughter is not here, and the wolves are gone!

—Oy-oy! —Kukki became frightened. —Vechovtyn must have done it. You know, he was here not long ago.

—There's only one wolf lying there without innards.

—I'll go there, put his innards in, revive him, and let him go home.

Kukki made innards from various pieces of meat and sewed them on inside the wolf.

—Oh-oh! —the wolf came alive. —Who did this to me?

—I've done it! —Kukki answered. —Go home. You see I woke you up. Our daughter is missing. She's probably at your place. Bring her back; don't hold her!

—Very well, we'll bring her back!

The wolf went home. He came to his own.

—Here I am, mother, welcome me!

—Oh-oh, who has come? No doubt it is my son who left yesterday?

—Yes, it's he. We left him there because he didn't have his innards; we didn't know what to do, —Vechovtyn explained.

—What did they do to you?

—Grandpa made innards for me and sewed them in. Then he awakened me. Tomorrow, after we sleep, we'll take their daughter back. But surely they'll do something to us again.

—Yes, yes, take her home; take her home now—the parents told them.

The wolves started for the dwelling of the ravens. They arrived there in the evening.

You wolves, you stay here, I'll do the talking first—Chinillymnylnakkut said.

—Mother, I've come, welcome me!

—Oy-oy! —Kukki cried out. —It must be that my mother-in-law arrived!

Miti went out.

—Oh, you've arrived!

—Yes, I have. The wolves brought me here.

—Where are they?

—Outside.

—Tell them to come in.

—Where are you, my wolves? Do come in!

—No, we'll not! Kukki will take revenge. We're in a hurry.

—Well, can we host you in any way?

—No, we're glad that we've brought your daughter. We were sorry for her. You didn't know at all where she was.

Miti led her daughter in the *zemlyanka*. Kukki still trembling with fear, hid himself under the bed covers. Miti said to him:

—Look, our daughter has arrived!

—Where did daughter come from?

—The wolves brought her here.

The wolves came home. They called out:

—Welcome us, we've come from grandpa's place, we've returned his daughter!

—What did grandpa say?

—He didn't show; he was afraid.

—Well, you were uneasy a little and that was enough, now you can calm down.

And Chinillymnylnakkut began to ask Kukki:

—And how did you rescue me?

—Well, I revived the wolf that didn't have any innards and I sent him home to his brothers. And he decided to return you. He said: "The old woman is miserable." But it's good that you came back.

I've finished telling the story, as much as I remember of it.

TALES AND LEGENDS OF THE KORYAKS

ETHNOGRAPHIC INFORMATION

The Koryaks are the native inhabitants of Kamchatka. Their self-appellations are Nymylany, Chavchuveny and Alyutortsy. Reindeer Koryaks called themselves Chavchuveny and the Maritime Koryaks called themselves Nymylany, "the village inhabitants" (Arutyunov 1988: 31). In 1959 they numbered about 7,400 (Menovscshikov 1974) and in 1994 about 9,000 residents with 4,600 speakers of the Koryak language (Chaussonnet 1995: 109). The majority of the Koryaks live within the confines of the Koryak National *Okrug* (Koryak Autonomous Territory). Separate settlements of the Koryaks are located outside the confines of the *Okrug* in the Bolsheretsky and Petropavlovsky *rayons* of Kamchatka *oblast*, and within the territory of the Chukchi National *Okrug* of Magadan *oblast* (see Figures 1, 2).

The Koryak language, which includes several dialects, belongs to the Chukchi-Kamchatka family of languages. "The Koryaks consisted of eight territorial groups, speaking morphologically and phonetically very different dialects. Because of the mobility of the Reindeer Koryaks, their dialect was the *linqua franca* and was chosen as the standard dialect for the modern written language" (Arutyunov 1988: 31).

The traditional economic activities of the Koryaks are reindeer herding, fishing, sea-mammal hunting, and land-mammal hunting. In recent years, the Koryaks started to develop sheep herding and milch-cow herding. During the Soviet period (1917-1991), the life of the Koryaks changed radically. With the establishment of large collective and state farms, the Koryak population moved from a nomadic society to a sedentary one. The *yarangas* were replaced with modern houses. Electricity, radio, public schools, modern medicine and other cultural and public service institutions became an integral part of living.

W. Bogoras and W. Jochelson begun the collection and scientific examination of the narrative traditions of the Koryaks at the beginning of the 20th century. During the Soviet period, in the mid-1930s, a large collection of Koryak texts, in various dialects, was recorded and published by the well-known linguist and ethnographer S. Stebnitsky. He was the first to collect a considerable number of texts from the cycle about the raven Kutkynneku-Kuykynnyaku. Even today the recordings and translations into Russian of S. Stebnitsky represent the nucleus of observed narrative folklore of the Koryaks.

The Paleoasiatic specialists I. Vdovin, N. Bogdanova, and A. Zhukova recorded many Koryak texts of diverse genres in the 1940s and 1950s. Some of these texts were translated into English and included in this publication.

13. How Kuykynnyaku Stopped the Rain

Recorded in 1928 in Kichiga village in the Koryak National *Okrug* and translated into Russian by S. Stebnitsky. Published in Stebnitsky 1938, p. 91 in the Koryak language with a parallel translation into Russian.

This happened long ago. It rained for a long time without letup.

Then Kuykynnyaku said to his sons:

—Now sons, go and round up some deer!

The sons rounded up the deer. Kuykynnyaku built a large boat. He drove the deer into it. Then he began to summon all the animals. Various animals came to him. Mice also came. Kuykynnyaku formed the mice into a team and harnessed them to the boat and they pulled it to the sea. He also took with him fly agaric.[19] He arrived at the sea. And all the time it never stopped raining.

He left the next day. For a long time he traveled over the sea. Finally he arrived at an island. He landed. He saw a settlement. He went to it. He saw a woman sitting there and combing her hair.

—Aha, that's why it's raining!

The woman said to him:

—Welcome old man! You've showed up!

—Yes, I have!

—Are you going on or are you going to stop here?

—I'll stay overnight and tomorrow I'll go farther!

And the woman was combing her hair all the time. He started to treat her to the fly agaric. She ate it and soon become intoxicated. The Kuykynnyaku began to cut her hair. He cut off all her hair. Then he took off all of her clothes. She was naked. He took the clothing and buried it in the ground. Then he said:

—Behave yourself or I'll torment you!

The woman was freezing, shivering and altogether intoxicated. She wanted to comb her hair. She jerked her hand toward her head. Then Kuykynnyaku cut her eyebrow and pubic hair off.

Then he sent the little mouse Kamchenanavut off:

—Swim across the sea and look around; maybe the weather cleared there.

The little mouse swam off. Soon she returned and told him:

—It's altogether clear.

Then Kuykynnaku started for home. He left the woman the way she was.

—Oy, I'm cold! I'm freezing! Give me my clothes! —the woman cried after him.

He did not. He returned home.

---

[19]Fly agaric — the Chukchi and the Koryaks used fly agaric mushroom [*mukhomor* in Russian] as an intoxicating, stupefying substance. These properties of fly agaric are reflected in the oral traditions of the Chukchi and Koryak peoples and also in the petroglyphs on the cliffs along the Pegtymel River in the Chukchi Peninsula.

14. The Travels of Kuykynnyaku

Narrated in 1928 by an inhabitant of Kichiga village, Avavu. Recorded and translated into Russian by S. Stebnitsky. Published in Stebnitsky 1938, p. 94, in the Koryak language with a parallel text in Russian. The image of Kuykynnyaku is not clearly expressed in the cycle of Koryak tales about the raven. Sometimes he is a man, at others a raven. In this tale he appears as a man.

One day Kuykynnyaku went to the seashore. He saw a ringed seal [*nerpa*].
—What are you doing here, ringed seal?
—I'm getting ready to sleep.
—I want to ask you something. Will you listen?
—Why me? I want to sleep!
Then Kuykynnyaku sang out:

> Ringed seal carry me
> To places where there's rich food, to the women of the sea people!

The ringed seal sat him on her back. She carried him. She brought him to the whale people.
—Good health to you, old man! What did you come for?
—How to say it . . . I'd like to eat some blubber.
—Well, come on in!
He entered.
—Well, bring him seal fins!
They did.
—There you are; you'll eat seal fins!
He started to eat the seal fins. He finished.
—Thank you, I've eaten. Only my throat is very dry. I could drink something. Give me a drink!
—Take a drink yourself! Over there is a wooden bucket with water.
—Eh, you still do without cups!
He went to the trough and had just begun to drink when suddenly he flew head first into the trough. He fell for a long time. He fell directly on the dwelling of the walrus people. He sat next to the entering hole. Then he started to sing:

> Oy, oy! The women of the far away land
> Are fetching water from the mountain streams!

They called out from the dwelling:
—Hey, a guest; come on in!
He entered.
—Now then, entertain the guest!
They started hosting him. He began to eat. He finished eating.
—Eh, I need to drink!
—Go, have your drink!
He went to the trough and had just begun to drink when suddenly he flew head first below. He fell directly on the dwelling of the bearded seal people. He sat next to the smoke hole and sang:

> Oy, oy! The women of the far away land
> Are fetching water from the mountain streams!

At that time, from inside, they called out to him:

—Come on in; be a guest!

—Oh! Give me some water! I feel sick. I'm dying to have something to drink.

—Go and drink yourself! Take this horn cup!

—They gave him a horn cup. He began to drink. He finished.

—O-ho! I've had my drink. I'm alive again.

—Now, entertain the guest with bearded seal fins!

They put in front of him seal fins. He began to eat them. He finished.

—Well, it's time to go home. Come with me. I'll give you my daughter.

—Why not! Very well, we'll come with you!

They got ready to accompany the guest.

They arrived at Kuykynnyaku's place. They began to make *tolkusha*.[20] They ate much *tolkusha*. Then they started to return. Kuykynnyaku gave them Tinianavut. They left with her.

They arrived at the whale people.

—Welcome! Where are you coming from?

—We saw Kuykynnyaku off.

—Good! What did they give you?

—You know, we're not given to mockery, like you. —And they showed them Tinianavut.

—Where did you get that girl?

—Since we did not jeer at anyone now, if you please, we are returning with the girl.

—A beautiful girl!

They took leave of the whale people. They returned home.

—Well, mother, light the fire, welcome the bride with fire!

They started to fumigate her with the fire. They got her accustomed to fire. People gathered and began to look at the bride. All of them exclaimed:

—Oy, what a beautiful girl!

Then they prepared a great feast.

---

[20]*Tolkusha* — a meal prepared from chopped tubers and stalks of a number of edible plants mixed with fish, blubber, berries, and other wild fruits. *Agutag*, or so-called "Eskimo Ice Cream," is a similar meal widely consumed by Eskimos. *Agutag* is an Alaskan Yupik word meaning "something mixed together" (e.g. seal oil, blueberries, Crisco, sugar, fish). It is also one of the favorite foods of the Alaskan Eskimo people and is considered a treat.

15. Kuykynnyaku and the Wolf

Narrated in 1928 by an inhabitant of Kichig village, Oonak (Kirill Popov). Recorded and translated into Russian by S. Stebnitsky. Published in Stebnitsky 1938, p. 96, in the Koryak language with a parallel Russian translation. The basis of this tale, widespread among the native peoples of both the Chukchi-Kamchatka region and Alaska, is the topic of the raven and the wolf sliding down the mountainside. In the Koryak version of this topic Kuykynnyaku slides down the mountainside on a sled and is joined by a wolf named Egymchychyn (cp. no. 16 of this edition). This variant (in differentiation from the Eskimo one) is not altogether an animal tale since its principal hero appears as a man. This tale illustrates small differences between a magical and animal tale in the Koryak cycle about Kutkynneku (Kuykynnyaku). Compare the Eskimo tale "Volk i voron" (The Wolf and the Raven) in *Eskimoskiye skazki i legendy*, Menovshchikov 1969, p. 23, and also the Chukchi text no. 55 in Dolitsky and Michael 1997.

The topic in this Koryak variant is contaminated by another topic in which the brother of the defeated wolf, Tayakhtyt, together with land and sea animals attempts to take revenge on Kuykynnyaku. The raven origin of the hero, his magical strength, is supported by the following occurrences: Kuykynnyaku dyes the sea with alder paint, which kills the sea animals and then he hangs his raven clothing inside-out from which the falling snow covers all land animals. As in this and in other tales about the raven Kuykynnyaku, the ancient myth of the raven-creator appears as the basis for the formation of animal tales in which the mission of the hero-creator is whimsically combined with the role of a cheat and simpleton. In its artistic theme, the mythological base of its content is enriched by satirical and comical motives, which express the ideological development of the tale.

Kuykynnyaku decided to go sledding. He went up the mountainside. He walked pulling the water-carrying sled behind him. He ascended the mountain. He sledded down to the very edge of the sea. He climbed uphill pulling the sled.

Then the wolf came by:

—Welcome, dear cousin! What are you doing? Are you sledding? Well then, cousin; I'll go sledding too!

—Don't you dare sit on it! You'll break it!

—Don't worry; I'll go only once!

The wolf started sledding. He sledded down the mountain three times. Then he said to Kuykynnyaku:

—All right, old chap, now I'm going home.

Kuykynnyaku also went home.

After some time the wolf decided: "I'll go to my cousin as a guest."

He started. He walked. Suddenly he saw Kuykynnyaku's legs scattered on the path.

—Oy! My cousin! How did he die? —and he ate the legs.

He walked a bit more and found Kuykynnyaku's arms. And he ate the arms. Then he found the head and also ate it. After that he found the body and he ate it too. The wolf walked on.

Suddenly Kuykynnyaku coughed in his stomach.

—Hey, cousin, where are we going?

—To your dwelling.

Then Kuykynnyaku asked:

—What's this?

—My kidneys.

—And this, cousin, what is it?

—My lungs.

—And what is this?

—My liver.

—And this is what? The thing that looks like a tent?

—Oy-oy! Don't touch it! It's my heart!

—All right, I won't.

After a short time Kuykynnyaku again asked:

—Hey! Cousin, where are we?

—Very close to your dwelling.

Again Kuykynnyaku asked:

—Where are we?

—We're now on the roof of the *zemlyanka*, we're going toward the entryway.

At that point Kuykynnyaku clutched the wolf's heart with his talons. The wolf died.

Kuykynnyaku called out:

—Miti! Quickly, come out! Cut the wolf open!

Miti took a knife and went out. She cut the wolf open. As soon as Kuykynnyaku got out of the wolf he said:

—Miti, let's make haste! Let's drag the wolf inside.

They dragged him in and cut off his head.

And Tayatkhyt, the younger brother of the wolf, was waiting at home for his brother.

He said to himself:

—Ey, where did my older brother go? I'll have to find him.

He started the search. He saw footprints.

—There he goes! It seems that he's gone to Kuykynnyaku!

Tayatkhyt came to Kuykynnyaku's place.

—Welcome, cousin! You're here! Well, come in!

Tayatkhyt entered.

—Now, Miti, host our brother-in-law with the head of a seal.

Miti put the head in a round bowl.

—Here, eat!

But he recognized the toothless jaw of his older brother and he said:

—No, I don't want it. Take it away. I kill such animals myself, all the time.

—Ey, Miti, serve the other treat, the head of a bearded seal!

Miti put the head in a long bowl.

—Here, brother-in-law, eat!

Tayatkhyt saw that it was the head of his older brother again. He stepped away from the bowl and went outside.

—I am going to invite all the people. I'll gather all of them!

Tayatkhyt set out. He gathered all kinds of animals: bears, wild deer, mountain sheep, moose. And the foxes were also there.

—Now let's go to Kuykynnyaku. They came there.

—Hey! Cousin, we're here!

—Coming. Wait a little. When I call you, then come in. I'm going to treat you with my supply of berries.

Tayatkhyt said:

— Well bear, what should we do?

—It's all right with me. I'll eat the berries. Let's go!

The animals went in. And Kuykynnyaku had just about time to bury fish gills and tails in the ashes of the fireplace. He buried them and said:

—Now, as they drag you outside, start smoking!

Then he said to the household people:

—Now then, take the food!

All of them went out. Only Kuykynnyaku remained in the dwelling. He watched over the people that had arrived.

And the household people already started to block the summer entrance with boulders. The stones rattled. The bear asked:

—What's rattling?

45

—A sack with nuts.

—I'll eat the nuts!

Again a stone rattled.

—And what is that?

—A sack with bilberries.

The bear began to dance with joy.

—Eh, I'll eat those berries!

Then from the outside they called out:

—The entrance log of the pile dwelling is broken. And the sack with the nuts is torn. Give us the bed cover! And bring the entrance log; take it to the entrance of the *zemlyanka*.

Kuykynnyaku went outside. They removed the entrance log. They put the bed cover over the upper entrance. Kuykynnyaku called out:

—Ey, fish gills, fish tails, start making smoke!

They made smoke. All the animals in the *zemlyanka* perished, only two barely escaped—the fox and Tayatkhyt. At once the fox ran into the tundra.

Again Tayatkhyt went to gather the animals. This time he went to the sea. He invited all sea animals—the whales, the walrus, the seals, bearded seals, and fish.

—Now let's go to Kuykynnyaku!

And because of the great number of animals, the sea looked like dry land.

—Hey! We've come!

Miti saw them and exclaimed:

—It's bad, Kuykynnyaku! You can't tell the sea from land!

—Quick, Miti, get me the dye made from alder bark!

She gave it to him. He poured the dye into the sea. All of the sea animals perished. Only Tayatkhyt remained.

Again Tayatkhyt went to get animals to help him. He arrived in the tundra. He invited all the worms and snails —the black worms, caterpillars, grubs, maggots, earthworms. They crept along.

The Kuykynnyaku family awakened in the morning—the entire land was covered with worms.

—Quick, Miti, get me the skis lined with deerskin!

She gave them to him. He put on the skis. He glided several times over the snow and crushed all the worms.

Again the wolf was the only one left. Kuykynnyaku called out to him:

—Don't you dare hang around me! I'll kill you!

So the wolf started for home. He returned home. He hung his [wolf] hide outside. The hide hung there all winter. He then took it down and carried it to Kuykynnyaku. He arrived:

—Good health to you, cousin! Where can I shake my wolf's hide? It's all covered with snow.

—Go directly over the upper entrance and shake it off.

He began to shake off the snow. "Well, —he thought to himself, —that should be enough. No doubt I've covered them all."

He looked inside, and nothing had happened, all were alive. There was only a heap of snow on the floor.

—Eh, I failed!

The wolf went home.

And Kuykynnyaku took his raven clothing and hung it outside. He left it hanging one night. The next day he took it down and carried it to the wolf's settlement. He arrived:

—Greetings, cousin! Where can I shake the snow off my raven's parka?

—Go over there and shake it over the upper entrance.

Well, he shook it only once and whole *zemlyanka* was filled with snow. And all of the wolves perished.

And Kuykynnyaku returned home.

16. Kuykynnyaku and the Vixen

Narrated in 1928 by an inhabitant of Kichiga village, N. Bezuglova. Recorded and translated into Russian by S. Stebnitsky. Published in Stebnitsky 1938, p. 100, in the Koryak language with a parallel Russian translation.

One day the vixen Chachuchanavut said:

—Eh, my children, what are you going to eat? I'm going to go to the seashore and look for something to catch!

She came to the sea and she sang out:

—My children, my children have not eaten yet!

She saw a small fish, took it and put it in a wicker basket.

And Kuykynnyaku heard somebody singing. He followed the voice, came, and asked:

—What have you found?

Chachuchanavut replied:

—I found a small fish. The children have to be fed.

Kuykynnyaku said:

—Well now, let me see your find!

—Yes, it's over there, in the wicker basket.

Kuykynnyaku did not waste time, took the fish, buried it in the sand and put a piece of wood in the basket.

Chachuchanavut took the basket and hoisted it onto her back. Then she said:

—Why has the load become heavier?

Kuykynnyaku said:

—Oh, it's such a big fish!

Chachuchanavut returned home. The little children ran to meet her.

—I-ka-ka! Mom brought a fish! Whom are you going to give the fish head?

Chachuchanavut said:

—You're the smallest one. I'll give the fish head to you!

She entered the dwelling. The little cubs were saying:

—Oh, mom, we're going to eat!

Chachuchanavut said:

—Get the fish; it's in the basket.

One of the cubs began to search and he said:

—There's nothing here!

Chachuchanavut said:

—There must be!

He searched and searched and again he said:

—There really isn't anything here! Look for yourself.

Chachuchanavut became angry:

—Get away from here! You're such a good-for-nothing!

Chachuchanavut ran to the basket, looked into it and found nothing. She said:

—This must be Kuykynnyaku's doing! He lives by cunning!

The next day Chachuchanavut went to the mountains to search for food. On the path she saw two wild deer; in a fight they had gored each other. She dug a hole in the ground, put her head in it, and sang:

—My children, my children, they have not eaten yet!

Then she quickly returned home and said:

—Now, we're likely to move to a new place! I've found two wild deer.

They arrived there. They built a stone *zemlyanka*. The little cubs were playing near the *zemlyanka*. Then they saw Kuykynnyaku:

—Oy! He's coming!

Chachuchanavut said:

—Better go inside!

They did. They covered the entrance. Kuykynnyaku came near and said:

—I-I-I'd like a bit of bone marrow!

Chachuchanavut said:

—Go and invite your wife!

He went to do so. He arrived and told her:

—Let's go to Chachuchanavut!

They went. They arrived.

—Well, come on in!

They entered. They covered the smoke hole.

Kuykynnyaku said:

—I-I-I'd like a bit of bone marrow.

Chachuchanavut tied a piece of marrow to a string made of sinew and gave it to him. He gulped it down. She pulled it out with the string. Again he gulped it down. Again she pulled it out. Yet again he gulped it down, but this time he managed to bite off a small piece.

The string broke and Kuykynnyaku swallowed all of the bone marrow.

While Chachuchanavut's family was amusing itself, Miti quietly hid fatty *tolkusha* in her bosom. Then unnoticed she threw it outside.

And Chachuchanavut went out and smeared the entrance log of the neighboring empty *zemlyanka* with fatty *tolkusha* and then she also smeared the handle of the hammer for breaking bones. Kuykynnyaku said:

—Now I'm going to go in the neighboring *zemlyanka*.

He entered the *zemlyanka*, swallowed a stone greased with the fatty *tolkusha* and the hammer for breaking the animal bones, and he came out. He nipped off the upper side of the entrance log and also swallowed it. Then he left the *zemlyanka* and went to the seashore. He arrived there.

He met the wolf.

—Welcome cousin! Where are you coming from?

—I tell you, from home.

The wolf said:

—Let's belch!

Kuykynnyaku answered:

—You first!

The wolf said:

—Spread out your parka!

Kuykynnyaku spread out his parka. At once the wolf vomited all sorts of food and bone marrow. He said:

—Now it's your turn!

Kuykynnyaku vomited the pounding stone, the hammer for breaking animal bones and a piece of the entrance log.

The wolf went to the tundra right away. And Kuykynnyaku gathered all that the wolf left and carried it home. He brought it and said:

—Miti, here's bone marrow!

Miti asked:

—Where did you get bone marrow?

Kuykynnyaku told her:

—I've killed wild deer. I've cached it there in the tundra.

—Well, quick, let's go and get it!

They got ready in no time. Miti took with her the deer hide from the bedding. Chichisen hoisted the stone for grinding bones to his shoulder, and Rira the hammer for breaking the bones. And Uala[21] rolled the fire bucket onto his shoulders. They all left.

Soon Uala yelled out:

—Oy-oy-oy, it's hot.

Kuykynnyaku said:

—We'll get there soon, soon!

They got to the cache. It turned out to be a hummock covered with bush cranberries.

Miti asked:

—Where are the wild deer?

Kuykynnyaku told her:

—We haven't come to them yet. There, over there, at that hummock!

They got there. It was another hummock covered with bush cranberries.

Miti asked:

—Where are the wild deer?

—They're over there; we'll get there soon!

They arrived and found nothing. Kuykynnyaku called out:

—Now, let's start running a race and see who will be first to get home! It could be that I'll turn out to be the fastest!

They started running home. They got there.

Miti said:

—He's exhausted us for nothing. He made his sons run with such heavy loads. He drove the children to exhaustion, and all in vain.

---

[21]Chichisen, Rira and Uala are the younger children of Kuykynnyaku and Miti.

17. Kuykynnyaku — the Collector of Bearded Seal Blubber

Narrated in 1928 by an inhabitant of Kichiga village, N. Bezuglova. Recorded and translated into Russian by S. Stebnitsky. Published in Stebnitsky 1938, p. 104, in the Koryak language with a parallel Russian translation. This tale involving the disguised vixen Chachuchanavut can be viewed as a logical continuation of the adventures of Kuykynnyaku presented in no. 16 of this edition. However, here he is represented as a simpleton who is tricked in revenge by the vixen transformed several times into relatives of the hero. In this tale the characters also appear as animals and people, as they do in other tales of this cycle.

One day Kuykynnyaku told his wife:
—Gather some berries, I'm going to trade them for bearded seal blubber.
He started out. He came to the shore dwellers.
—Welcome, Kuykynnyaku! What have you come for?
—Treat me with some seal blubber.
They gave him a *kalaus*[22] full of blubber. He started for home. On the path he found a dead vixen. He took her and put her on top of the *kalaus*. He said to himself:
—Good, I'll give this to Miti for the trimming of her parka.
But Chachuchanavut quietly gnawed a hole in the *kalaus* and let out all the blubber. She then ran away. The blubber froze on the snow and she collected all of it.
Kuykynnyaku returned home. Miti asked him:
—Where is the seal blubber?
—There, outside, in the *kalaus*.
Miti went out.
—There's nothing here!
Kuykynnyaku told her:
—Eh, it seems that Chachuchanavut made a hole in the *kalaus*!
So they did not have *tolkusha* to eat. No matter how hard Kuykynnyaku squeezed the *kalaus*, he could not squeeze anything out. It was empty.
Again Kuykynnyaku started out to trade for seal blubber. He came to the shore dwellers.
—Treat me to some seal blubber.
—And where is the *kalaus* that we gave you a while ago?
—Eh, Chachuchanavut made a hole in it!
They gave him another *kalaus*, full of blubber.
Chachuchanavut said to her cubs:
—Ey, quickly, cut my hair from half of my head, and the eyebrow and eyelashes of one eye!
The cubs did so. She ran toward Kuykynnyaku:
—Give me some blubber! Just a little piece! You know, I am your old relative.
He gave her some blubber. The vixen returned home.
—Now quickly, glue a moustache and beard on me. I'm going to meet with Kuykynnyaku again.
They glued them on. She ran out. Kuykynnyaku saw her and asked:
—Good health to you! Who are you?
—You know, it's me, your cousin. Give me a bit of blubber.
He gave her blubber. Chachuchanavut ran home. She came there and said:
—Eh, fast now! Shear all of me! I'm going to meet with Kuykynnyaku again!
They sheared her. She ran out. She met Kuykynnyaku. Kuykynnyaku said:
—Good health to you! Who are you?
—You know that I'm your first cousin!

---

[22]*Kalaus* — a container made from the bladder, stomach, or hide of an animal. It was filled with rendered seal blubber.

—What are you running after?

—Oh, for no particular reason. Give me a little bit of blubber.

He gave her blubber. He gave her all that was left in the *kalaus*. Kuykynnyaku returned home. Miti questioned him:

—Where's the blubber?

—There is no blubber. It couldn't be helped! My relatives emptied the *kalaus*.

Again Kuykynnyaku went to the shore dwellers. He came there.

—Good health to you! What have you come for?

—I'd like some blubber.

—You're eating a lot of blubber!

—Not really. All this is because I've met all my relatives on the path and all of them asked for blubber. This time I'll put it in my mouth.

He put the blubber in his mouth. He went off. On the path he met a Krivlyaka.[23] He burst out laughing and dropped the blubber. He went home. When he arrived Miti asked him:

—Where is the blubber? You're good for nothing; you can't bring home the blubber!

—What could I do? A Krivlyaka met me on the path, I couldn't keep from laughing and I lost the blubber.

He again went to the shore dwellers. He arrived there.

—Greetings, Kuykynnyaku! What have you come for?

—I'd like some blubber.

Again he put the blubber in his mouth. He started for home. Again he met Krivlyaka. He could not avert his eyes and he could not keep from laughing. He dropped the blubber. He went home with nothing.

Miti asked him:

—Where's the blubber?

—Well, I met Krivlyaka again. Since I couldn't look aside, I could not keep from laughing.

Then Kuykynnyaku decided to scatter pieces of dry fish around an ice-hole. Chachuchanavut arrived there with her cubs. The pieces of dry fish froze to the ice. The cubs could not tear them off. They started to urinate on them so that they would thaw out. However, they froze to the ice themselves and Chachuchanavut's tail froze to it also.

Then Kuykynnyaku arrived. Chachuchanavut yelled out:

—Get up, quickly!

But they could not stand; they could only twist their little heads. And Chachuchanavut was frozen to the ice herself and could not run away.

Kuykynnyaku came by and started to slaughter the cubs with a stick. And Chachuchanavut kept saying over and over again:

—Well then! And now kill another one! A-kha-kha-kha! Enjoy yourself! And in her rage her eyes were bulging.

Then with all her might she tore herself away and ran off.

She ran away without her tail. She left it frozen to the ice.

---

[23]*Krivlyaka* — in Russian language it is an affected person, a funny face with a twisted grin.

18. Kuykynnyaku and Mynkusyn

Narrated in 1928 by an inhabitant of Kichiga village, P. Belyakov. Recorded and translated into Russian by S. Stebnitsky. Published in Stebnitsky 1938, p. 106, in the Koryak language with a parallel Russian translation.

One day Mynkusyn went to the tundra to hunt. He arrived there. He hid in the moss.

Soon a wild deer came by. Mynkusyn took his knife and thrust it into the wild deer. He killed it and hoisted it to his shoulders. He carried it home. He came home. His mother asked him:

—Who gave you this?

—I killed it myself.

Mynkusyn went to the tundra again. He climbed up a large tree. Then suddenly he saw a bear walking on the slope of a mountain. The bear came close.

—Hi, Mynkus!

—Eh!

—What are you doing, Mynkus?

—I'm cutting trees.

—And why are you cutting it?

—For whatever they're needed.

—You've probably collected cedar cones, too?

—Of course! I've already filled two summer huts with cedar cones.

—What if I come to live with you?

—That I don't know; it could be that my mother would not want that.

—If you don't take me in, I'll eat you.

—Well, all right, come live with us.

The bear came.

—Hello, you bear creature!

—Hello to all of you! Here I am!

At once he drank two pots of tea, and ate two bundles of dried fish. He said:

—How many meals do you have left? I see that very little is left. As soon as I eat the half of the food in the summer house, I'll have to eat you and your mother.

Mynkusin went to the tundra. He got there and he began to cry. Kuykynnyaku heard him and caught up with him.

—Hello, Mynkus! What's wrong?

—Oh, it's bad! The bear said that when he finishes all of our food, he'll eat my mother and me.

—Don't worry Mynkus; don't cry! Tomorrow I'll come to your place with a spear. I'll make it very sharp.

Kuykynnyaku arrived the next day. Having eaten, the bear was sleeping.

Mynkusyn met him.

—Hello Kuykynnyaku! I see you've come.

—Eh! Indeed! I've come!

Kuykynnyaku looked around.

—What's moving under the parka over there in the corner! It seems that somebody is breathing under it.

Mynkusyn said:

—What's there is a bear fur hide covered with a parka.

Then he also said:

—I'm going to go to the yard to relieve myself!

His mother said:

—If you will, I will go too.

As soon as they left, Kuykynnyaku thrust the spear into the bear and killed him.

—Eh, it's been a long time since we've had bear meat!

Mynkusyn returned with his mother. Kuykynnyaku said:

—Well, here you are; I've provided you with a supply of food.

—Very good! Take some bear meat for yourself.

Kuykynnyaku hoisted to his shoulders a leg of the bear. He went home. He came there:

—Miti, take the bear's leg.

19. Ememkut and Khaeelgyt

Narrated in 1928 by an inhabitant of Kichiga village, N. Bezuglova. Recorded and translated into Russian by S. Stebnitsky. Published in Stebnitsky 1938, p. 101, in the Koryak language with a parallel Russian translation.

One day Ememkut said:

—Where have all our friends gone? No traces of them are to be seen.

Kuykynnyaku said:

—They went to propose marriage to Khaeelgyt.

Ememkut said:

—I'll go there and propose marriage, too.

Kuykynnyaku said to him:

—Why do you want to go! What kind of a bridegroom are you!

—No matter, I'll simply go.

He went. He arrived. Oho, how many people got together! They said to Ememkut:

—Well, we see, you've arrived. But we are getting ready to go home. It's time.

Ememkut entered the dwelling. He saw that two families were living there. On one side women's boots were hung, on the other side men's boots were hung. Ememkut sat down on the side where the men's boots were hung.

They began to host him.

—I'm not going to eat!

—Why do you refuse?

He said:

—I don't want to eat!

Just then the bride returned home. She wore man's breeches and was loaded with carcasses of wild deer. She had been hunting.

She came in and said to her mother:

—Feed me!

They began to feed her. Then Ememkut also started to eat. The bride took a piece of food and he grasped her hand. Khaeelgyt said:

—Why did you not feed the guest earlier? You let him be hungry.

Suddenly Ememkut struck her hand with a knife.

Khaeelgyt jumped up and ran outside. A short while later Ememkut went out after her. And what do you know—Khaeelgyt was nowhere to be found. He could not find her anywhere.

Then Kuykynnyaku's sister said to him:

—There is the entrance log to the sky itself.

Khaeelgyt returned again loaded with carcasses of wild deer. She said:

—Here take ten of the wild deer!

—Ememkut took all of them with his little finger. He went in. Khaeelgyt said:

—Let's play ball!

All started playing ball outside the dwelling. Ememkut by himself drove the ball. Nobody could take it away from him.

Then Khaeelgyt's father said:

—Since she refuses to go after you, take her as wife!

He took her as wife. They returned home. They started to live together.

20. The Son of Ememkut

Narrated in 1928 by an inhabitant of Kichiga village, Mullanvil. Recorded and translated into Russian by S. Stebnitsky. Published in Stebnitsky 1938, p. 112, in the Koryak language with a parallel Russian translation. The content of this tale is similar in its ending to the first part of the Koryak tale "Kuykynnyaku and the Wolf" (no. 15 of this edition) in which the ingested raven revives and kills the wolf.

Ememkut lived with his wife. They had two children. They sent them to catch fish. They caught a flounder. They cooked it. Ememkut said to the children:

—Go and pick some berries.

They went. Soon they returned.

—You know, there are no berries. There's not a single berry.

What was there to do? They began to eat the only fish. They finished eating. Then they fidgeted; they waddled. They grew hungry again; they needed food in their stomachs.

—Oh, how hungry we are!

—Let's go away from here!

They started with the first snow.

—Over there is a beautiful mountain, we'll stop there.

They stopped. It became dark. They lay down to sleep and fell asleep.

Ememkut had a dream. He awakened and said to his wife:

—It's bad! If we stay here a *nynvit* [24] will come and eat us.

Without delay they started to round up the reindeer. It became light. They gathered all of the reindeer. Suddenly it became dark.

—Oy, why did it get dark?

And that was the *nynvit* coming, howling like a wolf:

—Ehe! I'm going to eat you!

—Let's get out of here fast!

—Where will we go? Don't you hear? The *nynvit* is coming near, howling like a wolf, saying: "I'm going to eat you!"

All became frightened and cried in anguish. They quickly ran away from the *nynvit* and they left the newborn baby behind. The baby cried, drowning in tears.

Nynvit came up to him.

—Kheh! He'll grow up at my place; he'll be handy when I'm hungry.

So the little boy grew up. Then one day the *nynvit* became very hungry. He said to himself:

—Well, the boy has become handsome, big and heavy. So I'll eat him!

He began to eat. He smacked his lips.

Then the boy in the *nynvit's* belly started to claw it.

—Oy-oy! He's killing me! O-kho-kho-kho!

His belly burst. The boy walked out in one piece, and the *nynvit* died.

---

[24]*Nynvit* — a werewolf who in Koryak folklore played the role of a malicious being.

21. The Sisters of Ememkut

Narrated in 1928 by an inhabitant of Kichiga village, N. Bezuglova. Recorded and translated into Russian by S. Stebnitsky. Published in Stebnitsky 1938, p. 113, in the Koryak language with a parallel Russian translation. In this tale there is an account of the cosmogonic tradition about the creation of the whale by Ememkut, and a humorous story about his attitude toward a woman. This topic is found in Koryak folklore only.

Nypayvaelgyn[25] said:

—Let's test our sisters.

Ememkut said:

—My sisters are bad.

Nypayvaelgyn answered:

—Oh well, so what.

They went to the tundra for the testing. And Nypayvaelgyn went into a small river.

Khaysyaneru, Ememkut's sister, said:

—I want to drink!

They told her:

—There's water in the kettle over there, have a drink!

—I don't want that, I'm going to go in the water.

She went to the water, came to the river, and in it there was a trout swimming. She rolled up her sleeve to her shoulder and began to scoop up water, and the trout started to ridicule her.

The girl ran home, got there and told her older brother:

—You know, they saw my bare arm!

Nypayvaelgyn went about and told everyone:

—Ememkut's sisters are bad!

Then Ememkut went to test the sister of Nypayvaelgyn. He created a whale and entered it. He went to where Nypayvaelgyn's sister lived and came out onto the shore near her house.

The girl came out of the house and said:

—I'll go to the seashore. Maybe the sea cast out something.

She came there. She saw a small whale lying there. She took off her mittens, boots, parka, and then her [woman's] trousers. Altogether naked she clambered up the whale and started to dance.

Stealthily Ememkut came out of the whale's innards.

—Oho! She's dancing naked on the whale!

Well, he quietly took away all of her clothing—the parka, the boots, mittens and trousers. He left her altogether naked.

—Give me the mittens!

—No!

Nypayvaelgin came out and said:

—What is that over there? Could it be a polar bear roaming?

Then he recognized his sister. He went to her. And how angry he got! He scolded the girl roundly:

—You know, they saw you stark naked.

He carried her to the dwelling and forbade her to leave the *polog*. And how would she get out? She was so ashamed!

Just the same, all the bachelors moved to Ememkut's place. They married Ememkut's sisters.

---

[25]Nypayvaelgyn — lit. "The Envious One." *Zavistnik* in Russian.

22. Kutkynnyaku and the Shamanesses

Narrated in 1955 by an elder inhabitant of Karaga village, A. Pravoverova, age 73. Recorded by D. Pravoverova. Translated into Russian by I. Vdovin.

Kutkynnyaku's daughter could not sleep. Kutkynnyaku went to find a healing herb that would cure her. He went all over the land; there was only one cape left to search. Kutkynnyaku was tired; he crept along on all fours.

—If I go around this last cape and do not find a healing plant, it will be my last chance, and I might as well not look for it anywhere else.

He walked all over the land. He finally came to the edge of the land. Through an opening he saw little *yurtas*.[26] Two women with hand drums were dancing next to each other. Long hair flowed along their backs. From the very creation of life in the world they had argued with each other as to who was better in shamanizing. One was called Enentilnevvyt, the other Enenyaunevvyt. To all who were without life, they gave a long life, and sent them back to live on earth. They gave them pleasant dreams, happiness and the will to live compassionately. Kutkynnyaku heard them; he heard them and began to doze. Wearily he listened, then pulled the women up by their hair and asked them:

—What kind of sick people do they ask you to cure?

—It seems that when you were listening to us, you were dozing? People ask us to go to all the sick ones. We cure any sickness, we return them to life, and we give them a long life. When we untie the knot, we awaken in them the will to return to life. We give them a good appetite and a long, bright life.

Kutkynnyaku took the two women shamanesses and brought them home. He put them next to his daughter's temples, one on each side—so small were the shamanesses. They began to beat their drums and ask for a happy awakening in the morning. They knew the reason for her sickness from which she was dying. They started to sing about it in their songs. The sick girl heard them, fell asleep, and her life force returned. She stopped thrashing about and became restive. The shamanesses gave her a long life. They freed her from the evil spirits and in that way they cured her.

---

[26]The oldest *yurta* of the settled Koryaks was a semi-subterranean, cone-shaped dwelling. An opening at its peak served as a smoke-hole and a light aperture. The opening also served as the door and was reached by leaning an entrance log against it. Steps were cut into the log.

23. Kuykynnyaku and the Nynvits

Narrated in 1955 by an inhabitant of Koltushnoye village in the Koryak National *Okrug*, M. Barganov (Ivtakrat). Recorded and translated into Russian by I. Vdovin. In this tale, as in no other tales about the Koryak-Itelmen personage Kuykynnyaku-Kutkhe, the anthropomorphic personage is presented as a raven-creator, and the harmful "beings" as his disobedient helpers. He talks about the latter as "my playthings of yore". Also the geneology of the Kuykynnyaku family is given here in full. Namely, Kuykynnyaku himself, Amamkut (Ememkut), the oldest son of Kuykynnyaku, Kigygysynyaku, his second son, Tinienevvut, his daughter, and Kotganu, his third son. These are the steadfast members of the Kuykynnyaku family who are encountered separately in various Koryak tales of a given cycle. In the text of no. 16 of this edition other names of the children of Kuykynnyaku and Miti are given, namely, Chichisen, Rira, and Uala. One of the sons of Kuykynnyaku, Kigygysynyaku, kills with iron mittens the harmful "spirits" who escaped from the subordination of his father. This detail suggests a later interpretation or addition to an earlier content. Here Miti, the daughter of a magpie, like her husband, is a bird.

Kuykynnyaku lived with his wife Miti. Kuykynnyaku was a raven elder. Miti was the daughter of a magpie. When Kuykynnyaku married Miti, they started for home. On the way they came to a beautiful place. Kuykynnyaku said:

—Miti, let's stay here overnight.

The next day it dawned. Kuykynnyaku thought a bit and then he said:

—This is a good place to settle.

Then he said to his wife Miti:

—Let's start to build a dwelling here. This place is very beautiful.

Miti replied:

—Your father and mother and your parents-in-law are at home and what are we going to do here?

Kuykynnyaku told her:

—What do I need parents for now? I don't need them anymore. We're going to live by ourselves.

He began to build the dwelling. He built a solid dwelling. Miti gave birth to the first child. They named him Amamkut. Amamkut was very strong. Then she gave birth to a second child; they named this child Kigygysynyaku. He grew up frolicsome. But he also was very strong. After this Miti gave birth to a third child, a daughter named Tinienevvut. She was a very beautiful girl. She gave birth to a fourth child, a son. They gave him the name Kotganu.

One day they noticed that the fire they had kindled always made a strong noise.

Tinienevvut told her father Kuykynnyaku:

—Father, why does our fire make such a strong noise? As soon as I kindle it, it starts making the noise right away.

Kuykynnyaku told his children:

—Well, children, our fire is somehow making a strong noise. That means that some people want to attack us. As soon as it gets dark and the moon rises, you go outside.

As soon as it got dark the three sons of Kuykynnyaku went outside. Amamkut went first, Kygygysynyaku second, Kotganu third. They went to the dwelling's stronghold. Many people had gathered in it. The stronghold was a huge *yurta* and the *nynvits* had gathered there for a meeting. Amamkut, Kigygysynyaku and Kotganu started eavesdropping. The leader of the *nynvits* was Gyvkuku, and his helper, Nayykvat. The *nynvits* were saying:

—When the moon rises, we'll attack the Kuykynnyaku family and kill some of them.

Then one of the *nynvits* said:

—Quiet, you shouldn't talk so loud. It could be that our "friends" are nearby and could hear everything. And it could be that Amamkut and Kigygysynyaku are very much stronger than you!

Then Gyvkuku said:

—There are very few of us. It's going to be dangerous to measure up to them with strength. You know there are three sons there and Kuykynnyaku makes it four.

Amamkut, Kigygysynyaku, and Kotganu heard this and quickly went home. They came home and told their father:

—There are many *nynvits* in the stronghold. They're planning to attack us. As soon as the moon rises they will come and begin to kill us.

Kuykynnyaku asked them:

—Who is their leader?

Amamkut answered:

—Gyvkuku is their leader and his helper is Nayykvat.

Kuykynnyaku then said:

—They can't do anything to us; since days of old they've been my "playthings."

Just then Kuykynnyaku's family was attacked by a detachment of *nynvits*. Kigygysynyaku readied himself to fight them alone. He said to his brothers:

—Wait a bit, stay home, I'll cope with them myself.

Kigygysynyaku put on iron mittens and without delay attacked the enemy. He did not take his spear or bow and arrows. He began to crush the *nynvits*. He almost destroyed the whole detachment of *nynvits*. He returned to the *yurta*. Only the iron mittens were covered with blood.

His father said:

—Do you remember that yesterday I told you that those *nynvits* were in the past my "playthings?" I used to kill them with my iron mittens all the time. When they would attack me, I could not even warm up from fighting them.

24. The Raven Velvimtilyn

Narrated in 1954 by an inhabitant of Talovka village in Penzhinsky *rayon*, Koryak National *Okrug*, Kokok, age 18. Recorded and translated into Russian by A. Zhukova. Published in Voskoboynikov and Menovshchikov 1959, p. 458.

The raven Velvimtilyn swallowed the sun. The raven lay there, and a snowstorm started blowing; it did not stop because the raven swallowed the sun.

Ememkut said to his daughter Klyukenevyt:

—Go to the raven Velvimtilyn and invite him to come here.

She went outside and sat on a sled. A woman came and said to the raven:

—Get up! They came to you.

The raven asked:

—Who?

The woman answered:

—Klyukenevyt, the daughter of Ememkut.

The raven said:

—Well, I like that! M-m-m!

It did not clear. It snowed even harder. Klyukenevyt came home. Ememkut asked her:

—Where is the raven?

Klyukenevyt answered:

—He didn't come with me. He said: "I like that!"

Ememkut said to his daughter Inianavyt:

—Comb your hair nicely and go to the raven.

The beautiful Inianavyt combed her hair, dressed up, went to Velvimtilyn, and sat down. A woman came and said:

—Raven, get up! That's enough pretending! They came for you.

The raven asked:

—Who?

She answered:

—Inianavyt.

Velvimtilyn saw the girl and guffawed with joy: "Pa-ga-ga!" As he did so he spat out the sun. The skies cleared. It stopped snowing. The raven said to Inianavyt:

—We'll go together to Ememkut.

They went side by side. Inianavyt said to the raven:

—You go on ahead!

She took a long, sharp stick and pierced the raven with it. Let him not swallow the sun! Let it always be clear, let there not be a snowstorm!

And Inianavyt hung the stick with the raven Velvimtilyn on it high up.

25. How Rera Lost Her Bear-Bridegroom

Narrated in 1966 by an inhabitant of Karaga village in Karaginsky *rayon*, E. Gutorova. Recorded in the Karagin dialect by D. Pravoverova. Translated into Russian by I. Vdovin. In this tale the genealogy of the family of Kuykynnyaku and Miti is filled out with new members—daughter Rera and son Sisisyn (see text no. 16 of this edition in which the same names are given in a different phonetic rendering). For a similar subject matter see the Itelmen tale no. 67 in this edition.

One day Tinienevvut went far away from home to pick berries. She picked many berries and filled all the baskets. She went to a large open place and sat down to rest. Suddenly a she-bear appeared and threw herself at Tinienevvut. The bear dragged her over the ground and beat her, but Tinienevvut became quiet. She did not cry out, despite considerable pain. Suddenly the bear said:

—You're going to come with me to our house!

Without a word Tinienevvut obeyed. They came to the bear's home.

—Prepare the *kilykil*[27] and the fish heads, —ordered the she-bear.

Tinienevvut prepared the *kilykil* with the berries she just had gathered. There was much to eat—a heaping large dish. Then Tinienevvut split the fish heads. When she finished the bear said to her:

—You're going to sleep in my *polog*. In the evening my brothers will come, but don't be afraid, just sit quietly in the *polog*.

Again Tinienevvut listened to the she-bear. She went to the *polog* and lay down to sleep.

In the evening three bears returned home. They did not enter the dwelling at once but began to scrape the ground with their paws and they asked their sister-bear:

—Why is there a human smell here?

The sister-bear replied:

—Well, today I was around the ashes in the old fireplace that at one time people were using. So I brought their smell home.

The bears were satisfied and they entered the dwelling. The sister-bear put the dish with the meal in front of them.

—How come that today you made so much *kilykil* and so many fish heads? —asked the brother-bears of their sister.

—Today was a sunny day; you could see the berries clearly, so I picked more than usual. And my teeth don't hurt today, so that's why I prepared so many raw fish heads for you, —their sister-bear answered them.

The bears finished eating and started getting ready to sleep. The sister-bear tucked her brothers in on the other *polog*. In the meantime Tinienevvut sat quietly on the she-bear's *polog*. She felt terrible. Before the bears had returned, she had thoroughly kneaded their house boots, so they would sleep better in them. The she-bear put her brothers to bed, went to her own *polog* and lay down next to Tinienevvut.

Early in the morning, when it was barely light, the she-bear woke Tinienevvut and told her:

—Before you go outside, go around the sleeping bears in the direction of the rising sun and quietly push with your foot the bear who is closest to the entrance.

Tinienevvut went around the sleeping bears and carefully pushed with her foot the one at the edge. The bear grumbled in his sleep but did not awaken. Then the she-bear showed Tinienevvut where the path was and told her to go home on it. In doing this she said:

—If you see a bear following in your footsteps, don't get frightened or raise your voice.

Tinienevvut started for home on the path that the she-bear showed her. She looked back from a small hill and saw that a bear was chasing her. Tinienevvut remembered the advice of the she-bear and did not run off. The bear caught up with her, swept her off her feet and rolled her on the ground. Tinienevvut remained silent and did not offer resistance. Suddenly a child's cry was heard. That cry was

---

[27]*Kilykil* — a meal of cooked fish and berries.

from a son born to Tinienevvut. And at the same time the bear turned into a young man. He married Tinienevvut, took her home and they started to live together.

Winter came. Tinienevvut made warm clothing for the winter, and her husband, who had become a bear again, made a heated sled. They got ready to be guests of Tinienevvut's parents—Kuykynnyaku and Miti. They put their son in the sled and started the journey on foot. When they approached the house of Tinienevvut's parents, the bear again became a young man. The parents greeted them very cordially.

It was starting to get dark. Rera, Tinienevvut's sister, asked:

—Where did you find such a handsome husband?

Tinienevvut explained at length what had happened to her in the tundra when she went there to pick berries. She saw that Rera was ready to go to the tundra. She advised her to obey the she-bear all the time if she met her in the tundra. Rera listened to her sister then went to the tundra, to the same place where Tinienevvut met the she-bear. She sat down to rest. Suddenly the she-bear appeared. She began to beat Rera and rolled her on the ground. Then she took her home with her and ordered her to prepare a meal for her brother-bears. But Rera was lazy and didn't pick many berries so the *kylikyl* was almost without berries. And she split only a few fish heads. The she-bear asked her to knead the house boots of her brothers-bears so that they would be softer to sleep in. Rera did not knead the boots but cut from them the tendons and ate them. Then the she-bear bade her not to become frightened when her brothers come home and ordered her, before returning home in the morning, to go around the bears in the direction of the rising sun and quietly push with her foot the one at the edge. Evening came. Soon the bears arrived. Again they asked their sister why there was a human smell in the house.

The sister answered that she was near ashes of a fire made by people.

The bears sat down to eat.

—Very good *kylikyl*, —they said, —but why are there so few berries in it? And why are there so few split fish heads?

—Today the weather was bad, the berries were hard to see, —the sister-bear answered. —And my teeth were hurting, so I split just a few fish heads.

The bears finished eating and lay down to sleep. But Rera was so frightened of the bears that she wet herself.

In the morning Rera quietly lowered herself from the *polog*, immediately went outside and started running home on the path. Then she looked back from a small hillock and saw that a bear was chasing her. Rera became frightened, she cried out. The bear threw her to the ground; she cried:

—Oy, help me! Oy, he's killing me!

Her brothers Ememkutnek and Sisisyn heard her cries. They quickly ran down the mountain and killed the bear with arrows. A young man jumped from the hide of the dead bear and rushed in the direction of his house. Rera began to cry bitterly, rebuking her brothers for killing a man.

Her brothers told her:

—Why were you crying that you were being killed?

—Now you can chase after your bridegroom; here you have only his hide!

Rera became angry with her brothers. But there was nothing to be done—she lost her bridegroom because of laziness, cowardice, and disobedience.

26. A Tale About an Old Man Who Gave Away His Children

Narrated in 1958 by an inhabitant of Palan village in Tigilsky *rayon*, Koryak National *Okrug*, T. Kavav, age 47. Recorded and translated into Russian by A. Zhukova.

There lived an old man and an old woman. They had two children, a boy and a girl.

The old man was always setting fish traps. One morning he went to a fish trap, looked at it and went back home. The path passed by a spring. The old man wanted to have a drink and he touched the water with his lips. Suddenly something pressed his head down. He fell with his face directly onto the sand and he could not get up. He began to gasp for breath but still managed to call out:

—Hey, whoever you are, let me go! Go away, I'll give you my children!

He was released immediately. The old man jumped up and looked around. He saw nothing. He went home right away. He came home but did not tell the old woman anything.

And here's what happened next. The old man told the children:

—Some day maybe you'd want to go to look at the fish trap.

The brother and sister started for the fish trap. They got there, loaded themselves with something and left. They walked far. And then something stopped them in some sort of land. But they did not remember where they were going. It stopped them and sat them down and then said to them:

—There's a house!

And again:

—There's a house!

But, you know, the brother and sister were sitting under open skies. As it turned out, it was a *kele* who brought them there. The *kele* lay down on the ground and promptly fell asleep.

The children became hungry. They began to search for berries. Suddenly the *kele* awakened and ran to search for the children. He caught up to them, pulled them by the ears:

—Over there's the house, over there's the house!

He hoisted them onto his back and hauled them in the opposite direction. Again he told them:

—Quiet, quiet.

He set them down properly and he kept saying:

—There's the house! There's the house! Sit quietly.

They sat down and he, the godless creature, promptly fell asleep. He snored, and he rumbled like a tractor.

Again the children went to search for berries. Suddenly they saw a wild deer coming, and he stopped right next to them. They said to him:

—Will you let us ride on your back? We want to go home!

The wild deer asked the children:

—What are you doing here?

They said to him:

—Most likely a *kele* brought us here!

Then the deer said:

—Very well, sit on me. I'll take you home!

They sat on the deer's back. The wild deer ran fast. The children were riding as if on a bicycle.

But after a little bit of time they saw that the *kele* was chasing after them. He was yelling at the top of his voice:

—Wait a bit; wait a bit, you wild deer! Where are you running, you so-and-so?!

The wild deer heard this and he said to the children:

—Jump off quickly; jump off!

They jumped. The deer ran off. The *kele* caught up with him and said:

—Why were you leading those strange children away?

And the wild deer answered:

—I was not leading them away. I simply decided to entertain them. And those poor little things sat on me as if they were tied on!

Well, all right. But don't give them rides anymore!

The wild deer ran off. The *kele* seized the children by their ears and scolded them:

—Look of what they've thought! So small and they wanted to run away! You know, that wild deer can't run fast without my permission.

He led them home. He took them there and set them down.

—There is the house! There!

And he promptly fell asleep.

Again the children sat together and did nothing. Again they wanted to eat; so they went to pick berries.

Suddenly they saw a cub bear passing by them.

—Good day to you little children, —he said. —What are you doing by yourselves in the wild tundra?

And the children said:

—You know, he dragged us here!

The bear asked:

—Who dragged you here?

The children answered:

—Oh, some sort of scared crow, probably a *kele*.

And the bear said:

—So, a *kele*. And do you want to go home?

The children said:

—Very much. But how can we get home?

—Ah, sit on my back!

—You should know that very likely the cursed *kele* is going to catch up with us. But all right, when we go for a ride, things won't be so dull.

—Well, have a seat!

The children sat on him. The cub ran swiftly. He ran far, farther than the wild deer. Suddenly he said:

—Quickly, get off, jump down! He's catching up with us.

And the *kele* was already yelling:

—Wait! All the same, bear, I'll catch up with you!

The children got off right away. The cub stood there, waiting. The *kele* came to him.

—You, why are you giving a ride to strange children?!

The bear said:

—I didn't give them a ride. They said themselves: "Give us a ride, we're so bored."

—All right then. But I really thought that you would take them away.

The bear left promptly. The *kele* led the little children by their hands home. He went farther yet and said:

—There's the house! There's the house!

And then he fell asleep again, the so-and-so; he is so naughty!

The little children were simply sitting there. Then they saw a bull-calf approaching them. He was grazing. Suddenly he talked to them:

—Good day to you, brothers! What are you doing here?

They said to him:

—Don't you see that we're sitting at home!

—Where is the house? I don't see it.

Then they said to him:

—Don't yell! The master is sleeping there.

He came closer yet.

—Where did you come from?

They answered him very quietly:

—He dragged us in here.

—Maybe you want to go home?

They said to him:

—We want to, very much!

—Well, sit on my back!

But he was small and pot-bellied. The children laughed and said to him:

—Is it really possible for you to take us home? You know, others were stronger and more nimble than you and they couldn't do it.

And he said to them:

—All right, I'll just give you a ride!

He came closer to them. Anyway, the children sat astride him, laughing. The calf said:

—Oh, how heavy!

And he went toward the *kele*, and the *kele* started to snore louder. The children whispered to him:

—Don't go to the *kele*!

And the bullock replied:

—I guess we'll have to get started!

He stepped directly between the claws of the *kele*. He stumbled. He fell flat on the claws of the *kele*. The *kele* jumped up; he was startled and half asleep; he kicked them! So, the children and the calf flew into the sky.

The *kele* looked and saw that there were no children around. And there were no traces of anybody. Only the calf left small footsteps.

And the children and the calf found themselves on the shore of a sea. The *kele* sought them all day but did not find them. The children found themselves in a very beautiful place on the seashore. And the bullock disappeared—as if there had not been a bullock. The little girl glanced around and saw that she was already in a house. She went through the house and saw that it was a very beautiful house. She went out and walked around the house. And sure enough, it was very nice house. It had everything. It had all the utensils. There was food and many rooms.

Suddenly in one of the rooms she saw two long-eared dogs. They were happy with the little girl, and followed in her footsteps as if she was their mistress.

And the brother of the girl was in the tundra. He came home late. He saw the enormous dwelling and he said:

—Oy-oy-oy, what a big house!

He approached it. Suddenly his sister came out of the house. The two dogs followed in her footsteps. She started telling things to her brother. She said:

—Take a look at our big dwelling!

Her brother asked:

—Where did it come from?

His sister replied:

—Our little calf disappeared. I looked around and saw that I was already in the house. I walked around in the house. Then, in one of the rooms I saw these two dogs. No doubt they were selected to be our companions. They made me happy right away when they began to follow me like their mistress.

Her brother was very happy and he said:

—You know, this is beautiful! What a nice little calf we've found. He turned into a house. Very well, we'll stay to live here forever. The place is beautiful, untouched. There are many animals, many fish in the streams. Now, let's go in the house!

They entered. The house was very warm and bright. The dogs did not leave the pair, they were as if tied to them. The brother began to take them with him no matter where he went.

Yes, yes, and then something happened. The girl was combing her hair at the seashore. Suddenly she heard somebody cry out at the other shore. She started to look in that direction. She saw a human being walking about. He called out to her:

—Ege-gey, bring me across!

Immediately the girl threw her comb on the water. And look what happened! The comb turned into a large bridge: one end of it was where she was, the other on the distant pebbly shore. The human being started to cross on the bridge. And the girl held the "comb-bridge." He came closer. It turned out he was the *kele* of old. He said to her:

—Aha, so it turns out that this is where you are. All the same, I found you so-and-so!

The girl only said:

—Yes, so you have come.

—Aha, is that your house! Very well, let's go in it!

They entered the house. The *kele* said:

—Well, why is it that you ran away from me? I've been searching for you since that time. Finally I've found you! Look at you; you've become a grown up girl. Now we're going to live together. And if you don't agree, it's not going to be good for you.

What could she do? The girl agreed. She knew she could not run away; the *kele* would seize her promptly. The *kele* said:

—Now we only have to kill your brother.

The girl said to him:

—And how are we going to kill him?

The *kele* said:

—Prepare a poisoned meal. A soup.

The girl said:

—I don't have such food.

The *kele* gave her poison and said:

—Mix this with food. And a little later I'll hide in one of the rooms. When your brother comes, host him, talk to him in a friendly manner. Otherwise he will guess what's going on.

They waited for her brother. The *kele* hid himself, but the brother came when it was already late in the evening. When the brother started to approach the house, the dogs became ferocious. Their hair stood on end. They rushed ahead. The brother thought about them:

—Why are they like this, the little dogs? What's wrong with you? Earlier you never did this, — and he entered the house.

In the house the dogs showed even more anxiety. They threw themselves at the girl. Then she began to host him. The dogs spilled the food all over.

Something's wrong here, guessed the boy. He asked his sister:

—Why are the dogs behaving like this?

His sister said:

—No doubt they are hungry.

Her brother said:

—Although yesterday they also were hungry, they weren't like this. Maybe somebody bad came to you?

—No, no, who would come?!

Her brother said:

—Very well, in the morning I'll go to the tundra again.

And the *kele* was very frightened. He lay there afraid to even move a little. The brother fell asleep. The dogs lay down on either side of his bed. They guarded their master.

In the morning the brother went far into the tundra. He walked on. Soon he caught up with a pack of wolves. And then the wolves called to him. An old wolf said:

—Hey, where are you and your friends going?

The boy said:

66

—I've come a long way.

The wolf said:

—Why has your home become so bad for you?

And the boy said:

—At home I can't sleep well. It's as if there was some danger nearby. My friends guarded me through the night. That's why I left.

An old wolf said:

—Now, look here. . . All right, agreed! I'll also give you my two sons as companions. Don't refuse!

The boy was very happy:

—Oh, that's fine. Give me your sons as companions!

Two rather large wolves joined him promptly. And he only said this to them:

—That's nice; the number of my companions has increased.

He went on farther. With him there were already four companions. He then met the bear's family. The bears said to him:

—Well, you have many companions!

The boy said:

—Yes!

The she-bear told him:

—Very well, take my sons with you as companions!

The boy was even happier. Two yearling bears joined him. Now there were six companions. When he camped for the night six guards surrounded him. And on days, no matter where they traveled, they brought him food.

Then he again caught up with the fox. The fox said:

—Oh, my cousin, you have many companions! I'll also join you!

The boy said:

—Very well cousin, let's go! You're going to entertain me!

The fox said:

—Why not, in some way we can amuse each other.

They started out. The animals followed him. Then the boy thought to himself: "Now we could return home. I have many friends!"

They turned around. Then the house was already nearby. Suddenly the fox said:

—Cousin, wait a bit here with your companions. And I'll go and sneak up to your house. It could be that there is somebody bad in the house. It could be that they're planning something against you.

The boy replied:

—Very good, cousin, go ahead! We'll wait for you here.

The fox trotted to the house. He looked into the window. And, indeed, he saw the *kele* talking with the girl. The *kele* said:

—Your brother will come here now. You tell him: "Will you heat the bathhouse until it's hot enough? Then you can have a bath." When the bathhouse gets heated, the door will lock itself. He'll be inside there and he'll die; he can't get out. The house is made out of iron.

The fox heard all of this. They stopped talking and the fox returned to his companions. He came back and said:

—It's bad, cousin! And indeed they're thinking of doing something bad to you. The *kele* told your sister: "As soon as your brother comes here tell him to heat the bath. Let him make it very hot." As you go in to bathe, the door will lock itself and you'll die there.

The boy said:

—What am I to do?

The fox replied:

—Don't be afraid. Nothing will happen to you. When you heat the stove, don't heat it too much, just warm it slightly. As you come out of the bath, say to your sister: "I've heated the bathhouse, I'll go in there again." Then leave right away. The *kele* will go in the bathhouse. Then our friends and we will attack him and tear him to pieces. And now you go and take the dogs with you and let the others stay with me. Well, it's time!

The boy left. The dogs followed him. As soon as he came in the house, the *kele* hid himself again. His sister said:

—Aren't you very tired, my little brother? Would you first heat the bath and wash yourself?

—Well, you're right, I am tired! Perhaps you or somebody else wants to wash in the bathhouse. I'll heat it very well. I'll heat it and leave right away. It could be that somebody may want to go at once to wash up.

—Very well, heat it also for another person!

—I'll heat it.

He went out and started to heat the bathhouse. He heated the stove red-hot. The fox said:

—Now, that's well done!

He left the bathhouse. As soon as hc left, the door shut tight. And the dogs did not have time to jump out; they stayed in the bathhouse. The fox said:

—Don't worry, they'll get out! You know they have teeth of iron. There, you can already see them.

And true, they jumped out. Blood was dripping from their mouths.

The boy ran to the house and said to his sister:

—Well, I'm off. The bathhouse is heated.

And with the dogs he went to his companions. He came there and the fox said:

—I'm going there to have a look. It could be that the *kele* is already in the bathhouse.

He got there and looked in the window. He heard the *kele* say to the girl:

—Very well, I'll go in the bathhouse!

And the cursed one went to the bathhouse. The fox was looking. The *kele* went in. And the fox ran to his companions.

—Now cousin, let's go! He fell in our trap! He's already in the bathhouse, the bad one.

They started out. They came. The *kele* was still washing. They hid themselves around the bathhouse. The fox said:

—Soon the *kele* will come out. Then I'll amuse myself a little as he's being torn to pieces.

They looked. The cursed one appeared. The dogs were the first to attack him. They grabbed his legs. The *kele* fell and then the bears rolled onto him. And the wolves started to pull on his arms. So they tore the *kele* apart.

And the fox split his sides laughing; he almost died—he laughed so hard. They set the *kele* and his bathhouse on fire and went home. The brother was not angry with his sister. They ate together with his companions and lay down to sleep.

During the night the sister went to the scorched ruins and started searching. She found a fang of the *kele*, took it home and shoved it in the bed of her brother. Her brother got sick and died. It turned out that the fang of the *kele* went right into his heart. His companions were in an uproar. But the fox said:

—Well, now we'll have to try to take out the fang! The body of our friend is not cold yet.

He said to the wolves:

—And now, let's try! I'll pull from one side of the wound and you, with the bears, from the other. But we'll have to be nimble here; otherwise the fang will bounce into us and kill us all.

They began to pull. The fox pulled at one side of the wound, the wolves and bears at the other. Suddenly the fox jumped aside like a bouncing ball. The fang whistled away directly into the tundra.

The boy readily opened his eyes. Then the fox sat him up and said:

—Well, cousin, you woke up!

The boy asked:

—Oh, what's happened to me?

The fox said:

—You should know that your sister wanted to kill you!

68

At that the older brother became very angry. He then said:

—She's become a *kele*. Now I'll have to kill her!

He caught up with her, snagged her with a fishhook, threw her in the refuse shack and set it afire. She and the refuse shack came to their ends.

The companions began to live a good life. There were many of them and the fox lived with them. That's all. I've finished the tale.

27. The Clever Viksa

Narrated in 1960 by an inhabitant of Palana village in Tigilsky *rayon* of the Koryak National *Okrug*, A. Solodyakov, age 34. Recorded and translated into Russian by A. Zhukova. The detail about the enormous size of the wristwatches of the giants appears to be a superimposition originating among the Koryaks during the Soviet period.

There lived a rich man. He had a brother. The rich man had a wife and a daughter. Rich young men came to ask for the daughter in marriage. They drove large herds of reindeer to the rich man in order to buy the daughter for the reindeer. But the old man told all of them:

—What for do I need reindeer? They will not buy my daughter. All I need is a very strong man.

The young men returned home with nothing. Then again another one came. He was a very strong man.

The rich man told him:

—Here, in our parts, two giants roam. Kill the giants and I'll give you my daughter.

The young man ran back home because he saw that he could not kill the giants. They were very much larger than he.

A certain youngster heard about this. They called him Viksa. He was not in the least rich. His clothes were ragged. But he was very quick-witted and nimble even though he was not very strong. So Viksa went to the rich man. He arrived. The rich man said to him:

—Where are you going?

—Well, I've come to you, to serve you. I am very strong, the strongest of any of my people. Also very fast, very nimble, —Viksa bragged.

The rich man said:

—All right, very good. Here, in our parts, there roam two giants. They're very bad ones. If you kill them, I'll give you reindeer.

But Viksa said:

—I don't need reindeer! You give me your daughter!

The rich man said:

—Very well, let it be so!

Viksa went to the tundra. He had never seen the giants before. He walked and walked. Then he saw two men sleeping. Viksa became very frightened. But then he said to himself: "Oy-oy-oy, what is this, how long they are! Just like two whales thrown ashore by the sea. I couldn't ever hit them right." Then Viksa decided to hit one of them with an axe. And he hit one on the head. The giant kept sleeping; didn't miss a wink. Viksa hit him with all his strength once more. And the giant just rolled over on his other side. Viksa knew that he could not kill them. Then he thought of something. He gathered ten very large stones—he could hardly hold them—and carried them to a tree. Then he hoisted them up the tree and climbed up himself. He began to throw the stones on the heads of the giants. He hit one with the first throw. The giant became very angry. But then he fell asleep again. And Viksa hit the other one on the head. The giant opened his eyes, looked at his companion and went to sleep again. Viksa hit the first one on the head again. He got up and saw that his friend had turned on his side. And he fell asleep again. Now Viksa hit the other one on the head. That one woke up, looked at his friend and said:

—Maybe he's fighting something with his fists?

So he fell asleep again. Then Viksa took the largest stone and hurled it below. It hit the giant directly on the nose. It hurt him very much. He became angry, looked at his companion but he slept on as if nothing had happened. The giant turned around and hit his friend's nose with his fist. He awakened and said:

—Why are you fighting?

His friend replied:

—Because you've been hitting me with your fists all the time when I was sleeping.

The other said:

70

—You were the first to start it.

The giants threw themselves at each other. They started to fight violently, tearing their clothing to bits. One of them grabbed a stick to hit his friend! But he could not kill him. They fought for two days. Then Viksa saw that both were dead. At once he went home. He walked very fast. On the way he tore his clothing and scratched his face so that blood ran down it.

The rich man saw Viksa coming in a great hurry. The rich man was perplexed. He saw that Viksa's face was covered with blood and his clothes torn.

And he asked:

—Well, Viksa, have you come?

—I have.

—Who tore you up like that, a bear, maybe?

But Viksa said:

—No, that's from the two giants. They were really very much larger than me. I could hardly get the better of them.

And the rich man said:

—Is that really true?

Viksa said:

—Take a look; you know I've won.

—And where did you kill the two?

—There, on our river, a bit upstream.

The rich man gathered his lads.

—All right, we'll go there together! Maybe it's true that he killed them.

And Viksa said:

—I'll go with you. But the rich man said:

—You go treat your wounds! Only we will go.

They left and, truly, they saw the giants lying there beaten to death. And each of them had a wristwatch so big that it couldn't be taken off.

They returned. The rich man said:

—Yes, you are strong Viksa. You did tell the truth when you said: "I'm the strongest of my people."

And Viksa said:

—This is the first time I've killed such. Both of them were very strong. When they grasped my hand they almost broke the bones. And then one of them attacked me from the front and I hit his head with my fist. The other attacked me from the rear. I kicked him in the belly. He fell down. Then we fought each other again. One hit me in the cheek and drew blood. Then they grasped me and tore my clothing apart. I gathered the last strength I had and began to beat them with my fists. And I killed both of them. Then I felt pain myself and came back here straightaway. Now, will you give me your daughter in marriage?

But the brother of the rich man said:

—We'll not give her away yet. Our hunters cannot go to the tundra at all because there is a terrible bull there. He's killed many of our hunters.

Viksa said:

—What kind of bull is he?

The brother of the rich man replied:

—He's very large. From his forehead there sticks out a horn like a knife. If you kill him we'll give you our woman.

Viksa went to search for the bull. The brother of the rich man said:

—If Viksa tricked us, the bull will kill him. That means that Viksa is weak. But if he kills the bull that means that he's very strong.

Viksa saw the bull and he said to himself: "For sure that bull will kill me."

And the one-horned bull, when he saw Viksa, started to pursue him right away. Viksa started running for home. And the bull was right after him.

Viksa stopped. He saw that there was a big tree in front of him. Viksa ran to it and he only said:

—It will be better if he kills me at once!!

The bull took aim at Viksa, but Viksa, in a flash, hid behind the tree. The bull drove his horn directly into the tree and got stuck. Viksa saw that the bull was dying. He went to the bull and began to hit him with a stick. He then put a thong around his neck and cut the horn off him with an axe. He tied the bull to the tree. Then he cut the tree with his axe and took the horn out of it. He then led the bull away by the thong and started for home. He took the bull right to the house.

—Well, here, I've brought you your enemy. You can do with him whatever you wish.

The rich man said:

—Well, tell us Viksa, how did you get hold of that bull?

Viksa began to tell them:

—I barely found this bull. I looked for him for a long time. I couldn't find him anywhere. Then suddenly I saw him not far away. The bull ran toward me. And I sat on a hummock and got the thong ready. And as the bull threw himself at me I jumped to my feet. I grabbed his horn, threw the thong around his neck and started to tie him up. The bull tried to gore me. That made me angry. I lifted him, threw him to the ground and tightened the thong. Then I let him go. The bull got up. I was at the point of bringing him home when he decided to jab me with his horn. Uh, how angry I got. I took him by the horn, got my axe and cut the horn off. Then I came here.

All said:

—Very well, we'll give him that daughter in marriage. Viksa is a strong and nimble man.

And so they gave to Viksa the daughter of the rich man. I have finished the story.

28. Kaynyvilyu

Narrated in 1958 by an inhabitant of Palana village in Tiglysky *rayon*, Koryak National *Okrug*, T. Kavav, age 47. Recorded and translated into Russian by A. Zhukova. In Paleoasiatic tales about children born to a mother-animal and human husband or to a woman and a husband-animal, the unusual physical strength and deftness of the children is emphasized in comparison to that of those around them and even that of the mother and father. The episode about the Russian Cossacks, inserted into the magical tale, reflects actual historical happenings. The tale is changed further with the contaminated content of the Russian tale about the search for the "water of life" and the struggle of the hero with the Fiery Snake. In Koryak folklore the content is adopted to local conditions: the water of life is changed to "bile medicine" and the Fiery Snake to "old man Burning Spot" [with a Burning Head or a Fiery Head]. The hero "past the tenth door" kills the latter. The bile medicine returns eyesight to the hero's father. The influence of the Russian magical tale is quite evident here. (Cp. with no. 76 in Jochelson 1908).

There was a village. A hunter went from that village into the tundra. Then suddenly a snowstorm blew up. He got lost. He looked around and saw that a forest surrounded him and that he was at the very top of a hill. Suddenly he fell under the surface of the land. It was very warm there. After warming himself he started to think: "Where am I?"

He started to feel in the dark everything around him. He had the sensation of feeling fur under his hand. He thought: "What could this be?" And it turned out that it was a bear. Not just a bear but a she-bear. The exhausted hunter dozed into deep sleep. He then awakened because he was very hungry. He said:

—What is there to eat?

Then the she-bear passed her paw over his lips; he immediately felt sated and fell asleep again.

Spring arrived and the she-bear left the den. And the hunter also awakened and looked around.

—How come it's become light? —he said.

It turned out that the bear uncovered the den. So the hunter also left.

It was very warm outside. He said:

—Why has it gotten so warm? I only lay down to sleep yesterday.

The hunter forgot where he was to go, he even forgot about the village. He got very much used to the she-bear. In the second year, a son was born to them. His body was just like that of a man. Only his ears were those of a bear. So they called him Kaynyvilyu—Bear's Ear.

They began to live together, the three of them. So four years passed. Kaynyvilyu became strong—you know he was the son of a real bear.

He then said to his father:

—Let's go to your home.

His father replied:

—But how can I leave mother?

Kaynyvilyu said:

—All the same, mother could kill us.

His father agreed. He said:

—But how are we to go. No doubt your mother will follow us.

Kaynyvilyu said:

We'll run. She'll not see us.

His father said:

—She'll find us anyway; she'll smell us! She'll become even angrier if we run away on the sly.

Kaynyvilyu said:

—That means that we have to kill her.

But the father said:

—Why? It would be a pity to kill her!

Kaynyvilyu said:

—She'll kill us anyway. She'll get angry and kill us.

And so they ran away. At the time the mother was walking in the tundra. She returned to the place where she had left Kaynyvilyu and his father. They weren't there. The mother got angry and followed their scent. Daylight was coming to an end; it was almost evening. Finally she saw them walking. Kaynyvilyu and his father would stop often and look back. They saw mother. What bad luck! They quickened their pace.

The father became frightened—you know he was a human being! He said to Kaynyvilyu:

—She'll catch up with us! She's very fast on her feet!

And Kaynyvilyu said to him:

—Then I'll have to kill her!

They came to a gorge. Kaynyvilyu said to his father:

—You go ahead fast, I'll wait here.

His father ran with all he had and Kaynyvilyu hid at the edge of the path. He waited. He got a stone and put it in his fist. And his mother smelled that somebody was hiding there and she hurried to the place. Kaynyvilyu hit her with his fist between the ears. And the bear's eyes just popped out. She fell as if cut down.

Kaynyvilyu ran on the path after his father. He caught up with him. His father said:

—Where is mother?

—I've clubbed her to death.

He did this because he was bad and cruel. A real bear's son. No doubt even his heart was that of a bear.

The pair walked on silently. Finally they came to the village. The father led his son directly to his house. He said:

—This is our home!

But Kaynyvilyu did not go in the house directly. He saw many children. He went to play with them right away. Only he was too strong. They started to play. They jostled each other. He would very lightly hit somebody and tears would come to the playmate's eyes. Kaynyvilyu had a heavy hand.

Soon the whole village started to say:

—Where did our neighbor find such a Kaynyvilyu?! He's so naughty and strong. He maims all of our children.

But Kaynyvilyu did not know that people were talking like that. Then his father told him:

—My son, people are talking about you in a bad way! They say that you are maiming other children when you're playing with them.

But Kaynyvilyu said to his father:

—Yes, I just touch them lightly and they wail! You know that I don't use my full strength.

His father said to him:

—Please play with them gently.

Kaynyvilyu said to his father:

—Maybe it would be better if I went to the tundra?

But his father did not allow that. He said:

—You know if you go away you'll never return to me!

But Kaynyvilyu said:

—If I'm not killed or if I don't die, I'll return. And it could be that there is somebody stronger in our part of the world. Maybe I'll meet him.

His father became frightened, because he did not have such strength; after all he was only human. He said:

—Very well, go! Enjoy yourself! You can go right now!

—All right, I'll go, —Kaynyvilyu replied.

Kaynyvilyu walked downstream over the tundra. He saw that in front of him there was a moving birch forest. He stopped and said to himself:

—What's going on here; is it a hill with a forest on it moving?

The hill stopped. A human being appeared. It said:

—Welcome Kaynyvilyu! It's nobody but you, Kaynyvilyu, a hero, a strongman about whom they told me.

Kaynyvilyu said:

—Yes, that's me! Only I'm not a hero. But you're really a hero! You're carrying a birch forest on your shoulders!

To that the tundra-giant said:

All right then; let's go together where you started to go.

—So, we'll go.

They walked together downstream. They walked for a long time. Suddenly Kaynyvilyu saw **yet** another hill covered with cedars moving toward him. The hill came near and again a tundra-man appeared. He also called out:

—Welcome Kaynyvilyu! Are you the same Kaynyvilyu about whom they told me?

Kaynyvilyu said:

—Yes, I am.

—Where are the two of you going?

—Not too far. We're going down river. We're enjoying ourselves!

—Very good, I'll go with you too.

—That's fine! We'll enjoy ourselves more.

The three of them walked downstream. They walked. Again Kaynyvilyu saw that the entire tundra next to the river was moving. It came closer. Yet another tundra-giant came out of it.

—Welcome Kaynyvilyu, you're well-known strongman!

—Yes, I am. I am Kaynyvilyu. But I'm not a strongman.

And the giant who was carrying the tundra next to the river said:

—All right, take me also as a companion. I'll go with you.

Kaynyvilyu said:

—That's fine, a foursome is merrier.

They walked and walked. They saw a house as big as a cliff. Kaynyvilyu walked behind. The giants came to the house and said:

—Kaynyvilyu, this is our house.

It turned out that the giants were brothers. They said to him:

—Well, let's go in.

They went in. There were four beds in the house. They were covered with bear fur. Kaynyvilyu stumped heavily on the floor. The floorboards started to crack! He was angry because the beds were covered with bear fur. He purposely stumped more heavily.

The giants saw that Kaynyvilyu broke the floorboards. They told him:

—Hey, you! You good-for-nothing Kaynyvilyu! Why are you breaking the floorboards?

Kaynyvilyu said:

—If you must know! I'm not breaking them purposely. They are breaking by themselves. The wood is probably rotted through.

Right off the giants became quiet.

Kaynyvilyu lay down on the bed of the master who was not there at the time. True, the companions told him:

—Don't lie down there. That's the bed of our master.

And Kaynyvilyu told them:

How can you talk so badly to a guest?

—We're talking like this because our master is very frightening,

—All right then; when the master comes I'll get up!

They started talking. They asked Kaynyvilyu where he was from and where he was going.

Evening came. They heard a horse neighing. The master had arrived. Kaynyvilyu looked outside. Oh, what a giant of a man he was! And the horse was very beautiful; fire exuded from his mouth. The master tethered the horse and said to himself:

—Oho, it smells like a bear's ear! Could it be that Kaynyvilyu came here?

And Kaynyvilyu heard it all. The master finished tethering the horse; went in and saw that all the floorboards were broken and that Kaynyvilyu was lying in his bed. The master became angry, did not even say "Welcome!" and at once yelled out:

—Kaynyvilyu, get out of my bed!

But Kaynyvilyu did not get out. He just lay there as he did before. Then the master told him:

—Now, you better get up, you damn[ed] Kaynyvilyu! If you don't, I'll punch you!

Kaynyvilyu said:

—Now, look here friend! You're seeing me for the first time and you get angry!

The master came closer and said:

—If you don't get up right now I'll really shake you up!

Kaynyvilyu said:

—Well, that's your business!

The master threw himself at Kaynyvilyu. Kaynyvilyu got up and stood on his feet. Then, with his left fist he struck the master on his right ear. The master fell. He fell as if he had been hit with an axe. And Kaynyvilyu sat again on the bed. Then the other companions cried out:

—Why are you beating our master?!

Kaynyvilyu to them:

—He attacked me first and we didn't even get to know each other.

At that point the oldest of the giants threw himself at Kaynyvilyu. Kaynyvilyu struck him with the same force. He fell directly on one of his companions. And Kaynyvilyu again sat down. Then yet another of the giants attacked him. Kaynyvilyu became enraged because he knew that he was the son of a real bear. His strength and his heart were those of a bear.

Finally the last of the giants threw himself at Kaynyvilyu. Kaynyvilyu struck him hard, he fell, and Kaynyvilyu shoved him aside with his foot. He left the house alone and said:

—Could it be that there is nobody stronger than I? In there I've defeated such giants—the size of a hill.

He went farther downstream. He said:

—Maybe I'll see something interesting.

He walked and walked. Suddenly he saw in front of him a small *zemlyanka* with smoke coming out of it. He went to the *zemlyanka*. He entered it. A little old man was sitting there. He saw Kaynyvilyu and he exclaimed:

—Welcome Kaynyvilyu! Where did you come from? Are you the same Kaynyvilyu about whom they talk so much?

—Yes I am the very same!

The old man started to ask him:

—Where from and where to are you going?

Kaynyvilyu said:

—I'm coming from my house, from up the river. I'm simply walking, just for fun.

The old man said to him:

—Maybe you saw the giants of this place?

—Yes, I did. I went together with them to their house.

The old man to him:

—And where are they now?

—I left them in their house. We fought very hard.

—Why did you fight?

Kaynyvilyu said:

—We came to their house. We entered. I set my feet on the floorboards and they broke. The companions told me: "Why are you breaking the floor boards?" And I told them: "The wood is probably rotten and that's why they broke". There were four beds there. I sat on the empty bed. And the companions told me: "Why did you sit there. It's somebody else's bed". I asked them politely: "Whose bed is it?" They said: "It's our master's." I said to them: "Why can't I sit on it?"—"Because we are afraid of our master. He will scold us very much." I said: "Well, all right, somehow I'll get around it. Then they started talking to me. The giants were asking me where I was from. I told them all about my life. In the evening suddenly I heard a horse neighing. I looked out, and the horse was very beautiful and fire was coming out of his mouth. Then I heard the master saying to himself: "It seems that there is a smell of bear's ears here. Could it be that Kaynyvilyu came here?" You see, he sensed me with his scent! He then came in and saw right away the floorboards were broken. And he looked at me. He didn't even say: "Welcome!" and he became very angry. He said: "Why did you, you cursed Kaynyvilyu, break the floor boards? And why did you lie down on somebody else's bed?" And I said to him: "How nasty you are! We don't even know each other and you're so contrary." Then he started shouting again: "Now, you get out of that bed! And if you don't I'll beat you!" I said to him: "Well, as you will." As for me, I lay on the bed; I was not going to get up. He threw himself at me. Only then did I sit up. He started beating me but I swung my arm and hit him on the right ear. Then the others got angry and began to attack me in turn. Once they approached me, I struck them right away. I smashed them all and now I've come to you.

As it turned out, the old man was the father of the giants. The little old man said to him:

—Well, Kaynyvilyu, you're very strong and clever. You never make a mistake. It would be good for you to get married.

Kaynyvilyu said:

—Where would I find a good wife?

The old man answered:

—To be sure, you need a particular bride, one that's as strong as you are.

Kaynyvilyu became quiet and thoughtful. And the old man said:

—I know of a bride just for you. There is a very beautiful woman in the tundra; only she lives inside a hill.

Kaynyvilyu said:

—And have you seen her?

The old man answered:

—I've gone to that hill. At the top of it there is a hole. I looked in that hole and saw a very beautiful woman!

Kaynyvilyu said:

—How can I get to her?

And the old man spoke:

—I thought of that. I have a long thong. I'll let you down on it. You tie the thong around the woman. I'll pull her up. Then I'll let the thong down again and pull you up.

Kaynyvilyu asked him in earnest:

—Is it far to the hill?

—It's near.

—Very well then, let's go!

They took the thong and started out. They came to the hill. They climbed up it. And to be sure they saw an opening in the ground. Kaynyvilyu looked in the hole. In the darkness nothing was visible. He said to the old man:

—Why is there's nothing to be seen there?

The old man said:

—Maybe she went to the side—her place is very large. Why don't you let yourself down? Maybe you'll find her. And if you don't, I'll pull you back up. What would you do in an empty house?

Kaynyvilyu agreed. He said:

—All right, lower me with the thong!

The old man put the thong under Kaynyvilyu's armpits and started lowering him in the hole. As soon as he was hanging from the thong, the old man cut the thong and Kaynyvilyu fell below. He fell for a long time and finally hit solid ground. He looked up; the little hole above his head was barely visible, as if somebody pierced the darkness with a needle.

It turned out the old man tricked Kaynyvilyu. He decided to kill him because Kaynyvilyu was the undoing of his sons.

Kaynyvilyu walked and walked in the underground, but wherever he looked—there was no exit. He returned to the place where the white light was visible. He started to cry out:

—Hey! Hey! Get me out of here!

Nobody responded. Kaynyvilyu lived in the underground for a day, for two days. Without food he started to get weak. It was fortunate that he was a bear-human; if he had been simply a human he would have died of hunger long ago. One time when he was standing under the hole, he thought and said to himself: "It seems that death will come. After all my father said to me: "Don't go far, come back soon.' I didn't listen to my father and I went far. So I got in trouble."

Suddenly there was somebody's weak voice heard from above:

—Welcome, Kaynyvilyu! What are doing down there?

Kaynyvilyu became frightened. So at first he did not respond. He only looked up at the speck of light. And nothing was to be seen there. Then suddenly the same voice was heard. This time Kaynyvilyu answered:

—I'm dying of hunger here. A companion lured me down here!

And the voice asked him:

—No doubt you want to go home?

Kaynyvilyu said:

—I want very much to go home! Only I don't know how to get out of here.

And the voice again spoke:

—Very well, trust me. I'll try to lift you out with my thong.

And Kaynyvilyu said:

—Good, pull me up! I'd only like to get to the white light!

—Now look, I'll let down my thong. You just stand under the hole and I'll tell you what to do.

Kaynyvilyu obeyed and stood directly under the hole. And the voice from above said:

—Now I'm going to try to pull you up to the surface. You only have to put the thong under your armpits!

Kaynyvilyu did so. He tied the thong securely under his armpits. And again the voice said:

—How is it? Have you tied it well?

Kaynyvilyu only said:

—Yes, I have.

He felt that something was pulling him up. He crawled out and looked around. There was nobody to be seen. He said:

—Maybe I died? Or I'm simply dreaming that somebody had pulled me out.

Then a thin little voice was heard from the edge of the hole:

—It's me who pulled you up.

Kaynyvilyu looked at the ground. He saw a very small spider sitting there, looking at him and talking with him. Kaynyvilyu was very happy and he exclaimed:

—So it was you, it seems, who lifted me!

The little spider said:

—Yes, it was I.

Kaynyvilyu said:

—How can I pay you back? You know you've saved me from death!

The spider said:

—You don't have to pay! It's good that you were saved.

Kaynyvilyu said:

—Very well then. Maybe I'll be useful to you at some time or another.

He promptly went to the house of that old man. He arrived. He became very angry. He entered the *yaranga*, tore off the door and tossed it onto the tundra. The old man saw him and exclaimed:

—Welcome, Kaynyvilyu! So you returned!

But Kaynyvilyu did not even respond. He threw himself at the old man, grasped him by his feet and began to smash him against the wall of the *yaranga*. He broke all the bones in his body, drove a kettle hook under his ribs and hung him on the outside of the house. He set the house on fire and left.

He decided to go home to his father. He walked and walked and saw a village quite near. Kaynyvilyu rejoiced and said:

—Finally I'll be home soon!

He entered the village. He went directly to his house. Then he saw an old man lying [on the ground] between *yarangas*. He went up to the old man, greeted him and asked:

—Who are you? Get up.

The old man got up. Kaynyvilyu looked at him and saw that he was his father but without his eyes.

—How did it come to be that you are without your eyes? —Kaynyvilyu asked.

His father said:

—It was like this; the Russian Cossacks were celebrating a wedding and they gouged out my eyes. They're still in our house.

Kaynyvilyu lifted his father and carried him toward the house. They came to the house and Kaynyvilyu said to his father:

—You wait here! I'll go to them first.

Kaynyvilyu entered the house. The Russian Cossacks became frightened. How could they have known that Kaynyvilyu was to come! They started to talk to Kaynyvilyu. Kaynyvilyu said nothing to them. He threw himself at them. He grasped them all by their feet. He smashed them against the wall. He broke their arms and legs and tossed them outside. Afterwards he carried his father in the house. He put him on the bed. He was afraid that his father might suddenly die. So then Kaynyvilyu asked his father:

—Do you know, father, of any kind of medicine that will revive eyes?

His father answered:

—I've heard that there is such a medicine from the bile. But it's impossible to get it. All who have tried to get it never returned home. Go to our neighbor who is an old man. Ask him politely if he knows how such medicine can be gotten. It will be good if he knows!

Kaynyvilyu went to the neighbor. He entered the *yaranga*. The neighbor, the old man, said:

—Welcome! Where did you come from?

—Not long ago I came from afar. And now I've come to you to ask you, in a neighborly way, about some medicine. Maybe you know about some medicine that will revive eyes?

The old man answered him:

—Yes, true, there is such a medicine. But it's impossible to get it. Many brave men have gone after it but, so far, none have come back.

Kaynyvilyu said to the old man:

—Why is it that nobody has returned?

The old man replied:

—You know the old men say that there is a man called Fiery Head.

Kaynyvilyu asked:

—Why Fiery Head?

The old man answered:

—Most likely because his head is fiery. And in his liver there is bile. And this bile is the medicine that revives eyes.

Kaynyvilyu begged him:

—How can I get it?

The old man said:

—You have to kill Fiery Head and get it from his liver. But you have to get it very carefully, don't cut it through, and the neck of the gall bladder has to be firmly tied so that the bile does not spill out.

Kaynyvilyu said:

—And if it does spill out?

The old man told him:

—If it spills, then, they say, a fire will break out at once. It will be the end for you and Fiery Head will become alive again.

Kaynyvilyu said:

—And how is it possible to kill him?

The old man said:

—If you're going to go, I will give you a large saber. You grind it to be very sharp. And take it with you.

And Kaynyvilyu said:

Very likely I'll go. Only I don't know in which direction to go.

The old man said to him:

—Go where the sun sets. Go there for a long time; it's very far. Finally you'll see that the land has become somewhat red. That means that you have arrived. You'll see a *zemlyanka*. Quickly walk toward that *zemlyanka*. Just then Fiery Head will come out of it. He'll run toward you fast. His head is fiery but don't you be afraid and you also run toward him. He'll run up to you and start making circles around you. You just say: "We'll talk at home." And then run with all you have. If you linger, he'll burn you promptly. So rush to the *yaranga* in one breath. When you get inside start counting the doors. There should be ten doors. When you run through the tenth, stop and get the saber ready. Just as Fiery Head thrusts his head through the tenth door, cut it off without delay at the top part of the backbone. Fiery Head will fall down and you disembowel him. First get the liver, then the bile. See to it that you do this quickly. When you get the bile from the gall bladder put it in the pouch and run out of the *yaranga*. Again, run as fast as your legs will carry you because, if you linger, fire will surround you and you'll burn to death in the *yaranga*.

The old man stopped talking. Kaynyvilyu went home. He came in and told his father everything. His father said:

—Oh, my dear son, if I let you go, you'll never return home, Fiery Head will burn you up. But Kaynyvilyu said:

—If I do everything right, as the old man said, nothing will happen to me.

His father then said:

—Very well, go! Only take care to follow all the advice the old man gave you.

Kaynyvilyu left in the direction that the old man showed him. He took with him only a small bit to eat on the road and also the big saber of the old man. He walked and walked; he must go far, it's a long journey! Then he finally saw that the land was turning red. Kaynyvilyu said:

—Here I am, I've really arrived.

He walked a little more and saw a tiny *yaranga*. He said:

—That must be the *yaranga* where Fiery Head lives,

A man jumped out of the *yaranga*. He darted toward Kaynyvilyu. His head was really fiery. Kaynyvilyu also ran toward him. They met and Fiery Head started to run in circles around Kaynyvilyu. Kaynyvilyu merely said:

—We'll talk at home!

And he ran as fast as he could to the house. And Fiery Head just about caught up to him. With his left hand Kaynyvilyu pushed him and being light he flew backwards like a ball and fell down. Kaynyvilyu ran even faster. He then entered the *yaranga*. He started to count the doors. And Fiery Head just about reached the first door. Kaynyvilyu jumped through nine of the doors and hid behind the tenth. He took the saber in one hand and with the other he held the door. He got ready; he opened the door. Just then Fiery Head thrust his head through the door. At that point Kaynyvilyu struck his neck with the saber. The head fire went out. Kaynyvilyu did not linger, disemboweled him, took out his liver and separated the gall bladder. He tied it tightly and put it in a pouch and ran to the exit.

He came out and saw that from two sides, opposite one another, two fires were running. Kaynyvilyu darted along as fast as his legs would carry him. He managed to jump ahead between the two fires. The fires merged behind him and dashed after him in pursuit. It was a good thing that the old man told him: "Even if you outrun the fire don't stop, but run even faster. They're going to chase after you until the red land ends. Only then will they go out. Only then can you walk slowly."

Kaynyvilyu remembered those words. So he ran even faster to get sooner to where the red land ended. Then, finally the red land ended. Kaynyvilyu looked back. There was no fire, it had gone out. He walked on slowly. He walked and thought: "Well, it seems I've run away from danger."

When he was near the house, Kaynyvilyu started to worry: Maybe his father did not wait, maybe he died. Finally he came to the village, entered the *yaranga*, and there was his father, alive!

His father was very happy. He said:

—So, you have come back. No doubt you returned when you were halfway there?

Kaynyvilyu said:

—Why halfway? I went all the way to Fiery Head. I killed him. There was quite a bit of bile in his liver. I got it and brought it here. Only how is it to be used?

His father rejoiced even more and he said to him:

—Go to the old man and ask. Maybe he knows.

Kaynyvilyu went to the old man, the neighbor; the old man was also startled when he saw him. He said:

—Where did you come from, Kaynyvilyu? We thought that you'd never return, that Fiery Head would kill you.

Kaynyvilyu said:

—Thanks to you, old man! You've given me very good advice. I've done exactly what you told me to do. Also I've killed Fiery Head. And true, there was much bile in his liver. But I don't know how to use it

The old man answered:

—In olden times they used to say: Put the bile on a new small spoon and smear it around the eyes and then go to sleep. And when you wake up, the eyes will be the same as before.

Kaynyvilyu went home. It was already late in the evening. He came in and he said to his father:

—The old man told me: Put the bile on a new small spoon and smear it around the eyes. Then go to sleep. You'll get up in the morning and your eyes will be revived.

His father said:

—Well, all right, let's try it. Maybe it's true that that bile can heal!

Kaynyvilyu washed his father, put him in bed face up and let the bile trickle onto his eyes from the small spoon. His father fell asleep right away, as if the eyes did not hurt.

He woke up in the morning, opened his eyes and he saw everything. His eyes were like before. He also thought: Maybe I'm seeing in a dream?

The father cried out and began to wake up his son:

—Wake up little son, look at me! Is it really true that my eyes are like they used to be?

Awakened Kaynyvilyu became frightened. He jumped up. He looked at his father. And his father's eyes were exactly like they had been before.

—It's true, father, —he said. —Your eyes are completely cured!

Then his father finally believed it.

This is the whole story about Kaynyvilyu. Afterwards they lived well and Kaynyvilyu took care of the old man.

29. The Herder and the Bear

Narrated in 1952 by an inhabitant of Belogolovoye village in Tigilsky *rayon*, Tekel, age 40. Recorded and translated into Russian by A. Zhukova. Published in Voskoboynikov and Menovshchikov 1959, p. 461.

A herder got lost in a snowstorm and happened upon a bear's lair. The bear said:

—Welcome friend. Where are you going?

The herder answered:

—I'm in a bad way, I found myself in a snowstorm!

—And where is your family?

—I don't know. I'm lost.

—Very well, come to me in the lair. Take off your boots and fur-cap! We'll go to sleep!

The bear slept for a long time and the man slept with him. But then they awakened. The bear said:

—Who's with you at your house?

He answered:

—At home I have a wife and little son. There's still my old father and old mother. They are probably crying and saying: "No doubt our son has died."

They fell asleep again.

In the spring the bear went out of his lair. That man, it turns out, slept through the whole winter. The bear said:

—Hey friend, wake up! It's become light. It's getting warm. But the man replied:

—I want to sleep!

But after a while he went out and asked:

—Grandfather, where are my skis? I sat them right here.

And the bear said:

—They, my friend, were eaten by the vixen a long time ago.

The man asked:

—Where is my family?

The bear replied:

—They live nearby.

And the man said:

—I'd like something to eat.

The bear replied to him:

—Come over here!

He went in the lair and tore off a piece of his own shoulder.

Then he came out.

Hey friend, here's some meat for you!

And he said:

—Your family lives very close to here.

The man took the meat, went home, and told his parents how he slept through the winter with a bear.

30. Ammalyo

Narrated in 1952 by an inhabitant of Belogolovoye village, Kuteta Gammekovna, age 26. Recorded and translated into Russian by A. Zhukova. Published in Voskoboynikov and Menovshchikov 1959, p. 474. For other stories about a woman who refuses to get married and the unexplained shamanistic might of the heroine or hero see Dolitsky and Michael 2000, no. 15; Dolitsky and Michael 1997, nos. 1 and 7.

Long ago, when we still lived in the old way, there lived Ammalyo. She was then a young girl and she lived with her parents.

One time when they were sleeping a werewolf came into the *yaranga*. He looked at Ammalyo on the *polog*. Ammalyo became very frightened, cried out and started to call her parents. The people heard her, awakened—and the werewolf ran off.

Ammalyo's father said to her:

—Well, I better give you in marriage soon; you see, a werewolf wants to take you as wife.

Ammalyo did not want to marry. She refused point blank. She did not listen to her father.

Then one day Ammalyo went to the tundra to pick berries. The werewolf was watching for her; he seized her, sat her on a reindeer and took her far away to his land. Of necessity Ammalyo started to live there. She prepared food for the werewolves; they ate it and went to the tundra. But before they left they always said to her:

—Look here Ammalyo, don't you run away! We'll find you anyway and bring you back!

Some time went by. Ammalyo very much yearned for her home, for her parents. She began to cry. One day she got up early, began to cook the food and prepare the tea. When she was cooking the meat, she shamanized. She cast a spell over the meat. She prepared the meal and woke up the werewolves:

—The food is ready; eat it now!

The werewolves got up and began to eat. They finished and right away they fell into a deep sleep for many days.

Ammalyo started for home. She walked. She went off the path and sat down to rest. Then she heard somebody riding a reindeer approaching. She hid herself in a crevice. A reindeer jumped out of the crevice. Ammalyo became frightened and fainted. The reindeer rider passed by her. Ammalyo regained consciousness and started again to walk on the path. Soon she again heard somebody riding a reindeer in chase. She hid herself among the boulders. The rider was approaching over the boulders. Ammalyo became frightened again. She concealed herself and when the rider rode over the boulders farther, she came out and ran for home.

So the werewolf never found her. She came home. Her parents rejoiced. Her father said:

—Now you listen! I'm going to give you away in marriage. If you refuse, the werewolves will take you away forever.

Ammalyo listened. She got married. They moved to another village. And they lived there very well.

31. The Five Sisters

Narrated by A. Solodyakov. Recorded and translated into Russian by A. Zhukova.

There were five sisters who roamed over the tundra. They did not have mates. They were just women by themselves. They roamed from place to place pasturing their herd of reindeer. The youngest sister was the largest one. One day she said to her sisters:

—Why is it, my sisters, that we always roam over the same land? Then I got to thinking: "Should I ask my older sisters if they know of other lands, other countries." We're from year to year on the same land. You know, it's boring.

An older sister told her where there was another land; a beautiful and cozy one. She explained further:

—Beautiful lands are to be found only in the direction of the sea.

The youngest sister asked her:

—And the sea, is that what that land is called?

The older sister replied:

—The sea is like a river, only much larger. You can't see the other shore of the sea with your eyes. But, to be sure, the sea must have an end to it somewhere. And on that other shore there are hills.

The youngest sister said:

—Why not go there?

The older sister replied:

—This river flows to the sea. We'll go downstream along it. And when we get to the sea we'll see beautiful hills.

So they drove their herd toward the sea. They walked and walked. Suddenly the youngest sister said:

—What is that over there that is so bright?

The older one replied:

—That really must be the sea!

The youngest sister said:

—That must be right; the sea is very large! And our little river flows into it. And she added:

—That sea is so big because so many rivers, and all of them from one side, flow into it. And probably because of this the sea becomes deeper and bigger.

Her older sister told her:

—No, the sea is so big of its own. It was created as such.

Again her younger sister asked:

—Why does the river flow all the time? It flows and never stops. Why is this so?

Her older sister replied:

—A river has endless water. It also was created in that way.

And so the five sisters started to pasture their herd along the sea. The youngest one was their leader. She finally selected a place for their camp. They began to construct a *yaranga*. The oldest one told them:

—Hold back a bit; don't build that *yaranga*. I see a better place for it.

But the youngest said:

—Don't move on to another place.

Another sister said to the youngest:

—Sometimes you have to listen to the older.

And the youngest one said:

—It'll be better to stay here.

Again the other one said to her:

—Well, once in a while you listen to an older one.

The youngest one agreed and said:

—Very well then, we'll go there.

They built the *yaranga* at the new place. Suddenly the oldest disappeared out of sight. Then she returned.

The youngest asked her:

—Where did you go?

She replied:

—I simply strolled over the tundra.

The youngest one told her:

—Very well then, eat something!

She said:

—I'm not going to eat; I have a headache.

She made her bed and promptly went to sleep.

At night the sisters slept. The youngest also slept. Then she heard the older one get up quietly and leave the *yaranga*. She went out. The youngest started to listen. It was already dawn when, only then, did the older one return. She came in quietly and lay down. She was breathing very heavily. The youngest sister began to think: "Where did she come from? Where was she so long? And why did she return so tired?"

Morning came. The sisters awakened and started to eat. But the oldest sister was still asleep. Another sister went to her and said:

—Get up now; eat something!

And she replied:

—I'm not going to eat. I hurt so much.

Then again all of them fell asleep in the evening. Only the youngest one kept herself awake. She then saw that her older sister quietly got up, went out and returned only at dawn. She came in and promptly lay down to sleep. And the youngest observed her secretly. Again the youngest thought: "Where does she always go? And during the day she refuses to eat."

They awakened in the morning. The youngest went to the oldest and began to waken her. There was a bad odor coming from her older sister. As if something was rotting.

She awakened her:

—Get up; eat something!

The older one said:

—I'm not going to eat! I have a very bad headache.

And in the evening they fell asleep again. Only the youngest sister did not sleep; she wanted to learn where the older one went and why such a bad odor came from her. She decided to find out if the older one would again go somewhere.

The youngest sister lay there listening with her ears cocked. Then she heard the oldest one quietly eating something. And right then there was a strong odor of something sour.

In the morning the sisters woke up but the oldest one kept on sleeping. Then the youngest one said:

—Now, rekindle the fire outside!

The sisters rekindled the fire. They began to eat. The youngest sister said:

—Ever since we've made this our stopping place, our oldest sister goes out somewhere every night. And last night she was eating something. I heard it myself.

Another sister said:

—Why are you accusing our sister of doing something wrong? She is very sick and she can't eat any food. How could she begin to eat at night?

But the two other sisters objected:

—Our youngest sister is not trying to fool us. She never fooled us before.

And the youngest said:

—That is true, I've never fooled you. Tonight don't sleep and see and listen for yourselves.

Late in the evening the sisters lay down to sleep. They lay there quietly. They did not sleep. At midnight the oldest sister suddenly made a rustling noise with something. Right after that there was a bad odor! The sisters heard the oldest one start to eat something quietly.

In the morning the youngest told her sisters:

—Now you drive in the herd! We'll kill the best young reindeer.

The sisters drove the herd in. The youngest came out with a lasso. She lassoed the deer and brought him down. She hobbled his rear legs with the lasso, thrust a spear into his right side and released him. The young reindeer ran toward the *yaranga*. He ran around it and fell down at the fire pit as if he had been shot. The youngest sister became sad. Her older sisters questioned her:

—Why are you so sad, sister?

The youngest sister replied:

—You can see that something bad is happening to us. Go to that reindeer. Dress him and quickly cook him. I'll drive the herd away. When I am with the herd, our oldest sister may wake up and be about to go somewhere. At that time you tell her: "Go and get our youngest sister. She should come home and eat something. And kindle the fire for that." And I will try to hold her back a little. In the meantime you go and look at her bed. It would be very interesting to know what she eats during the night. Then put everything in its place so she will not guess what happened. I'll come back and you'll tell me everything. And look here, sisters, you listen to me and do everything the way I told you.

The youngest sister went off. The sisters began to hustle. They dressed the reindeer. One of them cooked the meat in a kettle. Then they went to their older sister. The began to wake her:

—Get up sister!

The older one got up.

—Well, —the sisters asked, —are you feeling better?

—A little better. My headache is gone.

—Let's go outside, we'll eat something. And you come with us; you'll eat with your younger sisters!

—I don't want to eat!

—All right, very well, come and sit with us, talk a little!

So the oldest sister came out and she said:

—And where is our youngest sister?

They told her:

—Right now she's with the herd. Won't you go after her? When she sees you she'll be happy. "Now look, —she'll say, —my sister has recovered. She's already walking." Make her happy; go get her!

The oldest sister listened to them; she went to get the younger one.

And the sisters did not tarry. They went in the *yaranga* and started to examine the oldest sister's bed. They found a human shoulder blade and bones of an arm. And on a finger there was an old fashioned very nice ring. They put everything back the way it was before. And they went out. They sat at the fire shaking with fear. One looked at the other.

The youngest sister returned with the oldest. They sat down to eat but three sisters could not put anything in their mouths. The youngest realized that something bad must have happened but said nothing. She began to eat.

The oldest sister said:

—I think I'll go to the *polog*.

The youngest said to her:

—Go and rest!

The oldest sister went off and the youngest said to her sisters:

—All right sisters, stop shaking and tell me!

The sisters began to tell her:

—We found a large human hand and a shoulder blade. On a finger there was an old fashioned ring, a very beautiful one. No doubt a woman's hand. You can see that our older sister gnawed that hand with her teeth.

86

The youngest sister told them:

—Very well. But tonight, again don't sleep!

They lay down to sleep. At midnight the oldest sister started to whisper:

—I have to eat something. When I eat this meat, what will I feed myself with? But if I kill another sister, there'll be food again. When I finish with her, I'll kill the next one. Two younger ones will be left. Then I'll eat them too. And after that what will I eat?

Morning came. The three sisters left the *yaranga* and cried. Their youngest sister told them:

—Stop crying. When I'm not anymore, then you can cry. But while I am alive nothing will happen to you. Now get yourselves together and do exactly what I tell you. We'll eat and go to the *yaranga*. I'll begin to talk and then it will come to you what I'm thinking about.

They entered the *yaranga*. The youngest sister said:

—My dear older sisters! We have a herd of reindeer. And that is all we own. Our entire life depends on them. Get ready to move. Here there is nothing more for our reindeer to eat.

The oldest sister cried out and said:

—My helpmates, my younger sisters! I can't go anywhere! The four of you will have to pasture the herd. And after you stay overnight for three days, let my most beloved sister, who is only a year apart from me, come to visit me. If I get seriously ill, let her stay with me. And if I am going to be sick longer and after you stay overnight for three days, let the middle sister come to me. You, my youngest sister, you send her to me. You know I'm very sick and could die suddenly. So you send the fourth sister. She'll bury me and return to you. Well, it is time for you to start the journey.

They left. The oldest sister went to sleep promptly. She was in very deep sleep, as if dead. They went out. The youngest sister was first. She looked to the right, she looked to the left, and she stopped and returned. She walked around the *yaranga* rapping with her staff. She came to the door and with her staff rapped on it three times. And she left promptly.

The sisters walked a long time. They stopped when it dawned for the second time. They sat down and started to eat.

The youngest sister said:

—Today or later I will not let anyone go to our oldest sister.

The sisters were quite happy.

—If I let you go she will eat all of us. She is really not our oldest sister but she is a *kele*!

Then the oldest sister woke up in the morning. She wanted to leave the *yaranga* but she couldn't, even though the door was open. She became angry and said:

—That's what my nasty youngest sister did! She must be a witch! But if I get out they won't get away from me anywhere.

She seized her parka and started dancing around the fire.

—Uttu-tu, uttu-tu, how can I get out!

She jumped up and flew outside through the smoke hole. She flew to seek out her younger sisters.

The youngest sister saw her, and she said:

—Look, sisters, there, far away, a raven is flying!

The sisters walked on paying attention all the time to the raven. Suddenly the raven started to grow. The youngest sister recognized her and said:

—Oh, you know, I've made a mistake! I forgot to cover the smoke hole. She flew out through the smoke hole. You see, she's coming toward us. Quickly, get together! Get reindeer and mount them. I'll be first and the oldest of us the very last.

Without delay the sisters mounted the reindeer. They went to the herd and the youngest sister in turn touched each reindeer with her staff. She rapped the legs of the mounted reindeer.

The oldest sister got closer and closer. The younger sisters heard that she was talking to herself while flying:

—You'll get nowhere! Tonight I'll eat all of you!

And the youngest sister said:

—I'm not going to give you my sisters! You're not our oldest sister; you're really a *kele*!

And that one said:

—*Kele* or sister, I'll eat all of you anyway!

The youngest sister jumped onto a riding reindeer. The reindeer started to run. The youngest sister cried out:

—Hold the heads of the reindeer upward!

The sisters were constantly looking around. The *kele* was already very close. The youngest sister waved with her staff and promptly the sisters started to fly. Then it started getting dark. The youngest sister looked back and said:

—She's already grasped one sister and thrown her down. She killed her.

She looked back again. The *kele* was just about to catch up with them. The two sisters started to cry. The youngest one told them:

—Don't cry, my dear sisters! I'm not going to let her kill you. I've purposely ordered the oldest to stay behind. Now I'm going to conjure and we'll all be saved.

And the sisters saw that the youngest really started to conjure. She built three fires and told them:

—Each of you lead your reindeer to a fire!

The reindeer went to the fires themselves. The sister-witch fell into the fire. And in the fire there was an old man holding a knife. And he cut to pieces the oldest one who was a *kele*. And the others were saved.

With this the tale ends.

32. The Shamaness Kytna

Narrated in 1955 by an inhabitant of Koltushnoye village in the Koryak National *Okrug*, M. Barganov (Ivtakrat). Recorded and translated into Russian by I. Vdovin.

Kytna had a daughter by the name of Ralinavut. Ralinavut got lost. And in the neighborhood there lived a large pack of wolves. There were twenty-eight wolves in it. It was they who took Ralinavut and moved away. The people searched for Ralinavut in all of the settlements but found her nowhere. Nobody saw her. So they decided: "No doubt, Ralinavut has died."

Six years went by and she had not returned. Then Kytna said:

—I'm going to learn how my daughter died.

And she began to shamanize.

Kytna had a helper. He told her:

—Your daughter Ralinavut did not die. She lives in the north with wolves in a place called Talkap. Long ago there lived a large pack of wolves—there were twenty-eight of them—it was they who took your daughter Ralinavut away.

In the morning when it dawned, Kytna said to her husband:

—Now I know where our daughter lives.

Her husband asked her:

—Where is she?

Kytna replied:

—Our daughter is far, far away in the north, at Talkap!

Her husband said in earnest:

—You must not go there by yourself. It bodes ill, you'll get lost.

Kytna said:

—I can't get lost. Even if I can't get my daughter out of that pack of wolves in which she is living, I'll return directly home.

Her husband said:

—All right, let's prepare the provisions for the road.

They started to prepare them; they made meaty tallow and cut up some dried meat. Kytna was well equipped for the trip. In the morning they awakened and ate. It was barely dawn when Kytna started out. She walked briskly and after she took about a hundred steps she became a wolf. You know that wolves run fast and so did Kytna. She ran toward the first camp of the reindeer herders and became a human being again. She arrived there. A herder saw her and said:

—Welcome, where are you going on foot?

Kytna replied:

—I'm going north, to Talpak.

The herder asked her:

—Why are you going there?

Kytna told him:

—My daughter lives there with the wolves.

The herder said to her

—You're getting to be an old woman; it must be difficult for you to walk! Ride one of our reindeer.

Kytna said:

—It's frightening for me to ride reindeer, it's better I go on foot. Maybe if I go on fast, I'll find my daughter sooner.

The reindeer herder said:

—All right, as you wish. Then tomorrow at dawn be on your way.

When on the morrow dawn came, Kytna promptly started out. She barely took a hundred steps—and the herder looked—and there was a wolf running.

The reindeer herder exclaimed:

—So that's why we couldn't convince her to ride our reindeer!

Kytna, it seems, changed her body again.

On the path Kytna met a wolf. The wolf befriended her. Kytna began to question the wolf, saying:

—Have you seen in any of the packs an unusual wolf?

The wolf replied:

—Far north, still farther beyond Talkap, there lives with a large pack of wolves someone unlike a real wolf. In that pack there are twenty-eight wolves; it is with them that she lives.

Kytna said:

—That perhaps could be where my daughter is. Her name is Ralinavut.

The wolf said:

—Indeed, there is a little girl with that name.

Kytna said:

—Thank you, now I have learned everything.

And Kytna started directly for the north as the wolf had told her. She ran to a sumptuous camp of Chukchi reindeer herders. She came to the master of the camp as a guest. The master began to question Kytna, saying:

—Where did you come from walking, little old woman?

Kytna replied:

—I'm from far away, from warm country, from Kichiga.

The Chukchi master said:

—Oh, you're really from afar and you've come on foot. I know your village Kichiga. Why did you start such a long journey, on such a difficult path?

Kytna replied:

—Isn't there near you a large pack of wolves? Don't they disturb you?

To that the Chukchi man said:

—Oh yes, nearby there is a big pack! Oh, and they do bother me! Every night they attack our herd.

Kytna said:

—Six years ago those wolves took away my daughter. Well, it is only this year that I've started to search for her. Maybe I'll not be able to take her away from the wolves.

They prepared to sleep. Kytna told her hosts:

—We'll get up before dawn and eat.

The next day they got up before dawn. They ate and drank tea when it just began to dawn. Kytna started for the place where the pack of wolves was eating the reindeer killed by them. She saw the pack and went around it against the sun so that the wolves would not catch sight of her. She walked and sang a song. When she had circled once, she called out the name of her daughter:

—Ralinavu, oh!

At that point Ralinavu stopped eating and asked:

—Who's that calling?

Again Kytna made the same circle around the pack. She called out the second time:

—Ralinavu, oh!

Ralinavu said:

—Somebody is calling again. It is as if my mother had come here.

Kytna went around for the third time. She walked singing and again called out:

—Ralinavu, oh!

Ralinavu went in the direction from which her mother was calling her. She came up to her mother and said:

—Mother, you've come here!

Kytna told her daughter:

—We'll go to the camp. We'll stay there for a day; I'll rest there. You know it took very long to get here. But I'm your mother.

They came to the camp. There already was some light. Kytna brought her daughter there.

The Chukchi man, the master of the camp, said:

—Oho, you've returned yourself and you've taken your daughter from the wolves.

They stayed in the camp for a day and rested. The Chukchi man said to Kytna:

—Can I take you home on harnessed reindeer?

Kytna said:

—No, we'll go on foot; we're in a hurry. Tomorrow we'll start back.

In the morning, as soon as it dawned, Kytna and her daughter started on the way back. The Chukchi man followed them with his eyes. At first Kytna and her daughter walked like people. But when they were about a hundred steps away the Chukchi man saw only two wolves running.

The Chukchi said to himself:

—Oho, the little old woman took on another appearance to run to the faraway country.

And Kytna and her daughter came home. The husband of Kytna was outside. He looked and saw two wolves coming closer. They ran side by side directly to the village. Then the old man said to his friends:

—Very likely those are my old woman and daughter coming back.

Other people at once came out of their dwellings and saw two wolves running toward the village. The people said:

—But those are not people; they are wolves!

Kytna's husband said:

—That's not so. They are my wife and daughter. Why would animals run directly to a village?

Then the wolves ran nearer. Within a hundred steps from the *yurta* Kytna and her daughter became people again.

33. Why People Started to Die

Narrated in 1960 by an inhabitant of Palana village in Tigilsky *rayon*, K. Kechgenki, age 25. Recorded and translated into Russian by A. Zhukova.

At one time there lived two brothers—Aka and Oyo. Aka was an able hunter. He walked over the tundra for days, killed many animals, and was never hungry. But Oyo was very lazy. He stayed at home all the time, and slept for days. All he did was to cook the meals for Aka.

Then one time Aka went far into the tundra. Suddenly he saw a *yaranga*. He went to the *yaranga* and a girl came out of it, a very beautiful girl. Aka was very much taken by the girl. They entered the *yaranga* together. Aka even forgot about hunting. He spent the whole day with the girl. Only toward the evening did Aka remember Oyo.

He told the girl:

—Well, you know, I have to go home! My brother is waiting for me there.

Aka went home thinking of the girl all the time. He arrived home; he did not eat anything. He said to Oyo:

—I've walked very far. I met with no animals. I'm very tired today.

And he lay down to sleep right away.

Aka awakened before dawn. He left the house promptly and did not return until evening; and again he returned without any prey. Finally the food gave out and there was nothing left for Oyo to eat.

Oyo left for the tundra. He walked and he thought: "Maybe I'll find something to eat." He walked for a long time. Suddenly he saw a large crevice in the ground. He went to the crevice, looked at it, thought a bit and said:

—Could it be that below here life could be good?

And he bent down. He fell; he got on his feet. It was dark around him as if his eyes had been picked out. Oyo walked at random—wherever his feet would take him. He walked and walked and finally it started to get light. He saw that he was walking on a path. He noticed a small *yaranga* in the distance. Only there was no smoke coming out of it. He came up to the *yaranga*. He thought: "Probably there's nobody there." He entered and saw an old, very old woman sleeping at the far end of the *polog* wall. Oyo woke up the old woman and said to her:

—Feed me something right away!

The old woman told him:

—Don't be in a hurry! Lie down to sleep and in the meantime I'll prepare the food!

Oyo lay down but began to watch the old woman on the sly.

The old woman prepared two kettles. She took a knife, cut out meat from her hip and threw it into a kettle. And in the other kettle she blew her nose. She then put the kettles over the fire.

When the soup in the kettles began to boil, the old woman awakened Oyo.

Oyo got up and said:

—Old woman, I'm not going to eat that food. You've cooked your own meat and in this one you blew your nose.

The old woman said:

—You mean you don't want to eat? Very well, don't eat!

Oyo said to the old woman:

—How can I get out of here? Take me back to my own land!

The old woman said to him:

—Now, listen to me! Not far from here is a small river. When you come to it, lie face down. Then you'll see a small *garbuscha* [pink salmon] going up the river. Take that salmon and cut a small piece out of the hump on her back. Only be sure that you cut only a small piece.

Oyo left right away. Soon he saw the river and promptly lay face down. Then he saw, to be sure, a salmon is swimming upriver. He grasped the salmon and sank his knife deeply into it.

The salmon jumped up, and struck Oyo with all her strength and knocked him off his feet. Oyo fell onto an ice-floe and promptly got stuck to it. He could not free himself. So Oyo died on the ice-floe. From that time on people started to die.

This is the end of the tale.

34. The Disobedient Children

Narrated in 1952 by an inhabitant of Paren village in the Nenzhinsky *rayon*, Kamlil, age 43. Recorded and translated into Russian by A. Zhukova.

There lived a brother and his sister. They never listened to their parents. So one day their parents left them in the tundra, and went themselves to another place. The children were in the *yaranga* by themselves. *Kele* came to them and wanted to eat them. They threw the children into a pit and led into it a bear so that he would tear them to pieces. But the bear pulled the children out of the pit. He began to feed them; he wanted them to grow up for himself to eat.

Then the *kele* went to pick berries and they said:

—Let's go and eat the children!

And the little boy and girl decided to run away from the bear. They ran and ran and suddenly there appeared a small river in front of them. They began to beg a small forest bird to carry them across the river. But the small bird replied:

—My wings are very small; I cannot carry you across. Let the gull carry you across!

The sea gull flew forth and carried the children across the river. The children ran farther. Then the *kele* came to the pit. They looked and saw that the children were not there. They started to search for them. They came to the river. They wanted to get across it but they couldn't. They asked the little bird how the children crossed the river. The little bird tricked them and said that the children drank up the river. The *kele* started to drink the river. They drank and drank and they burst.

And the children returned home, and from that time on they obeyed their parents.

35. Oyo

Narrated in 1952 by an inhabitant of Belogolovoye village in Tigilsky *rayon*, Atna Ichovich, age 74. Recorded and translated into Russian by A. Zhukova. The subject matter about seven brothers seeking brides is met with, in various variants, also among other peoples of the Chukotka-Kamchatka region (see the story *Pyat bratev* [Five Brothers] in Menovshchikov 1969, p. 68). The theme of securing brides by following released arrows is widespread even in Russian folklore (compare *Tsarevna-lyagushka* [The *Tsarevna*[28]-Frog] *et al.*).

At one time in the past there were seven brothers. The youngest of them was called Oyo. He was a simpleton and fool, altogether a dupe. Then his older brothers began to think about wives, since none of them were married.

The brothers said:

Oyo, we're going and you are staying home!

Oyo replied:

—Why should I stay here! Yes, if you go without me, you'll go for nothing; you'll find nothing.

The older brothers said to him:

—You can't come with us. You're awkward at speaking, your clothing is not in good shape, you don't have winter boots, and the lining of your skis is worn out.

Oyo said:

—That doesn't bother me. I'm used to it. I won't freeze!

The older brothers agreed:

—Very well, let him come with us. He'll be worse for it! The skis of the older brothers were in good shape; they were lined with *kamus*.[29] But Oyo had only snowshoes and summer boots.

They set out. As soon as they started Oyo fell behind. They walked and walked and toward evening they came near to a village. They looked back and saw that Oyo was catching up. The older brothers skied very fast but even so Oyushka[30] hurried after them as if somebody was pulling him with a rope. True, his skiing snowshoes and boots were thoroughly frozen. Yet he caught up with his brothers and, not slowing down, he started to overtake them. Now it was his older brothers that fell behind. They said:

—Well, what do you know! Our Oyushka, it seems, is very fast!

Only now did they recognize this. Earlier all would say: "You're worthless, Oyo, you so-and-so."

Oyo arrived in the village. The masters went to meet him and said:

—Don't go farther! Stop here!

It seems that in this village they always acted in this way. Then the master Kagynkan and his helper Nyune came to meet with Oyo.

They said to him:

—Are you with friends?

Oyo replied:

—Yes!

What have you come for?

Oyo said:

—To tell the truth, we've come to ask in marriage.

They said to him:

—When your friends come here, let them stop here also! Then we will tell you all what to do.

Oyo waited until his brothers arrived. The brothers arrived. He told them:

---

[28]*Tsarevna* — the daughter of a tsar.

[29]*Kamus* — the tough lower leg skin of hooved animals.

[30]Oyushka — diminuative of Oyo.

95

—We're to wait here! Soon the masters will come and tell us what to do.

At last Kagynkan came and told them:

—Now you can go there!

The brothers started out. Kagynkan said:

—This is the place where you fight. We have a custom that when a suitor comes he has to first prove himself in a contest.

And the place for the contest was a small, blood-stained square of ice.

It seems that the defeated were grasped by the shoulder[s] and their heads pounded directly on the ice.

Kagynkan went toward the *yarangas* and began to call out:

—Where is our fighter-*bogatyr*?[31] Suitors came here to marry. Come and meet the suitors!

The fighter came out challenging them. And so far nobody had been able to defeat the *bogatyr.* The oldest brother started to take off his parka. But Oyo said:

—Hold back! He'll kill you. You know, not for nothing did I overtake you even though your skis were better. It would be best if I try!

The oldest brother said:

—Very well, but do put on my fighting boots and breeches!

Oyo said:

—I don't need your boots and breeches. You know that I've overtaken you in my clothing. And I'll fight in it.

The older brothers with the oldest one said:

—Well, what can you ask of a dupe?! Be it, as it will!

Oyo took off his parka. And the *bogatyr,* whom Kagynkan had called out, was already waiting on the ice. Oyo said to him:

—You attack me first!

The *bogatyr* attacked Oyushka. Soon he got tired. The *bogatyr* said:

—I matched my strength against yours and I see that I can't cope with you!

And the older brothers saw this and thought: "He's just about to bring down our Oyushka."

But Oyo said:

—Well, hold on! Now I'm going to attack you.

Oyo threw himself at the *bogatyr,* turned him around several times, threw him down on his back and pounded his head on the ice. He only grunted once.

The people yelled:

—Kagynkan, what happened? They killed our *bogatyr*! Oyo finished him.

Kagynkan said:

—That cursed Oyo! All the same, he killed him!

Then Kagynkan told Oyo:

—Put your parka on. Now you're going to compete in running.

He then called out:

—Now send here those who can catch up to wild deer on foot!

And so the fastest of all the people, one that could catch up to wild deer running, came forth. The older brothers began to prepare themselves for the race. But Oyo said to them:

—Stop getting ready! They'll catch up to you. Better let me try.

The brothers said to him:

—Very well, but put on our very best skis and boots lined with fetlock from deer legs [see *kamus*]! But Oyo said:

—You know that I've outrun you on my skis and in my boots not so long ago.

The brothers said:

—Very well, let him run. He'll be worse for it!

---

[31] *Bogatyr* — figuratively a big, strapping man. In Russian folklore a *bogatyr* is an epic hero.

Then Kagynkan said:

—You'll finish your run over there at that spring. The one that gets here first, let him stop here and get hold of that club. The one that comes in second let him bend over the spring and drink of water. And the victor will hit him with the club with all his might. That is the rule. Now run!

The runner pulled ahead right away. Oyushka on his skis, black pads, in his first strides dropped back. They went on all day without rest and then turned back. Oyushka suddenly caught up to his rival as if someone was pulling him with a thong. He caught up to him, overtook him and left him far behind, as if he was standing rather than running. Late in the evening one of the runners came into view and the other one was not to be seen.

The people shouted:

—Over there, one showed up!

And little man looming on the horizon came closer and closer.

Oyo's older brothers talked among themselves in whispers:

—Oh, it seems that he is our Oyushka!

They recognized him by his motions. They ran to the spring. It was really Oyo. His older brothers said to him:

—Oh, Oyo, did you run only half the distance?

Oyo said:

—No, I was just at the place where you turn around to come back!

His brothers said:

—And where is your rival, the one who could catch up to wild deer?

Oyo said with contempt:

—I left him behind at the turning place!

The people shouted:

—Kagynkan! What's going on?! Oyo outran our most fleet-footed man!

Kagynkan also began to cry and said:

—Oy-oy-oy, such a good-for-nothing Oyo overtook the swiftest!

He then went to Oyo and told him:

—Go to the spring. When our runner comes in and begins to drink, you hit him with that club.

The slow one ran in. So, such was his fate! Promptly he started drinking from the spring. At that point Oyo hit him with the club.

The people shouted:

—Kagynkan, what's going on! Oyo killed our fastest!

Again Kagynkan started to cry. He said:

—Very well then. Now call for a man as nimble as an ermine!

Then there came a man, very short, but very well muscled.

Kagynkan then said to Oyo:

—Now you're going to compete in jumping and bounding. The place of the contest will be up there. And down here our people will stand bristling with spears. The one of you that doesn't reckon correctly will fall directly on the cluster of spears. And that's a sure death.

Again the older brothers began to prepare for the contest. But Oyo said to them:

—It would be better that I, the worthless, good-for-nothing die. Nobody will then have to say: "Oh, our famous Oyo died."

The older brothers said:

—All right, let him fight if he wants it that way!

Immediately the two left for the cliff to fight. Once there, Oyo said:

—You leap at me first, and I'll go after you slowly!

The man as nimble as an ermine prepared for the fight very thoroughly. He jumped and Oyo did so right behind him. He also jumped nimbly and high. Oyo flew over the head of his rival, hit him with his foot on the head, and the rival fell onto the terrible, sharp spears. But Oyo landed in a safe place. At that point the people cried out, lamenting:

—Oy, Kagynkan, what's going on here?! Our nimble as an ermine is dead!

Kagynkan cried:

—Oy, oy, oy, that cursed Oyo defeated us! So, now bring Nyune here! Where is he? Let him carry all his weapons!

Nyune appeared loaded with arrows and two bows. He came forth. Kagynkan told him:

—You know they've defeated us!

—Well, It's clear that we'll have to give them wives!

Kagynkan said:

—Yes, it's really so.

Nyune said to the brothers:

—Come over here!

They came up to him. Nyune said to them:

—Here I have seven arrows. I'm going to release them myself. The first one I'll shoot for your oldest brother, then for the second, then for the third, altogether seven times.

He released the first arrow for the oldest brother, then the second for the following brother. And so he released all the arrows. He said to Oyo:

—You're winners! You have achieved the best of your goals. Now go and follow the arrows. At the place where the arrows fell you'll see *yarangas*. In those *yarangas* are your brides. Let our oldest brother go first.

The oldest brother followed the path of his arrow. He saw the *yaranga*. He went to the *yaranga*. He looked in. A girl was sitting there sewing clothes. The *yaranga* was a very nice one. Around the *yaranga* a large herd of reindeer was pasturing. That was her dowry.

The second oldest brother also followed his arrow. And like his older brother he found a *yaranga*, and in it, a girl. All of the brothers found themselves brides. And all of them had reindeer. But Oyo's bride was prettier than the others, and her clothing was the most beautiful, and the *yaranga* the nicest. At once Oyo took the beautiful clothing and put it on. You wouldn't recognize him; he didn't look like Oyo.

In the evening they got together, began to prepare the food, and talk together. They said:

—Let our younger brother Oyo be the elder over us. He's gotten for us such a good life! Yes indeed, let him be our leader! And tomorrow we'll all go home!

In the morning they politely asked Kagynkan:

—May we now leave for home?

And Kagynkan told them:

—You are the masters now! It's your decision. Even if you'll go home, nobody can say: "Why have you gone home?"

Promptly they got together a caravan of reindeer-drawn sleds. Oyo was the very first to leave. They all returned home and started to live well.

Now I've finished the tale about Oyo. The end.

36. A Narrative About Those Who Lived Before

Narrated by A. Solodyakov. Recorded and translated into Russian by A. Zhukova. The toponymic and anthroponymic details and the accurate portrayals of the actions of the heroes are indicative of the origin of this legend in the stories about actual historical events during the period of the fighting of the Chukchi and Koryaks for the control of reindeer herds.

There lived a Chukchi, the strong man Kechgyntakyav. He lived with his wife and they had two children. Then one day the husband set out to hunt for wild deer. He took with him bow and arrows and a spear. It was fall. He had barely set out when a driving rain occurred. It was fortunate that he had taken a raincoat with him. It began to get dark. And he had not killed anything as yet. He climbed up a hill where there were always mountain goats to be found. As soon as he reached the top, he came upon a mountain goat and he killed it. He decided to prepare the meat. He made a fire with dry branches and put a fatty brisket on a spit. Suddenly he looked to his left, at the cedar forest, and he saw a long file of enemies coming closer to him. All of them had spears. "What am I to do?" —thought Kechgyntakyav.

Kechgyntakyav concealed himself in line with the fire and waited for the enemies to appear. Suddenly the meat on the spit moved. An arrow had stuck in it. After a short while it moved again but it did not fall in the fire because it was on a spit. The enemies apparently thought that it was the Chukchi sitting there. They came up to the fire and burst out laughing. They started to eat right away.

"That there scoundrel is no doubt the oldest of them. He is the only one eating the fatty brisket," —Kechgyntakyav thought.

He promptly aimed his bow and arrow at him and released an arrow. The arrow struck the enemy and killed him. The Chukchi started to make noises and yelled out:

—There are many of us; let's attack them together and kill them all!

The enemies became very frightened. They started to think: "True, they could kill us," —and in their fear they ran off every which way. They left behind all their equipment. Kechgyntakyav was supplied with many arrows for his bow. He was rich in arrows.

So our Chukchi, brave and sharp-witted, saved himself from the enemy.

37. Ymka

Narrated in 1955 by an inhabitant of Koltushnoye village in the Koryak National *Okrug*, M. Barganov (Ivtakrat), age 73. Recorded and translated into Russian by I. Vdovin.

There lived on Kuutuk[32] Island a strong man named Ymka. He had a wife, a daughter by the name of Kunavvyt and one son named Pininan.[33] Ymka had a first cousin whom they called Tavityn. He had two wives, both of them childless.

Ymka and his kinsmen destroyed many enemies. Somehow the word spread that a large enemy group was coming near. At this Ymka began to talk things over with his relatives. Tavityn said:

—We're going to fight here, in this fortified place.[34] This way we could destroy all of those enemies.

Ymka said:

It's going to be difficult to fight inside the fortress. It could be that much blood would be lost among the *yurtas*. It would be better if we fight farther away from the *yurtas*, in the tundra.

The group of enemies came closer. Promptly Ymka's people came out of their fortified place, went to the nearby tundra and started fighting. By now they started to kill the enemies. They stopped shooting arrows, and began to fight with spears. Much embittered Ymka threw his spear, took his axe and attacked the enemy. He began to hit the enemies' heads with his bone axe. But then he hit wrongly and the axe got stuck in a cleft of the helmet's sidepieces.[35] He got even more furious. He reeled in the enemy in whose cleft the axe was stuck from side to side. He could not free the axe so with it he shook that enemy. Somehow the enemy managed to sink his spear under Ymka's armpit. He pulled out the spear from the wound. Before he died Ymka killed ten more enemies. Finally Ymka became quiet and passed away.

His son Pininan was wounded in the right hand. Tavityn was the only one left to fight and while doing so he told his relative:

—Stop fighting; go home. I'll be the only one to attack them. You know, there're only a few enemies left. I'll finish them alone.

Pininan started for home promptly. He arrived.

His mother asked him:

—Where are your father and uncle?

—Ymka is no more; he was killed. And I have left Tavityn there; he's the only one fighting. You know an arrow hit my right hand. Because of that, uncle told me: "That's enough, stop fighting, go home."

There were few of the enemy left when Tavityn glanced at the riverside and saw that his relative Kunavvyt was running away. Tavityn finished off the rest of the enemies and started for home. He came home and said to his wife:

—Let's eat and then we'll go and bring Ymka here.

---

[32]Kuutuk (a Koryak place name) is a small island at the eastern coast of the Kamchatka isthmus, to the north of Kichiga village.

[33]Pininan, lit. "burning chip," is the name of the son of the hero of Koryak epic folk legends, Ymka.

[34]Fortified place (*krepnost* in Russian, *Vyyvyn* in Koryak) — the dwelling place of settled Koryaks; usually composed of from one to four semisubterranean *yurts*. S. P. Krashenninikov called such fortified places *ostrozhki* [pl. "little islands"] (Krashenninikov 1819). Quite often the dwellings of the settled Koryaks of the 17th and 18th centuries were on small islands close to the coast, but also on heights with steep slopes along rivers, the seacoast and capes.

[35]To protect the head of the fighter from the arrows [missiles] of his adversary, the ancient Koryak helmet had two loose sidepieces, right and left, which consisted of a squarish plate covered with walrus hide.

They ate and started for the tundra to get Ymka. They got there and went on to Ymka. Ymka lay in a pool of blood. Ymka's wife began to cry. They then put him in a canoe. They brought the dead Ymka home. Only then did Ymka's wife regain her self-possession and she asked:

—Where is Kunavvyt, where did she go? I haven't seen her for a long time.

Tavityn said:

—I saw her not so long ago. She was running down-river on the bank.

Kunavvyt's mother said:

—Could it be that Kunavvyt ran off to some settlement? When did they cremate[36] Ymka?

Tavityn asked:

—I'm going to search for Kunavvyt.

First he came to the settlement of Kichiga. Tavityn arrived there and he asked the Kichiga people:

—Did Kunavvyt come here to Kichiga?

The Kichiga people answered:

—Kunavvyt did not come here.

Then Tavityn set out for the Rekinnikii settlement.[37]

He arrived at Rekinniki and asked the people:

—Did a girl by the name of Kunavvyt come here?

The Rekinniki people said:

—There is a girl by the name of Kunavvyt in our village.

Tavityn rejoiced and said:

—Oh, how wonderful that my niece Kunavvyt is alive!

He went to Kunavvyt and began to talk with her. He asked her:

—Would you like to go home with me? What is your wish?

Kunavvyt told her uncle:

—I don't want to go home; here I'll find a husband for myself.

Tavityn went home by himself. He arrived home and said to everybody there:

—Kunavvyt went to Rekinniki. I told her: "Let's go home," but she didn't want to.

To that Kunavvyt's mother added:

—Well, she stayed there at her own wish. If that's what she wants, let her have it. Whether she finds a husband or not, it's all the same.

Tavityn said to his nephew Pininan:

—Heal yourself faster. If an enemy group gets here before long, I could not fight them by myself.

By winter Pininan healed a little. So one day Tavityn told him:

—Pininan, go and get some *yukola*.[38] The *yukola* is in a storage pit on the Kaluvvit River.

In the morning Pininan went after the *yukola*. He came to the pit where the *yukola* was stored; he opened the pit and let himself down into it. He started to prepare a bundle of *yokula*. Then suddenly the enemies looked down into the pit and said to Pininan, Burning Chip:

—There, if you will, Ymka's Burning Chip has burnt out!

Pininan looked up. He said to the enemies:

—I think that Ymka's Burning Chip will burn as long as it is fatty and thick.

Pininan said this but how was he to jump out of the pit!

The enemies did not expect that Pininan would jump out so soon. They wanted to spear him but they speared themselves. True, they watched the opening of the pit. They prepared their spears for the attack. They were saying to one another:

—When Pininan starts to come out of the pit, spear him.

---

[36]Interment after cremation of one killed in battle was a mode of internment practiced by the Koryaks until recent times.

[37]The village of Rekinniki is located on the western coast of the Kamchatka isthmus.

[38]*Yukola* — dried fish.

But Pininan jumped out of the pit so fast that the enemies could not take good aim. So deft was Ymka's son Pininan! So, that's why they speared each other.

Having leaped out of the pit, Pininan stood on the ground far from it. He began to jump on one foot, saying to himself: "Ymka's Burning Chip cannot go out, it will burn forever!"

Afterwards Pininan said to the enemies:

—Get your reindeer ready and I'll prepare my feet as you chase after me. True, you're riding reindeer and I'm on my feet!

The enemies flung themselves into the pursuit of Pininan. Pininan flew like a bird! He ran home to a place where a high post, around which games were played, was sunk in the ground. Pininan climbed onto it and stood on one foot atop it. The enemies just began to come closer. They saw Pininan standing on one foot on the post. They said:

—Pininan has become very deft!

Pininan cried out to Tavityn:

—Uncle, get our bows ready!

Tavityn said to his nephew:

—What are you doing there? Better get in the fort fast, you know the enemies are very close!

Pininan answered:

—They are coming, as they will. And I'll be in the fort soon.

The enemies ran up and began to shoot arrows at Pininan who still stood on the post. They had barely drawn their bowstrings when Pininan jumped into the fort. All of the enemy's arrows were stuck in the ground. Yet, they started to fight. Pininan and Tavityn destroyed the entire enemy group. They spared only one of the enemies and let him go home. He returned to his home and told his companions:

—Never, never again will I go to that village to fight. Our enemies are very strong and deft to boot. You know, we surrounded Pininan when he let himself down in the storage pit to get *yukola*. We surrounded the pit and got our spears ready. And we all lost him. He jumped from the pit and left us behind. And those of my companions, who were guarding the pit, killed one another with their spears. Indeed, one time we were chasing after him on reindeer. He was on foot but he flew like a bird on wings! We then came up to Pininan's dwelling and saw him standing on one foot on the top of a post. We promptly started to shoot arrows. And how he did jump again, and directly to his fort! And our arrows were stuck in the ground. Then they started fighting. And they almost destroyed our group. I was the only one they let go home. That's why I now tell you: "Never again will I fight them, or in the end even I will be killed for something."

38. The Settled and Nomadic Reindeer Herders

Narrated in 1955 by an inhabitant of Koltushnoye village in the Koryak National *Okrug*, M. Varganov (Ivtakrat). Recorded and translated into Russian by I. Vdovin. This is a historical story about the fighting of the Koryaks with the Chukchi for the control of reindeer herds. The settled Coastal Koryaks were on the side of the nomadic Koryak reindeer herders fighting the Chukchi; on the side of the Chukchi reindeer herders engaged in fighting with the Koryaks were the settled Maritime Chukchi and the Asiatic Eskimos. (Compare with the text "Viyutku-predvoditel" [Viyutku-the Leader] in Menovshchikov 1969, p. 123).

The settled Coastal Koryaks waged war with the reindeer herders—the Evens, Kamchadals, and also the Chukchi. The Chavchuveny[39] were a weakened people. Thus in the end they were almost destroyed. Only seven camps of the reindeer herders were left; all the others were destroyed. However, somehow one old reindeer herder became bold and said to his son:

—Go and seek a bride.

The son asked his father:

—Where am I to go to propose?

His father replied:

—Go over there, to our enemies, the settled dwellers, to propose marriage. Go where there are ten sons and one daughter. Propose marriage to her.

The son said to his father:

—Very likely our enemies will kill me!

The father said to his son:

—Very well, let them kill you! Death comes only once!

After this the son went off to propose. He arrived and he saw that many people were practicing shooting with bow and arrow. One of them saw the new arrival and he said to the others:

—Look, there's a "wolf" all by himself.

The others said:

—Let's kill him.

But one of the older ones said:

—No, we'll not kill him; let him come here and we'll ask him where he is going.

The suitor came up to them and they asked:

—Where are you going?

He said:

—I came to you to propose marriage. I came to the place where there are ten sons and one daughter. It's to her that I want to propose.

At once ten people went toward a *yurta* and entered it. There the oldest one said to his father in a loud voice:

—A suitor came to work off time[40] for our sister. We ask of you, would it be not better to kill him?

Their father said:

—It's going to be bad for us if you kill him. He came to propose, and to kill him would be sinful. I've lived a long time, almost a hundred years, and I've never seen a suitor put to death.

Then the suitor entered. The little old woman exclaimed, saying:

—Well, now, our guest, do sit down!

The suitor sat down. The old man said to his wife:

—Let the guest have something to eat.

---

[39]Chavchuveny (pl.) — Nomadic Koryak reindeer herders.

[40]The custom among some northern peoples for the suitor or bridegroom to work for the bride's family for a specified length of time.

The old woman started to prepare a meal. She cut the meat. She put human excrement in the soup. She used a pot instead of a platter. She mixed the excrement with the meat. And she handed it all to the suitor. The suitor dipped a wooden spoon into it, scooped a spoonful, and carried it to his mouth. All of a sudden the old woman struck the suitor's hand. The spoon fell to the side. Filled with indignation the suitor exclaimed:

—Why did you hit my hand when I began to eat?

To that the old woman replied:

—Did you ever see any man who ate human excrement?

The suitor told her:

—I thought that once a pot with food was offered, it meant that it was edible.

The old man said:

—It seems that you really want to marry our daughter. Well then, take our daughter in marriage; marry her!

The bridegroom promptly went to the *polog* of the bride, and he stayed with the hosts for three months. At that time the old man said to his son-in-law:

—By all means, this is enough. Go home with your wife. You can't live with me here forever; go to your home.

They started for home. They arrived at their dwelling. The old reindeer herder went out and saw his son driving up. At once he went into the *yurt* and called out to his wife:

—Come on out, our son has arrived with his wife!

Both of them went out, the old man and the old woman.

They turned to their son and told him:

—We thought that they had killed you, our only son. And now it seems that you've already married.

The old man told his son:

—Go back and ask your father-in-law and your mother-in-law as to how we are to live now. Last year the Chukchi enemies took the herd from us. Talk things over with them about what happened. Maybe they'll say to you: "Very well, we'll go and search for the reindeer; now that we know for sure that they are yours."

The young reindeer herder went to his father-in-law. His father-in-law said to him:

—Welcome, you've arrived!

—Yes, I've arrived!

The oldest son of his father-in-law asked:

—What did you come for?

The young reindeer herder told them:

—True, I've come here because of a very urgent problem.

And his father-in-law asked:

—What has happened to you?

He said:

—I want to discuss with you our living conditions! Last year the Chukchi drove off our reindeer. Can we take back those reindeer from them?

Then all of the relatives of his wife said:

—Very well, we'll go right now, without fail, if you know where these Chukchi robbers live.

The reindeer herder said:

—I know very well. The Chukchi live not very far from here.

Then they all started to get together. They prepared themselves well and started to trek to the north. They arrived at the Talkapskaya tundra, and found the Chukchi who had taken the reindeer away. The oldest Koryak brother called out:

—Well, you Chukchi, we've come here! Now you answer us! Last year you took a herd of reindeer from us? We've come to take that herd back!

In answer a Chukchi strongman by the name of Kvararu called out:

104

—You're not taking any reindeer!

The Koryak strongman said:

—It's not going to be difficult to pick out our own reindeer! You can't prevent us [from doing it]!

The Chukchi strongman Kvararu said:

—And I say, you'll not take them!

Then the oldest Koryak called out to his younger brothers:

—Well, my younger brothers, get ready, we're going to fight!

They got ready. The Koryaks made it clear to the Chukchi:

—Let us fight!

At the same time Kvararu said to his fighters—all young men:

—We're going to fight; the settled Koryaks have arrived!

The Koryaks fought for two days but they defeated the Chukchi. They took in captivity the Chukchi women. They also took in captivity the poor and the very young. They then started for home. They drove with them a very large herd of reindeer. The old reindeer herder was very happy about it and he said:

—Look at them; they brought our own reindeer back!

39. The Revenge of Rynnynalpylyn

Narrated in 1955 by an inhabitant of Koltushnoye village M. Varganov (Ivtakrat). Recorded and translated into Russian by I. Vdovin. Published in Voskoboynikov and Menovshchikov 1959, p. 470. The basic plot of this narrative about the blood revenge of the Koryak hero is apparently the same as that found in the Itelmen stories about Tylval.

At one time there lived two brothers and their sister. They called her Kilivnaut. The brothers grew up and began to train themselves to develop strength and deftness. Soon they became so strong that when they shot arrows with the bow they broke the wooden nock of the arrow. So they then began to shoot arrows with nocks of bone.

Their sister was not married.

Then Kilivnaut began to go to the tundra every day. It turned out that she was secretly meeting an alien tribesman. However, her brothers knew nothing about this. When Kilivnaut became pregnant she met her husband, the alien tribesman, in the tundra and began to say to him:

—Kill my brothers.

But her husband, the alien tribesman, replied to her:

—Why should I kill them? You know they are your own brothers! Yes, and I couldn't kill them; they are too strong. If I attack them, it's more likely that they will kill me.

Kilivnaut then said:

—If you don't kill my brothers, then, when your son is born to me they will kill me and they will say: "You have married our enemy!"

Then her husband, the alien tribesman, said to her:

—Very well, then. Only, how are we going to kill your brothers?

Kilivnaut replied to him:

—Very simple. I go back home; as soon as they fall asleep I'll go to the *yukola* storage where they keep their bows and arrows. I'll cut the bowstrings with a knife and I'll take the spears far into the tundra. You'll come during the night and we'll easily kill them.

The alien tribesman said:

—Very well then, go home!

Kilivnaut started for home. She came in. Her brother asked her:

—Kilivnaut, why have you been away from home for so long?

Kilivnaut replied:

—Simply because I've walked the tundra for a long time.

It got dark. The brothers fell asleep. Kilivnaut went to the *yukola* storage. She took the bows of her brothers and cut the bowstrings with a knife. She carried the spears to the tundra. During the night her husband, the alien tribesman, came in. At that time Kilivnaut called out to her brothers:

—Oy, the enemy has come to us, get up!

The brothers sprang up and ran to the *yukola* storage. They came to it and found out that the bowstrings of all their bows were cut. They then rushed to the place where the spears were stored. There were no spears. The brothers ran back home. The enemy attacked them. As soon as the first blows struck them, the brothers pretended to be dead. Then her husband, the alien tribesman, said to Kilivnaut:

—Come here! You've said: "Let's kill my brothers!" I've told you the truth: they must not be killed. Look what we have done to them. You know, we've killed them.

Kilivnaut came up, looked at her brothers and said to her husband, the alien tribesman:

—It could be that they haven't died yet. Now then, let's check to see if they're dead! Test them, cut off their upper lip. Start with the older one.

Her husband, the alien tribesman, cut off the upper lip of the older brother, but that one did not even stir. Kilivnaut said:

—He really died. And now cut the younger brother's lip off!

Her husband, the alien tribesman, cut off the upper lip of his wife's younger brother. The younger brother shuddered. He did not have as strong a heart as the older one. He was still young and it was very painful to him.

Kilivnaut told her husband:

—Kill him!

The alien tribesman speared the younger brother of Kilivnaut and he died at once.

The alien tribesman said:

—Now, we'll go home to my place.

They started for home; they arrived there and began to live together.

Rynnynalpylyn got up and cremated his brother. He then began the journey to his relatives. He did well and went to Alyutorka, where his relatives lived. There he began to recover. Soon he was completely recovered. Rynnynalpylyn lived with his relatives for ten years and he became even stronger. Then he finally said:

—I think the time has come. Remember I have a sister. I'll find her and torture her to death.

Rynnynalpylyn began to assemble his kinsmen: his cousins, and other relatives. He gathered them all and he said:

—Let's go and find my sister and torment her to death!

They replied:

—Well, let's go!

In the early spring they started out traveling to the north over the thin ice that covered the snow. Next morning they came to a camp. Rynnynalpylyn asked the workers of the reindeer herders:

—Which is the *yurta* of my sister?

The workers showed him the *yurta* saying:

—Over there, you see, that's their *yurta*.

Rynnynalpylyn took a lasso and went there. He came to the *yurta*, threw the lasso onto the tied upper ends of the poles that supported the frame of the *yurta*, tugged at it strongly, and toppled the *yurta* on its side. His sister jumped up and said to her husband:

—Hey, from which side are we being attacked, who are the enemies?

Rynnynalpylyn said to her:

—Be quiet, the lipless enemies have attacked you!

The sister recognized her brother and said to him:

—Be careful, here you have your nephews and your kin.

Rynnynlapylyn replied to her:

—Here I have no nephews or kin—no relatives at all.

Then Rynnynalpylyn said to the workers of the alien tribesmen:

—Now, drive a herd of reindeer here!

The workmen went off to the herd. They drove the reindeer to the camp. They selected two old, untrained wild bulls and took them very close to the *yurta*. The relatives seized Rynnynalpylyn's sister and dragged her toward the reindeer. Rynnynalpylyn pierced her ankles, threaded thongs into the openings and tied them firmly. The other ends of the thongs were tied to the untrained bulls. They released the bulls. Quickly the bulls darted in different directions. They tore Kilivnaut in two. They then captured the bulls and brought them back. One of them dragged behind him one of Kilivnaut's legs, the second the other.

Kilivnaut's husband started to cry. Rynnynalpylyn killed the children of Kilivnaut reasoning: "If those children are not killed, then afterwards, when they grow up, they'll become my enemies."

Rynnynalpylyn told Kilivnaut's husband:

—I'll not kill you. You're not to be blamed. Our sister alone is to be blamed for everything. That's why she deserved to be tortured to death.

Rynnynalpylyn then said to the enemies:

—We're now going to get ready to return. I'm going to take with me half of your herd. You're going to ask: "Why is Rynnynalpylyn taking half of our herd?" I am taking half of your herd because you were the first to kill my younger brother. You acted rather poorly toward us. If you had not been first to do me ill, I would not be taking half of you reindeer. I would have not tortured my sister to death. I would not have killed my nephews. And also I am angry with you because you have cut off my upper lip. Not one of you said: "It's not necessary to cut his lip!" So, for that I'll take half of your workers also, the other half I'll leave with you.

Rynnynalpylyn divided the herd in two, took half of the workers and left the other half.

Then Rynnynalpylyn and his people started for home. He returned home and they started to call him Avamylkaki, the Lipless.

Avamylkaki told the workmen of the alien tribesmen:

—Now you may live as you want. It's your herd; protect it. You only have to kill a reindeer when I want reindeer meat.

And so they lived that way.

40. Mivit

Recorded in 1934 by a student of the Regional [Communist] Party School in the Koryak National *Okrug*, Enagit (Savva Khlebnikov) from the Alyutor nomadic *kolkhoz* [collective farm]. Translated into Russian by S. Stebnitsky. In the oral tradition of the Koryaks, the story about the legendary giant Mivit, endowed with lightning speed and strength, was widespread. Mivit is presented as a man who, when hunting, does not use bow and arrow but overtakes birds and animals because of his fantastic speed.

Long ago there lived an ancestor by the name of Mivit.

That man was very fast on his feet. When he saw a flock of geese, he flung himself on them right away. The geese could not fly off and he captured all of them.

He tied the geese that he had caught to a strap. And he ran home. He arrived there, and only the beaks of the captured geese were hanging from the strap. Their bodies were worn to nothing because of the speed he ran at.

When Mivit went to the mountains to hunt he did not take with him bow and arrows. When he arrived in the mountains he overtook in an instant one or two mountain sheep and killed them.

He wanted to go to the other side of the bay. From there, following a flock of ducks, after a day's crossing he arrived to our place. His footsteps are preserved here since that time. I've seen them myself. He walked with long steps. I've measured his steps: there were ten of my steps to his one.

And nobody could kill that man.

One day when he was returning from the land of the Chuvantsy, the Chuvantsy chased after him. And Mivit was carrying a large bundle of wood. And even though the bundle was heavy, the Chuvantsy could not overtake him. They could not kill him. They stopped and looked for his footsteps. By the time they found his footsteps, he had gone far away.

Then the Chuvantsy said:

—We're not able to kill him. There's no use trying. Let him go. We'll not be able to catch up to him anyway.

And the Chuvantsy returned home.

Then, at one time, Mivit made his way from Chuvan country all the way to Alyut.

And when he got to Yygoyva hill, the bundle of wood, which he was carrying on his back, caught fire by itself; it flared up because of his fast running. He then threw off his load.

41. The Rich Man and the Worker

Recorded in 1934 by an inhabitant in the lower reaches of the Apuka River in Kamchatka, Kechgayat Nutenii. Translated into Russian by I. Vdovin. Published in *Skazki koryakov reki Apuki*, Leningrad 1936, in the Koryak language.

There lived two brothers. They were poor. When living became unbearable, one of them said:

—Let one of us stay home and the other go to work for the rich man.

They did what they thought. One stayed home and the other went to work for the rich man. He arrived there. The rich man said:

—You'll work for me until next spring. When the cuckoo cuckoos [calls], your work will come to an end.

The rich man told the worker:

—Know that my condition is that you do not get angry. If you get angry or offended, you'll have to give me a hundred reindeer. If I get angry or offend you, I'll give you a hundred reindeer.

The worker said:

—I don't have a hundred reindeer.

The rich man said:

—It doesn't matter; then you'll work for me until the following spring.

The worker thought for a long time and he then said:

—Very well, I agree!

And he added:

—I will not become angry and I will not be offended.

The next morning the rich man sent the worker to the herd:

—Go to the herd; work there as long as there is light in the yard. When it gets dark, go home.

The worker toiled with the herd all day. As twilight arrived and the sun set, the worker returned home.

The master asked him:

—Why did you come here?

The worker said:

—The sun set, it became dark, so I came home.

The rich man said:

—I really said: "When it gets dark, go home." True, the sun set, but the moon rose.

The worker said:

—What is this? So, I beg you, am I to work all night as well?

The rich man said to the worker:

—Oho, you are, it seems, angry!

The worker said:

—I'm not angry and I'm not offended.

And the worker went to the herd again.

The moon shone all night and the worker toiled all night around the herd. In the morning the moon set but then the sun rose. The worker sank to the ground and began to get angry with the rich man:

—Oho, so, if you please, I'll be working all the time! He doesn't work himself and he eats well. He doesn't pay me for my work. And he doesn't give me food.

At that time the rich man was nearby. And the worker did not see him. Suddenly the rich man said to the worker:

—It seems that you're angry! So now, you give me a hundred reindeer! If you don't, then work until the following spring.

The worker spent the time working until the following spring. He got nothing for his work. He went home with empty hands.

He came home and his brother met him with these words:

—Welcome! Are you bringing back many reindeer for your work?

His brother told him how the rich man tricked him. Then the brother, who had stayed home, said to him:

—Now you stay home and I'll go and work.

He went to work for the rich man. He arrived. The rich man said:

—You're going to work for a long time for me. You're going to work until the cuckoo bird flies in. And this is my condition: see to it that you don't get angry. If you get angry you'll have to give me a hundred reindeer. If I get angry, I'll give you even more reindeer than that. The worker said:

—Very well, agreed. But in my opinion a hundred reindeer is not enough. It would be better if we agree to this: the one who gets angry first will give a thousand reindeer.

The rich man thought for a long time and then he said:

—Very well, agreed!

But he thought to himself: "I'll have even more reindeer."

Then next day the sun rose in the morning but the worker was still sleeping. The rich man began to waken the worker:

—Hey, wake up. You're a lazy man! The sun came up long ago and you're still sleeping!

The worker said:

—What is this, are you beginning to get angry?

The rich man said:

—No, I'm not angry; I'm simply saying to you that it's time for you to go to the herd.

The worker got up, barely standing.

—Hurry up; it hurts me that you're taking to the road so slowly!

Again the worker said to him politely:

—Are you sure you're not angry?

The master replied:

No, no, I'm not angry. Simply, you should know that it's a long way to the herd. And I have to take you there.

The worker took a long time to put on his shoes. He took even longer to wash himself. And it was already noon. The worker said:

—It's not time to go to work now. Soon it'll get dark. Let's first eat well; then I'll go to work.

They finished eating. The worker said:

—I ate well. I can't work. I have to sleep a little. He lay down on the grass and slept until evening.

The rich man cried out:

—Well, how long can you work? The others have already returned from work and you have not started as yet!

—Oho! Could it be that you're getting angry? —asked the worker politely.

The rich man said:

—I'm not even thinking of getting angry, I'm simply talking with you. So, very well, go home; it's getting dark.

—Well, it's nice that you are not angry, —said the worker, —it's time, if you please, to go home.

Two months went by.

There was little cause for the rich man to be happy with such a clever worker. He did not work and he never got angry with the rich man.

The rich man decided to trick the workman—you know, he also was very clever. The rich man thought: "How can I trick that clever workman? How dumb I am! Why did I tell him: 'You're going to work for me for a long time, until the cuckoos fly in!' But spring will not come so soon."

The rich man thought for a long time, then he said:

—Very well, now I'm going to trick that worker!

He came home and he said to his wife:

—We'll go to the woods and there you'll climb up on a tree. As soon as you see me with the worker, start cuckooing right away. Only see to it that you are well hidden, not showing.

The rich man returned home and said to the workman:

—Let's go hunting!

They took guns and they set off. They approached the woods. The wife saw them. She began to cuckoo:

—Cuckoo-cuckoo! Cuckoo-cuckoo! Cuckoo-cuckoo! Coock!

The rich man said:

—Hear, the cuckoo is calling! She already started cuckooing!

He then added:

—Well, your work has come to an end! Today you can start for home.

The worker realized that the rich man was tricking him. He said to the rich man:

—Has it ever happened that a cuckoo made her calls in the winter? What is a winter cuckoo like? I'm going to shoot her. Then we'll see what's going on. How about it?!

The worker began to aim at the calling cuckoo. The rich man saw him do that, darted toward him and began to take his gun away.

He took it and yelled out:

—You can't shoot at a human being! Don't kill it, you know, it's not a cuckoo!

The worker said:

—Oho! And now you're angry!

The rich man began to curse:

—You almost killed my wife!

But the worker then said:

—You said yourself: "Let's go to the woods and hunt!"

The master yelled out:

—Very well, that's enough, go home! Take the reindeer!

The worker took the reindeer promptly and started for home. He returned. From then on the brothers lived well.

42. The People of Palana

Narrated in 1955 by an inhabitant of Koltushnoye village in the Koryak National *Okrug*, M. Barganov (Ivtakrat). Recorded and translated into Russian by I. Vdovin. According to the ancient customs of the coastal inhabitants of Kamchatka and Chukotka, a whale thrown by the sea onto the shore became the property of all of the inhabitants of the given locality. The members of the community regarded the acquisition of such a gift of nature by one person as a serious offense. This work must be viewed as belonging to the genre of economic (short) stories that reflect the realistic conditions of life in the Koryak community during the period of the disintegration of egalitarian social relationships and the appearance of social gradations based on property.

Long ago there lived the Palana people. Among them was a strongman named Nyrygyrnyn. He built his dwelling on the bank of the Palana River, near a cliff. Nyrygyrnyn had two daughters and a wife, but no son. The daughters trained themselves to be very strong and deft. And soon they became strong, but not as strong as their father. And in the village of Kakhtana there lived two brothers-strongmen. The older was named Nutemi, the younger Mikiflyu. One time a large whale was cast onto the shore at the very mouth of the Taskyt River. The people of Kakhtana saw the whale that had been thrown by the sea onto the shore, and soon the people living in the four small villages along the Kakhtana River gathered there. They came there to prepare the whale and divide it amongst themselves. The old man Nyrygyrnyn also started for the whale. He arrived at the place where the whale lay on the seashore. He saw that all of the people were sitting on the seashore and doing nothing. Nyrygyrnyn asked them:

—Why are you sitting here and not working? There's a lot of whale meat lying on the shore!

The dwellers answered:

—We can't divide the whale. They won't allow us.

Nyrygyrnyn asked them:

—Who is it that will not allow you to divide the whale?

All the people answered:

—They are the two strongmen who are atop the whale, —Nutemi and Mikiflyu.

Nyrygyrnyn climbed onto the whale. But Nutemi threw himself at him and pressed him down. Nutemi said to Mikiflyu:

—Now cut some small pieces of whale blubber!

He cut some and dragged it to Nyrygyrnyn. Then they took off his breeches and began to fill them with whale blubber. They filled the breeches with blubber and Nutemi said:

—Well, now you march home! You take the whale blubber, which we gave you to your daughters.

Nyrygyrnyn immediately started for his home on the Palana River. Nyrygyrnyn came home and his daughters came out to meet him. The older one asked him:

—Well, father, did you get some whale blubber?

Nyrygyrnyn replied to his daughter:

—Here, I've brought you whale blubber. Eat.

Their father began to take out the blubber from his breeches. The older daughter became angry and she asked her father:

—Who filled your breeches with blubber?

Nyrygyrnyn told his daughter:

—The strongmen filled the back of my breeches with blubber.

The older daughter asked her father:

—Who are the people that were laughing at you?

Nyrygyrnyn said:

—Nutemi and his brother. They have become very strong.

There and then the older sister cried out and told her younger sister:

113

—Let's go and measure our strength with them. We'll put on our overalls made of walrus hide and we'll go to the whale where those two strongmen, Nutemi and Mikiflyu, insulted our father.

The two girls started out together, and the two strongmen were sitting on the whale and cutting blubber. The two girls climbed onto the whale right away. Nutemi said:

—Why are you climbing up here? You know we did not tell you: "Come up here."

Then the girls said:

—Why did you fill the back of our father's breeches with blubber?

Nutemi said:

—Because my brother and I are strong.

Then the older sister became angry and said:

—Let's measure our strengths on the carcass of the big whale.

Nutemi said:

—You can't defeat my brother and me. Nobody can defeat us.

The girls said:

—Well, we'll see! We'll take the whale from you by force. The ones who prove to be weak will be thrown down from the whale.

They started to test their strength atop the whale. And, would you know, the girls threw Nutemi and his brother from the whale. They invited all the people and said:

—And now, come here and divide the whale!

All the local people began to divide the whale. And Nutemi and his brother stood on the shore and looked on. They wanted to go to the whale but the people would not let them, they pushed them back. They could not overcome the girls, they were afraid. And so Nutemi and his brother went home with empty hands. And only when the local inhabitants finished dressing the whale and went to their homes, did Nutemi and his brother dare to go to the place where the whale lay. They came there and began collecting the pieces of blubber that had fallen onto the sand. The others had thrown those pieces away but to them even they seemed good.

Nyrygyrnyn did not want his daughters to get married. To be sure many suitors arrived but Nyrygyrnyn turned all of them down, sent all of them back. His daughters had already grown fully, but still they lived without husbands.

Then one morning all of them sat down to have breakfast. The daughters said to their father:

—We want to give you some advice: don't clean your teeth anymore with a toothpick after a meal. Then live with the teeth with the remnants of food on them. Then maybe you'll understand how wrong you are by not letting us marry.

And so the father quit cleaning his teeth after a meal. Then things became bad: he could not eat; he could not sleep. At that point Nyrygyrnyn said to his daughters:

—Yes, now I'm beginning to understand what suffering I'm causing you, how unhappy you are without husbands. I'm now going to start searching for husbands for you.

43. Yintalat

Narrated in 1955 by an inhabitant of Koltushnoye village, Koryak National *Okrug*, M. Varganov (Ivtakrat). Recorded and translated into Russian by I. Vdovin. The realistic adventures of a hunter whose mind was dulled, and who had left his family, are intertwined here with a tale subject of cohabitation of man and animal, which is widespread among Paleoasiatics. The realistic and fantastic story and the tale are intertwined in its oral rendition. (Compare with Dolitsky and Michael 1997, no. 26, and no. 29 of this publication).

Yintalat was a man from Kichiga village. Something had happened to his mind. Gradually he lost the ability to judge. When he lost his mind, he took to the tundra. He took with him only a shotgun and a spear and nothing else. Yintalat roamed the tundra for five years. He recognized nothing and remembered nothing. Then gradually his mind came back to him. He saw the countryside and began to recognize different places. Yintalat then said:

—Maybe I've come to Cape Lopatka? I recognize the land near Petropavlovsk-Kamchatsky.

He then went in the direction of the dwelling; he simply went in that direction. Then he lost his mind again. After that he again saw the countryside, which was not far away from his family. He recognized it and said:

—Now, if you please, I'm going home.

He came to a herd of reindeer, saw a tent, and headed directly toward it. He came to the tent and found there a man by the name of Avvak. Avvak saw him and exclaimed:

—Welcome, you've arrived, old man!

Yintalat also said:

—Yes, I've arrived!

But then Avvak began to be afraid of Yintalat. He began to fear him very much and would have run away but Yintalat told him:

—Don't be afraid of me, Avvak. I now seem to be an insistent person, but all I want is to go home.

Avvak replied:

—Well, then let's kill a reindeer; maybe you want to eat!

Yintalat said:

—True, I very much want to eat!

Avvak captured a calf, killed it, dressed it, and they began to cook the meat. They finished cooking the meat and ate it. After they finished eating, Avvak said:

—Now we'll lie down to sleep; tomorrow morning we have to get up very early.

Yintalat replied:

—It could be that I'd reach my dwelling even today, even if it will be at night.

But he stayed with Avvak. The next morning they awakened, drank of tea, and Yintalat started for his home in Kichiga. It was becoming dark and was still a long way to his home. The ground was already covered with snow and Yintalat could not walk very fast. And then he came to the foot of a mountain. It was already dark. The slope of the mountain was covered with trees. Yintalat looked to his left and saw that on the slope of the mountain, but higher than the place on which he stood, there was a dot of light. Yintalat said to himself: "No doubt somebody is staying overnight there. I'll go there. I cannot get home today anyway. It's completely dark."

And Yintalat went toward the fire [light]. A man came to meet him and said:

—Welcome man, where did you come from?

Yintalat replied:

—I am from Kichiga. For a long time, for five years, I've lived in the tundra. Now I'm going home.

The man said:

—Yintalat, stay overnight in my house and tomorrow you'll go home to yours.

They entered the dwelling. The master started to cook bear meat and fat. They finished eating and the master said:

—Well, my guest, it's time to sleep!

Yintalat replied:

—Well, let's go to sleep very soon; I'm very tired. I need to rest.

The master said to Yintalat:

—When I begin to heat the dwelling it will be midnight; if you waken, don't be afraid of me, don't be scared of anything.

Yintalat said:

—Nothing will scare me.

And he fell asleep right away. The dwelling was gradually becoming cold. The middle of the winter arrived. The master started to heat his dwelling; he roared like a bear. He started to pound the sidewalls with his forepaws. Yintalat almost awakened, looked around and saw that his companion was a she-bear, and he fell asleep again. And when spring came the master awakened. He began to waken Yintalat. Yintalat did not want to get up and he said:

—Why are you awakening me so soon?

The master replied:

—What do you mean: "So soon." Spring is already here.

Yintalat shot back:

—Why are you laughing at me? How could it be spring? You know that we went to sleep just last night.

To this the master said:

—Not yesterday, but last year, as soon as the first snow fell outside. You know you came to me then and at that time we went to sleep.

Yintalat went outside and saw his flintlock and spear. And the hide [sling] of the flintlock had been already eaten by the foxes. Yintalat thought: "What's happened to me? I know I came here only yesterday. But then I came with the first snow and now it's spring." And then he went back into the dwelling.

The master asked him politely:

—Well, how is it outside?

Yintalat replied:

—Well, it's true that spring has arrived. But how could that have happened? You know that when I came to you, the ground was barely covered with snow. And now it seems to be spring in the courtyard.

Then the master said to Yintalat:

—Well, you'll eat some bear meat and when you finish eating, you'll start for home. Now your house is quite near and it's become warm outside. Now you will not freeze, although your clothing is in bad shape. Well, that's all right. You'll get to your house anyway.

Yintalat finished eating the bear meat and started to get ready for the journey. He took the flintlock from the shelf, fitted it with a sling, put it over his shoulder, and grasped the spear with his hands. The master said to Yintalat:

—From here you'll go over there to the high ridge. When you get there, look back at me. You'll then learn what I am, who I am. Then you will also say: "What has my companion turned out to be!" Well, now it's time for you to start. Look back from the enclosure and then you'll learn who I am.

Yintalat started out, climbed onto the enclosure, looked back at the place from which he had started his journey. From there he saw the companion with whom he wintered. It turned out that he was a large bear. Yintalat then said:

—What do you know! It turns out that I spent the winter with a bear, but I thought that I was a guest of a man. It seems that I've become friends with an animal. It is then likely that I lived in the tundra for five years, I've had no real food and yet I didn't die. But I really must have done something to keep on living. I must have done something when my mind was dulled, because I remember nothing. And also I wasn't aware of my body.

Yintalat waddled over the enclosure and started going down the other side. He came up to the house when it was only midday. The inhabitants saw Yintalat coming nearer. They began to speak to each other:

—Who is that man who is coming to us?

Yintalat came up to them.

The inhabitants said:

—Welcome, who are you, where did you come from?

Yintalat said:

—I am Yintalat, I am from here; I am a human being.

The inhabitants said:

—Oh, you have finally come Yintalat. And we thought that Yintalat had died long ago, and we even stopped missing him. We waited a long time, a very long time. Then we decided that he died. You know it's been five years since you went to the tundra. The local people started to question Yintalat. They asked:

—What did you eat when you were living in the tundra?

Yintalat told them:

—How I lived, I don't know. I don't remember anything about that life. One day I saw the land, the cape near Petropavlovsk, I recognized the region and thought: "To be sure, my *yurta* is to the north of this place." And I walked from there in the direction of my house. Then, I remember, I saw a wild stag and I decided: "I'll kill it and eat it." I started to steal up to the wild deer, got very close to it and took aim. I looked and it was a large gray boulder, not a deer. I thought: "What happened? What took place here? As if I didn't see a wild stag." I carefully started to go away from that boulder, so that nothing would happen again. I went on for about three hundred steps, looked around and again saw at that place a wild deer. I then thought: "Why save a single bullet? Be as it may, I'm going to shoot." Again I began to steal up, got there, took aim, glanced at it, and again there was a large boulder in front of me. Very well, I decided, I'm going to shoot anyway. I shot, looked, and a wild stag fell to the ground. I hurried to it and began to dress the deer. As soon as I had skinned it, I began to eat the marrow. Then I separated the fat from the meat and I said to myself: "You should take the fat for food on your journey. I cut the hide of the wild stag in the middle and put it over myself as a raw parka. I warmed up and went farther toward my house. Soon I saw a herd of reindeer, a tent, and a man named Avvak.

Yintalat began to live at home. He lived alone in a *yurta*. True, he had a wife but she lived in a neighboring *yurta*. Yintalat said to his wife:

—Don't live with me until my mind is altogether right.

And he added:

—If we lived together I could suddenly kill you or do something bad to you. So I am afraid to live with you. When my mind completely repairs itself then I'll say to you: "Now, my wife, let's live together again, like we did before."

And, to be sure, later they began to live together again. The name of his wife was Yintalata Navyayvyt. They lived on for five years. Then Yintalat died.

44. The Hunter

Narrated in 1958 by an inhabitant of Palana village in Tigilsky *rayon*, I. Mokhnatkin, who had been the chairman of a *kolkhoz* (collective farm). Recorded and translated into Russian by A. Zhukova. There are several variants of this story. In one of these, a hunter by the name of Kechgyntavav kills only one of the enemies and the rest run away.

There lived a Chukchi hunter near Palana village. He was deft and strong and he was very good with the bow and arrow.

One day in the morning he got ready to go hunting for wild deer. In leaving for the woods he told his wife:

—If I don't have any luck in the hunt, I'll return early.

He took a bow and arrows and went to the woods on foot.

He had not yet come to the high mountains when he saw in the tundra two wild deer, very large ones. He stole up to them but for some reason he could not shoot them. A lot of time went by. Finally the hunter loosed an arrow. It hit the stag but only wounded him lightly. With great leaps he started running in the direction of the mountains, but the doe just stood there and looked at him as if she were wondering what had happened. Then a second arrow found her. It lodged directly in her back. Then the doe also ran off.

—Eh, what luck! —the hunter cried out.

And the wounded deer ran farther into the woods in different directions. The hunter gathered his arrows and went after the stag. For a long time he chased the prey. Finally he caught up with him at a place where he could get close to him by stealth.

—"Eh, it would be better for me to miss, so the deer does not see me—thought the hunter, —then I'll aim the second arrow directly into his heart."

He released the first arrow. The deer did not move; he stood there as if rooted to the ground.

—Aha, the deer is standing! Now I'll send him a second arrow.

But while the hunter was drawing the bow, the deer fell down dead.

The stag was very large. The hunter couldn't carry so big an animal by himself. And it was already late and far to the camp.

The Chukchi decided to spend the night next to his prey at the edge of the woods. In past times, the people of Kamchatka lived as families, each family by itself. There were no villages. And each family defended itself. At that time there roamed over the tundra small groups of enemies. The Chukchi called these enemies the *tangs*. The *tangs* often attacked the Chukchi families and robbed them.

And the Chukchi believed in some sounds in the darkness of night. If partridges cry out during the night, it means that the enemy is near. Disturbed partridges take to the air and always cry out. At this point the Chukchi ready themselves for defense or they run away.

So the hunter stayed in the woods for the night. He dressed the deer, collected a large heap of dry wood and lit a big fire. The fire burned brightly. The hunter decided to sear a lot of meat so that he could take with him a little more. He impaled large pieces onto a stick and placed them around the fire to sear them.

Night came, a very dark one without a single star. It was already very late when the hunter began to prepare to stay for the night. He removed the charred meat from the sticks, put them on clean grass, and put other pieces on a spit. He put some more dry branches onto the fire and it lit up even brighter. He barely lay down to sleep when he suddenly heard a partridge cry out somewhere nearby. "Well, —he thought, —either a bear is roaming nearby or it is the *tangs*."

The hunter quickly doused the fire. He listened attentively and thought to himself: "If I stay here, the enemies will kill me; if I run away, the meat will be theirs. No, I'm not going to give them my booty." Soon he heard the call of the partridge again. It was very close by and he began to prepare to defend himself in a hurry—just in case. He threw dry branches into the smoldering fire and it flared up again. He placed the meat a little higher around the fire. He backed into the darkness and saw that if people were to sit around the fire; the fire would light their faces.

Then there were voices heard. The hunter went to the fire hurriedly. With his second light parka he made a scarecrow and for its face he hung onto it a piece of fat. He then left the fire and hid himself in the darkness. He selected a place from which he could see what was happening at the fire.

Suddenly he saw that arrows embedded themselves in the scarecrow. The scarecrow swayed a bit and fell down. And pieces of meat also fell down. "They're shooting badly, —thought the hunter. — Their arrows didn't even go through my thin parka."

And the *tangs*, there were three of them, as soon as the scarecrow fell, ran up to the fire and cried out:

—Ey, there's nobody here! They ran away. Only the seared meat is left.

The hungry *tangs* rushed to the food; the meat was already thoroughly prepared.

When the *tangs* had eaten about half of the meat, the hunter drew his bow taut and released an arrow into the *tang* who was sitting under a tree. The *tang* began to slowly incline toward the tree. The other two laughed and said:

—Our chap must have gotten tired! That fatty meat was too much for him!

The Chukchi hunter was very strong. His arrow went directly through the heart of the enemy. It went right through the man and continued for a long distance. The other *tangs* saw nothing of this. With greed they again attacked the food.

The hunter killed the second one the same way. Only then did the third one guess that it was not sleep that overcame them but that they were dead. The *tang* jumped up and he would have run, but he did not get far. The hunter shot an arrow through the legs of the *tang* and the arrow pierced both of his calves. In pain the *tang* sat down and in a flash the hunter got to the fire. He bound the *tang's* arms and covered the wounds with pieces of resinous cedar bark and tied them on with thongs made of raw deer hide. Immediately the blood stopped running from the wounds.

In the morning, at daybreak, the hunter loaded his captive with meat and led him to his house. He arrived there and ordered his old wife not to kill the captive, saying:

—We cannot kill him. I'd rather free him and tell him to pass the word to all his people that they should stop robbing and killing the Chukchi. They would be better off by hunting, fishing, and collecting grass and root plants. The *tangs* have robbed many of our people and they died of hunger.

The hunter thought for a while and said:

—Yes, the *tangs* have done nothing bad to me. But, to be sure, if they had taken me captive they would have, no doubt, robbed me of everything and would have done me in. You know they roam around almost naked. Because of them I became an orphan. The *tangs* attacked my family, robbed it of everything and killed my parents. But anyway, I'm going to let him go as soon as his legs heal.

And he released the captive after three days. From that time on, the *tangs* did not attack as frequently. They released many such enemies. And then the *tangs* stopped plundering altogether.

45. Do Not Brag Too Soon

Narrated by G. Kechgenki. Recorded and translated into Russian by A. Zhukova.

At one time there lived in the sea a very large bullhead. He was the leader of all of the sea fish. His mouth was so large that an entire *yaranga* could fit in it. This bullhead was very old. Also his back was rigid because of age. He was the strongest and most bragging among the sea fish. For that they selected him as their leader.

And among the river fish, the salmon was the leader. He also was the strongest among the river fish.

Somehow the bullhead heard about the salmon, the leader of the river fish. He became very angry. He, the bullhead, was the strongest among all fish, sea and river, and not some salmon! He started to say to everybody:

—I'm going to eat the leader of the river fish, the salmon, and then I'll be the only leader of all fish!

He started to think as to how he could become the leader of both the sea and river fish. He thought for a long time. Then, as the tide started to rise, he swam to the river. He entered the river and opened his mouth so wide that it blocked the river. He would wait until the salmon showed up and then would swallow his rival. The bullhead was in the lower reaches of the river and the salmon swam a little farther upriver.

Then a little salmon learned about the bullhead waiting at the mouth of the salmon's river. He swam to the salmon to forewarn him. He swam up to the salmon and said:

—The bullhead is lying in wait for you. He blocked the whole river; he wants to eat you alive.

The salmon thought for a while. He thought out how to defeat the bullhead. He swam to the bullhead. He swam and blew himself big with air. He blew himself very big. He entered the mouth of the bullhead on the run and came out of his belly. He came back a little distance, he looked at the bullhead— and he was already dead.

And so the braggart-bullhead found his death. They say that to this day no bullheads live in the rivers, only in seas. But the salmon enter the rivers as masters.

46. The Clever Fox

Narrated by Mullanvil. Recorded and translated into Russian by S. Stebnitsky. Published in Stebnitsky 1938, p 120, in the Koryak language with a parallel Russian text. The nature of the subject matter of this tale reveals its heterogeneous origins. The tale was composed as a result of the contamination of several plots originating during several historical periods and in multilingual social settings. The episode about the competition of the fox and bear, as to who is cleverer, is tied to the general Paleoasiatic group of tales about animals. The episode about the meeting of the fox and the vixen Chachuchanavat belongs to the Koryak cycle of tales about animals. The episode about the meeting of the fox with the Russian priest-collector introduces the realistic historical events of the end of the 18th—beginning of the 19th centuries when the Russian priests-missionaries tried to convert the Koryaks to Christianity while also filling the function of tax collectors. The episode of the meeting of the fox with the prince Ivan signifies the penetration of Russian magical tales to the Koryaks oral tradition. In these, the prince Ivan is portrayed as a national hero. Each episode of the tale has a pointed social message. People and animals appear as personages reflecting the social hierarchy of a Koryak community of the 19th century. The priest-collector of taxes orders the vixen to give her daughter in marriage to the bear, so that the sable furs, given to the bear for the vixen's daughter, would serve the priest as taxes.

The clever fox said:

—Well, tell me who here is smarter?

—I am smarter! I, the bear!

—Well then, outsmart me!

—All right! And if I can't outsmart you, I'll give you a motley parka.

—Very well, and I, if I can't outsmart you, will do the same.

Suddenly the fox exclaimed:

—Just look and behold, a rider on a motley reindeer is driving up!

The bear looked in that direction.

—Oh, it was easy to outsmart you! After all, a fox is smarter!

The fox took the motley parka and a hide of an otter to boot.

—After all this is not the first time that I'll outsmart you!

They went in different directions to their homes. They returned.

One day the vixen Chachuchanavut said to herself:

—Well, now I'm going to outsmart the fox.

She went to the seashore. She arrived there and found many shells. She collected them and brought them home and began to make a *tolkusha*.

And the fox went to hunt for ducks. What could he hunt for? However, with much difficulty he killed a small duckling.

—O-ho-ho! It's going to be hard for me to carry it home to my wife. I'll just take a foot, put it over my shoulder, and carry it home. He put the duck's foot over his shoulder. He went home. As he walked toward the house, his little children saw him and cried out:

—Oy-oy! Father killed a duck!

They ran to meet him. They met their father. The smallest of them put the duck's foot over his shoulder. He carried it home.

Then the vixen Chachuchanavut went as a guest to the clever fox.

—Welcome Chachuchanavut! You've arrived!

—Yes, I have arrived. Here's *tolkusha* for you.

They began to eat the *tolkusha*. The *tolkusha* was frozen hard. The clever fox broke all his teeth eating it.

—Oy! I can't fool anybody anymore!

Chachuchanavut said:

—You can fool them even better now that all your teeth are broken.

—Ah, is that so! Will you host Chachuchanavut with blubber?

Chachuchanavut left. She returned home. Her husband became angry with her:

—Where were you?

—What of it! I took *tolkusha* to my uncles on my grandfather's side.

—Well, that's nice. What did they host you with?

—With blubber.

Then there appeared a priest at the clever fox's. He came in and started talking in Russian:

—A-tke-pro-se-se-se!

He entered.

—What's with you older brother?

And he again repeated:

—A-tke-pro-se-se-se!

—What do you want, older brother?

And as before he said:

—A-tke-pro-se-se-se!

Then they invited him to go outside. He did.

—Could that be the prince Ivan who is talking out there?

—Yes, it is I!

—Come here!

He did. They asked him politely:

—What did that good-for-nothing, who was here a while ago, want?

—Well, that was a priest. He was collecting fox and sable hides. He came to collect tribute.

The clever fox went to hunt for foxes. He encountered a vixen. He shot at her. He did not kill her.

—Eh! What luck! So I'll make a trap!

He made a trap. He walked away some distance and hid himself. No animal took the bait. There was only a vixen running in the distance.

—How can this be? I outsmarted the bear so easily but I can't catch a vixen! What luck!

He started for home. He arrived.

At once the priest said:

—Where are the fox hides?

—I can't outsmart them in any way.

—And the bears you could?

—Well, why not? I'll give my little daughter in marriage to the bear for sable hides and then I'll pay my debt.

His wife agreed to give their daughter in marriage to the bear.

But the little daughter started to cry:

—I'm not going to go to the bear!

You don't have to cry! We're giving you to a rich man so that you won't be hungry ever again.

—All right, it's all right. Let him take me for wife!

The fox brought his daughter to the bear. Even from a distance he cried out:

—Hey, you bear! I'll give my daughter to you as wife!

—Very well, I'll take her. How many sables do you want for her?

—Yes, five hides!

—Very well, I'll take her.

The bear gave him five sable hides. Then they promptly went to their homes. The bear took the little girl to his house, looked—and there was a boy!

—Ah, that rogue, the clever fox! He fooled me again! He won't get away with it.

Then the boy started running! He ran home and told his father:

—Father, —he said—you're smart, but you're going to pay for it.

The fox said:

—All right, let him try to take revenge, I'll outsmart him easily!

122

47. The Vixen

Narrated in 1928 by an inhabitant of Kichiga village in the Koryak National *Okrug*, Avakka. Recorded and translated into Russian by S. Stebnitsky. Published in Stebnitsky 1938, p. 128, in the Koryak language with a parallel Russian text.

An old woman came out, sat on the roof of her *zemlyanka* and began to sew. Suddenly she heard the vixen Chachuchanavut scratching under the *zemlyanka*. The old woman said:

—Come here little sister! I have a lot of blubber. Take a piece for yourself!

The vixen came running. The contriving old woman caught her and killed her. She dragged her into the house, skinned her, chopped her up, and started to cook the vixen meat. She finished the broth and took it off the fire. She went out again, sat on the roof, and began to sew.

A boy was lying down in the *zemlyanka*. After a while he cried out to his mother:

—Mama, come soon, we'll eat!

The old woman said:

—Wait a little! Don't hurry! We'll eat soon. You'll have your fill. And you should not feel hungry yet.

After a little while the boy called out again:

—Come, mama, we'll eat!

—Wait a little! Don't hurry. You'll eat soon. You'll have your fill. And for the time being you should not feel hungry yet.

Again the boy cried out:

—Come right now, mama, let's eat! Somehow the vixen became whole again!

—Wait! Don't hurry! You'll eat soon. You'll have your fill. You're not hungry yet.

The old woman came in; she wanted to serve the food. She looked at the kettle. There was nothing in it; it was empty. Only the fat boiled from the meat was there. She then asked the boy:

—Where's the meat that was in the kettle?

The boy said:

—I've said to you several times: "Come soon, let's eat," and you always had your own: "You couldn't be hungry yet!" So you were late. The pieces of vixen meat stuck together, the vixen put on her hide and ran away.

TALES AND LEGENDS OF THE ITELMENS

ETHNOGRAPHIC INFORMATION

The Itelmens are one of the native peoples of southern Kamchatka. The term *Itelmen* is a Russian adaptation of the ethnonym *Itelmen* that means "real" or "living." The principal part of the Itelmens live in the Tigisky *rayon* of the Koryak National *Okrug* (Koryak Autonomous Territory), Kamchatka *oblast* (Figures 1, 2). In 1959, the Itelmens numbered about 1,100 (Menovshchikov 1974) and in 1994 about 1,500 with only 100 speakers of the Itemen language (Chaussonet 1995: 109). "The Itelmens were once a large people, who were almost completely assimilated in the 19th century by the descendants of the Russian Cossacks and peasants who had settled in Kamchatka in the 18th century. The result of this assimilation was an ethnographic group of Russians known as Kamchadal" (Arutyunov 1988: 34).

The Itelmen language belongs to the group of Chukotka-Kamchatka languages. In terms of cultural and economic relationships the Itelmens were, since early times, closely tied to the native people of the region, the Koryaks. These ties continue in present times. With the consolidation of local collective farms into larger ones and the organization of state farms, the Itelmens and Koryaks living in small settlements transferred to large ones. The mixed nature of the population, the strong influence of the Russian language, from the 18th century on, and mixed marriages, led to the loss of the Itelmens' native language. And with this loss also the loss of their rich and distinctive folklore, which, in the main, consisted of the tales about the man-raven Kutkh. The contemporary Itelmens retained their language and ethnic identity only in a few villages in the south of the Koryak Autonomous Territory (Arutyunov 1988: 34).

Their principal occupations are fishing, hunting for furbearers, breeding milch cattle and horses, food gathering, and also commercial gardening. Today, economically, the Itelmens are no different from their neighbors, the Russian population of Kamchatka (Arutyunov 1988: 35).

The earliest ethnographic information of the Itelmens of the 18th century came from the Second Kamchatka Expedition under Vitus Bering between 1737 and 1742 (Krasheninnikov 1755, 1972). The Russian ethnographer W. Jochelson recorded the largest collection of Itelmen tales, particularly those about the raven Kutkh, at the beginning of the 20th century. In 1961, the American philologist D. Worth published the Itelmen texts with a word for word English translation. Some of these texts are included in this publication. During the Soviet period (1917-1991), ethnographers and linguists could record, from those who retained their native language, only a small part of the oral traditions of the Itelmens.

48. The Legend About Tylval (Variant A)

Narrated in 1966 by an inhabitant of Napana village in Tigilsky *rayon*, P. Nasedkin, age 52. Recorded and translated into Russian by A. Volodin.

At one time Tylval lived on the Kulka River. His sister Ryngena lived with him. Tylval had a bow made of a whale's rib. Tylval used to collect firewood. He walked very far—all the way to the Stolovaya volcano. He loaded himself with firewood, came home, threw it down—and the whole earth trembled. Then one time he went after firewood, and when he returned home he saw that there was an unknown to him man lying on his stove bench. The man had come from the north. They greeted each other, sat down and ate. Then the man said:

—They say that you are strong, so I've come here; I'd like to test your strength.

Tylval said:

—Am I really strong? Look, I am so small compared to you.

The man said:

—I came here from far away. Well, it doesn't matter; let's test our strengths.

Tylval rested a while on his stove bench. Then he said:

—Well, since you want to test me, lift me with your little finger.

The man could not lift Tylval with his little finger from the stove bench. Tylval said:

—Now you lie down and give me your little finger.

He took the man's little finger, pulled, and lifted him like a feather. Then he said:

—Take your bow and I'll take mine. You give your bow to me, I'll shoot with yours, and you with mine. See that cloud. We'll shoot at that cloud.

Tylval took the man's bow and barely started to draw it—and the bow broke. The man took Tylval's bow, tried to draw it but he could not even bend it. The man spoke again:

—Will you wrestle?

The man's sister said:

—He came from afar; try to wrestle with him.

They squared off and began to wrestle. The man grasped Tylval but could not lift him from the ground. But Tylval took that man, lifted him overhead and threw him on the ground. All of the man's joints were dislocated.

—Here, take him, —he said to his sister.

 And he threw him at her feet:

—Take care of him yourself.

And so the life of that man ended.

49. The Legend About Tylval (Variant B)

Narrated in 1968 by an inhabitant of Tigil village, a native of Verkhnyaya Sedanka village, N. Grigorev, age 45. Recorded and translated into Russian by A. Volodin.

Tylval lived with his sister. They lived on the Kruglaya volcano. They lived there for a long time. In the winter, Tylval, when he expected enemies, would wet the volcano with water. At a certain place there was a rise where he would wait for the enemies. Then, one day a Palana Koryak came by and called out from below:

—Who lives here, on the Kruglaya volcano?

Tylval went out and said:

—I, Tylval, live here.

—I have come from Palana to compete with you. When are we going to compete?

—We'll compete this way: first we'll see who will be the first to get firewood at the Talnishnaya River.

—Well, let's run.

They ran. Tylval ran slowly but the Koryak ran with all he had. Even before the Koryak reached the Talnishnaya mountain ranges he exhausted his strength and he lay down. Tylval ran around him, tied together a bundle of firewood and on the way back said:

—Are you tired? Well, let me put you on my shoulders. You'll then know who I am. I'll take you to the volcano, throw down the firewood, feed you, and tomorrow we'll compete again. We're going to go after bears and take them with our bare hands.

They woke up the next day.

—Who is going to be the first to capture a bear and kill him with his hands? —asked Tylval.

The Koryak said:

—I'll go.

Tylval told him:

—Be quick about it so we can have supper here, at home.

The Koryak walked and walked, and he did not find anything. While the Koryak was walking Tylval brought in three bears. One of them he did not kill. He seized him by his hind foot and threw him down onto his back, thus stunning him. The Koryak came. Tylval said:

—Why didn't you come for supper? I've already eaten; I've brought in three bears. And what have you managed?

—I couldn't find a bear.

—Very well. Now, if you are such a strongman—you see the bear lying over there. I've stunned him. When he recovers, grasp his left hind leg and throw him on his back so that he won't get up again.

The bear came to and the Koryak right away flung himself on him, but became confused, did not seize him by the foot, but grasped his ears and began to wrestle with the bear. Tylval ran up, seized the bear's hind leg and threw him onto his back. So he killed the bear and the Koryak rebounded far off in the other direction. It was fortunate that he fell on something soft. The Koryak said:

—Yes, you are really strong.

And Tylval's sister thought to herself: "It would be nice to have the Koryak for a husband." And she said to him:

—Sleep over for three days in Shchekakh, which is on the Tigil River. And I will send my brother after firewood; I'll find his bow and I'll nick its bowstring slightly. When he draws the bow, the bowstring will split. And don't you hesitate, shoot at him with the crossbow right away and kill him.

The Koryak said:

—Well, Tylval, you've defeated me. Next year I'll come again and then we'll compete in the Koryak way, naked.

And he made as if he was leaving, but he spent three nights in Shchekakh by himself. On the fourth day he came to the Kruglaya volcano. There the girl was waiting. She had already nicked the bowstring. The sister purposely called out:

—An enemy is coming!

Tylval drew the bow and the bowstring split. The Koryak climbed to the volcano and said:

—Now I'll finish him. And he shot at him with the crossbow.

The arrow entered above the right shoulder blade. Tylval fell down and purposely feigned convulsions. The Koryak embraced his sister; he wanted to kiss her. Tylval pulled the arrow out, seized the Koryak and hit him in the forehead. Although he did not want to kill him, so strong were his arms that he killed him there and then. He tied up his sister and said:

—Tomorrow morning I'll put you to death.

Tylval awakened in the morning and said:

—Right now, I'll go to the Blizhniy [Near] range, then to the Ostryy [Sharp] range where I'll catch two wild deer.

He went and captured the deer. He lowered his sister from the volcano. He tied one deer to his sister's left leg, the other deer to her right leg. He nudged the deer in different directions. They ran and tore his sister in two. Tylval said:

—This, my little sister, is your punishment for wanting to kill me. Let the deer drag you now, and I'll go and I'll cook myself of the good meat I've provided you. I thought that you'd be friendly with me, your own brother, and seek advice. Then you would have asked: "My brother, I want to get married." I would not have denied you. And now let the wolves eat you, let the magpies squabble over you, or the ravens with the carrion crows. I am very angry with you. Now I'll live by myself so that nobody can split my bowstring again.

50. The Legend About Tylval (Variant C)

Narrated in 1926 by an inhabitant of Sedanka village, I. Kosygin. Recorded and translated into Russian by E. Orlova.

Some twelve to fifteen *versts*[41] upstream from Tigil there lived the Itelmen Tyval. He had a beautiful sister. As it was, he lived with her, but he would not give her in marriage to anybody. Still, she was cunning and she and a simple, non-Christian Koryak from the north, they say from Voyampolka village, loved each other. The beautiful one, Tylval's sister, always used to walk around the volcano on which she lived with her brother. While walking she sang and the Koryak heard her. That's why the birch grove opposite the volcano beyond the river is called *Pesennyy* ["Singing"]. The beautiful one arranged to escape with the simpleton, but her brother knew about it. He prepared his bow, made from a rib of a whale and arrows with stone points, and he waited. It seems that he wanted to meet with the simpleton to tell him not to come there anymore. He waited and waited and then he fell asleep. And his sister was just waiting for that to happen: She broke off all the points of the arrows and came down the mountain and ran to the birch grove. There the Koryaks' riding reindeer were already waiting for her. They quickly sat her on the sled and whirled away to the north. Her brother awakened and his sister was not there. He guessed what had happened and ran in pursuit of the offenders. Soon he caught up to them, killed all of the Koryaks, tied his sister's legs to two wild deer and drove them in different directions. They darted off and tore his beautiful sister in two.

The volcano on which Tylval lived, he renamed *Izmennaya* ["Treacherous"] because of the treachery of his sister. So, all that was left of his beautiful sister are the names *Izmennaya sopka* ["Treacherous Volcano"] and *Pesennyy bereznyak* ["Singing Birch Grove"].

And where Tylval went, we don't know.

---

[41] *Verst* — Pre-Soviet system of lineal measurement in Russia. One *verst* is equal to 3,500 English feet or 1,060 meters. (Editor).

51. The Legend About Tylval (Variant D)

Narrated in 1926 by an inhabitant of Tigil Village, A Mironova, age 45. Recorded and translated into Russian by E. Orlova.

It happened long, long ago; my grandfather was still living. I really don't remember whether it was before the flood or after the flood when Tylval lived in Kamchatka. (My grandfather still had an oil lamp made of stone, which was given to him by Tylval as a gift, but Akhtamosha, my little son, tossed it out somewhere).

Tylval was of great stature. His legs were long; with one step he could cover fifty *versts*. He lived on *Izmennaya sopka* [Treacherous Volcano]. From there to Tigil it was one step for him, from there to Mayak, another step. The hollow of Tylval's hand was this big: they would bring him berries—a tribute from the entire village of Voyampolka—he would tell them to pour them in the hollow of his hand and all of the berries would just cover the bottom of the hollow. He could see through anything, he could hear everything from a hundred *versts* around him. Everyone feared him and obeyed him.

At that time there lived on Kamchatka not orthodox Russians but non-Christian [pagan] Koryaks. So the Koryaks who lived south of Voyampolka decided to steal Tylval's sister and take her in marriage. They got a sled ready and started out on reindeer for *Izmennaya sopka*. Tylval heard about this and took his bow and stone-tipped arrows. He decided to kill the Koryaks and take back his sister. He sat there for a long time, waiting on the crest of the volcano, became tired and fell asleep. At that point the Koryaks ran toward the volcano, and the beautiful one, Tylval's sister broke off the stone tips of the arrows, and poured water on the mountain (the *Izmennaya* River flows from there since that time) so she could slide down easier. She sat in a trough, slid down the mountainside to the Koryaks and left with them.

Tylval awakened, did not find his sister, realized what had happened, and started to chase them. He killed all the Koryaks, and for her treachery and love affair he tied his sister's one leg to a deer, the other leg to another deer. He pushed the deer; they darted in different directions and tore her in two. Tylval named the volcano on which he lived *Izmennaya* for the treachery of his sister.

Even today the dwelling of Tylval may be seen from the *Izmennaya* River, from near Tigil. Others say that he lived on the Kulki River [Kuluk] not far from Tigil.

52. Tylval's Revenge

Narrated in 1953 by an inhabitant of Sedanka village in Tigilsky *rayon*, G. Fedotov. Recorded and translated into Russian by E. Orlova.

Long ago Tylval lived on the Izmennaya volcano. From there he went everywhere. One day he met two strongmen who were looking for him. They said:

—Who are you?

—I am Tylval from Sedanka.

They looked at him and said:

—True, we thought he was a very big man. In vain we've come such a distance!

—Since you've come, let's go to my home, my dwelling!

The newcomers agreed and they started as a threesome. It was getting dark and they stopped to spend the night. Tylval said:

—You get the firewood ready and I'll catch something for supper!

He started off and soon he drove home a deer, a big and fat one. He told them:

—Catch the deer and then we'll eat!

They jumped up and ran after the deer. They could not catch it; they stopped and asked:

—Is there a lasso?

—What do you need a lasso for?

—We can't get it without a lasso. We can only do it with a lasso.

Then Tylval jumped up, seized the deer by its hind legs, dashed him to the ground and also cut it in such a way that there were two even halves.

The two ate and said:

—We're going to return, we're not going to your place!

He became very angry:

—Didn't you already tell me that you're coming home with me?

—And how far is it to your house?

—We'll get there today!

And he told them to start running. At first they ran very fast, head over heels. It became dark and they asked:

—Really, shouldn't we spend the night here?

Tylval said:

—Why spend the night here? My little house is very close by.

He seized them by their hair and started running dragging them behind him. One was bleeding so much that he died, but the other one he somehow dragged to the village but he too soon breathed his last.

Tylval lived with his mother, father and sister. And his sister had a suitor. She often wandered to the woods and met him there.

One day Tylval came home and saw the suitor. He took his bow wanting to shoot at him. But earlier his sister had split the bowstring. He drew the bowstring and it broke. Tylval guessed that his sister had split the bowstring. He became very angry, yet he did not kill his sister.

He went into the house and killed his father and mother. He cut his hip with a knife, smeared the blood [over himself], and became quiet and lay there as if dead.

Then the suitor entered and hit Tylval's head with a log. Tylval did not even shudder. Promptly the suitor and sister jumped out of the house and started for the suitor's village.

Tylval got up as if nothing had happened and started after them. The Koryak and the sister saw him, became frightened and began to move faster. Tylval shot at the sled and only wood splinters remained of the sled.

Tylval came up to them and killed his brother-in-law right away. As he was killing his brother-in-law, he said:

—If you had come to propose in a nice way you would have lived in a nice way. But you did it in a bad way, so, now die!

To his sister he said:

—And you wanted to ride away on deer; well, now you will ride deer!

He made her catch two deer and harness them. When his sister had caught the deer and harnessed them, he tied her to the reindeer and nudged them in different directions. That's the way he killed his sister.

53. Tylval and Nemal-The Man

Narrated in 1926 by an inhabitant of Napana village in Tigil *rayon*, N. Nasedkin, age 52. Recorded and translated into Russian by E. Orlova.

Some say that Tylval was of great stature but one also hears that he was small but very solidly built and strong. Many men came to compete with him, and he was always the winner. Tylval used to go to gather firewood to Ambon toward Mayak, some fifty *versts* from the Kulki [Kuluk] River. And he would bring not only firewood back but would hunt down a wild sheep and bring it home with the wood. He could see thing far away, like an eagle, and even better than one; he could hear exceedingly well.

Rumors about Tylval traveled quickly all over Kamchatka. They even reached Nemal-The Man who lived beyond the ranges to the northeast. He had black hair and he would plait it into two braids. Nemal-The Man was a real giant. As soon as he heard about Tylval, he did not hold back and went to the southwest to compete with him. He took with him only a bow made of a whale's rib and also stone-tipped arrows. He climbed over the range to its western slope. He arrived at Voyampolka and asked:

—Where does your strongman Tylval live?

And the Voyampolka people said to him:

—We've heard about Tylval but we don't know where he lives. Go to Tigil, there they know!

Nemal-The Man came to Tigil and asked:

—Where does Tylval live here? I've heard that nobody can defeat him so I want to contend with him!

—Go to the Kulki River, that's where his house is, —they said to him.

—Is he really very big? —Nemal-The Man questioned them.

—No, he's not big but, to be sure, he's strong.

So Nemal-The Man went to Tylval grinning to himself and thinking how he was going to defeat the little Tylval. So he went over the tundra, came to the Kulki River, and saw a *yurta* built of earth and stone—a big, big one. Nemal-The Man took out his bow made of a whale's rib, got his stone-tipped arrows ready, walked toward the *yurta* and asked:

—Is there a man living here?

—There is, —a woman's voice answered him from the *yurta*. —Come on in, if you've come as a good person!

Nemal-The Man entered the *yurta* and saw a woman sewing boots in the dark corner of the *yurta*, and a little boy or girl playing on the floor.

—Who are you? —the giant asked.

—I'm the wife of Tylval and this is his child, —the woman answered and she began to prepare dinner for Tylval.

The giant started asking about Tylval—is he big, does he become angry—and when he learned that he was smallish and did not get angry, he thought to himself: "It's so much of a pity to compete with him; I came for nothing . . .."

—And where is he now? —he asked.

—He went to the Ambon for firewood, —Tylval's wife answered.

After those words Nemal-The Man became quiet; he realized that Tylval must be strong. The people did not say to no purpose: "You know that the Ambon is some fifty *versts* from Tylval's house." Nemal-The Man sat there and waited for the master; the mistress hustled about getting supper ready, cooking the meat and fish. Suddenly there was a terrible crash and rumble, as if lightning had struck very close by.

—What's thundering like that? —asked the giant

That's Tylval returning. He brought the firewood and threw it on the ground, —the wife answered at ease.

The giant looked through a slit and saw that there was virtually a mountain of firewood and a carcass of a ram on Tylval's shoulders and that he was small in stature. The giant became altogether quiet and waited until the master would enter the *yurta*. He hid the bow and arrows behind his back.

Tylval came in, saw the guest, greeted him, and did not ask why he came—he already knew. Nemal-The Man wanted to tell him right away as to why he came but was on his guard. He thought: "Let me see what else is going to happen."

—Well now, feed us! —Tylval said to his wife.

She brought to the table grilled meat of a wild deer. They began to eat without a word spoken. Tylval gnawed off the meat from the longest leg bone of the deer, gave it to the giant and said:

—I'll compete with you if you can crush this bone! The giant looked at him in astonishment thinking that the master was joking. Then he saw that he was not joking. He took the bone in his hands, tried to crush it and then said:

—There isn't a man in this world who could crush such a bone!

Then Tylval took the bone with his left hand, pressed it in his fist, crushed it and said:

—Look!

And from the hollow of his hand small pieces, like powdery white flour, fell to the *yurta's* earthern floor. Nemal-The Man realized that he would not be able to cope with Tylval. He hid his bow and arrows behind his back so they would not be seen. He wanted to leave the *yurta* but was afraid. "As soon as I leave the *yurta*, —he thought, —Tylval will kill me."

Nemal-The Man did not sit in the *yurta* very long, but it became necessary to leave!

Then all of them got up and went toward the exit. In the darkness at the door they broke Nemal-The Man's left leg and right arm. And when they got to the courtyard, Tylval grasped him by his unbroken right leg, lifted him above his head, twisted him—and how his back hit the ground! The giant only groaned. All of Nemal-The Man's ribs and bones were broken, and he died right there.

54. Kutkh

Narrated in 1929 by an inhabitant of Utkholok village in Tigilsky *rayon*, M. Zayev. Recorded and translated into Russian by E. Orlova.

Kutkh lived with his wife. One day Kutkh went to the sea to fish. He took a fishing rod. He came to the lake and promptly started to fish. He caught many. The small fish he threw back. The big ones he kept for himself. He harnessed the large fish and started for home.

At home his wife prepared many *tolkushas* to feed the fish with. Kutkh, as they were going home, promised the fish that at each stop he would feed them a plate of *yukola*.

Kutkh put the *tolkusha* on the sled and they left. He rode quite fast. They arrived at a birch grove. The dog-fish stopped and immediately asked:

—Well now, feed us!

Kutkh said:

—Ride me just a little farther!

The dog-fish again dashed off very fast. Kutkh even laughed a little. They dragged him to a low lying place, stopped again and said:

—Well, Kutkh, feed us!

Again Kutkh said:

—Ride me just a little bit farther!

The dog-fish got angry and darted off directly to the lake. Kutkh became frightened and began to cry out:

—Salmon, salmon, salmon, you stop! I'll give you *tolkusha*!

But the fish, as if deaf, dragged him on. Kutkh wanted to jump off but his foot got snagged in the sled.

The fish arrived at the lake and leapt into the water. And Kutkh drowned.

55. How Kutkh Frightened the Vixen

Narrated in 1969 by an inhabitant of Tigil village V. Ponomareva, age 60. Recorded and translated into Russian by A. Volodin. The subject matter about the drowning of the vixen in the first part of this tale has a parallel in Eskimo folklore (see no. 52 in Menovshchikov 1974 and no. 52 in Dolitsky and Michael 2000), where under similar circumstances the vixen is drowned by the ducks-teals who build a boat of their own wings.

There once lived a vixen. She very much wanted to marry. One day she was running along the bank of a river. Suddenly she saw fish spawning roe lying there, full of worms. The vixen took the roe, and cradling it like a child, picked the worms from it and ate them. Oy, what an experience for a child!

Suddenly she saw loons swimming on the river. One of the loons said:

—Kakakre, kakakre, look at that young woman sitting there!

The vixen said:

—It is I, your wife! Take me with you; we'll swim together!

A small loon answered:

—I'm not the father of your child; his father is swimming back there!

The loons swam away. Again the vixen sat on the bank, smoothing the roe, eating the worms. The child became fully lice-ridden!

She saw sea gulls swimming over the bedrock. A sea gull said:

—Keyya, keyya, keyya, who's the young woman sitting there?

—It is I, your wife, —said the vixen. —Take me!

—Well, come, sit down like a wife!

The vixen was happy; she sat on the rock. She said to the roe:

—There's your father!

And the sea gulls talked among themselves:

—Keyya, keyya, keyya, let's go over there to that deep place and sink the boulder, and fly away.

—What did you say? —the vixen asked.

—We were saying: Swim carefully; don't drown the beautiful young woman, because there are still relatives [nieces] here.

The vixen was happy:

—To be sure, are you really my husband?

Then they came to the deep place. The vixen, picking lice off her child, did not notice anything. Suddenly the sea gulls flew up and the boulder started to go under water. Yet the vixen did not drown. She threw the roe [onto the bank] and with difficulty got on the bank and sat on a sandbar.

—Well, now I'll dry my breeches and my eyes too.

She took off her hide and took her eyes out. She put the eyes in a bush and hung her hide on a tree. She lay down.

—I'll rest a little.

And she fell asleep. All of a sudden Kutkh came to the bank. He came upon the vixen and the sight seemed funny to him:

—What do you know; she's lying here naked! Now I'm going to frighten her.

He went to the river, took water in his mouth, and again he laughed at the sight, and the water poured from his mouth.

—All the same, I'll frighten her!

He went to the river again, put water in his mouth and covered his lips with his hand:

—This time I'll frighten you!

Kutkh went to the vixen, and again the sight made him laugh and all of the water came out through his nostrils. Again he went to the river:

—You know, all the same I'll frighten her, but I'll have to send my laugh to Miti.

135

Miti was sitting at home and sewing when suddenly she was overcome by a laugh, like a belly laugh.

—What's happening to me? No doubt Kutkh is up to something.

And Kutkh again took water in his mouth:

—Well, now I'll really frighten her!

The vixen lay there naked and sleeping. Kutkh splashed water on the sleeping vixen. The vixen got very frightened, jumped up, bumping into everything because of poor sight. Kutkh was dying of laughter. Suddenly somebody called out to the vixen:

—Why are you running around naked?

—Kutkh frightened me, —the vixen said. —And who is that here?

—We are bog bilberries; we're picking each other.

—Give me two small bilberries.

They gave them to her and she placed them in her eye sockets. Everything around her became much more visible. At once the red bilberries began to pick themselves a little farther away:

—Vixen, why do you walk around like this?

—Kutkh frightened me. Give me two red bilberries.

The vixen threw the bog bilberries away and inserted the red bilberries. Now everything became red. She walked farther. The [tree] cones were picking each other. They asked the vixen what was wrong with her. The vixen told them:

—Kutkh frightened me; I've lost my eyes, I've lost my breeches. Give me two cones so I can make eyes.

They gave them to her. She threw the red bilberries away and inserted the cones. She found the place where she left her eyes and breeches. She looked and she saw that her fur had entirely dried out and became warped. The vixen wet it in a puddle. Her whole body ached and was covered with scratches from the bushes.

Kutkh came home full of laughter:

—Miti, listen to this!

But Miti was angry. Kutkh said:

—Miti, why are you angry? Listen to the funny thing I'm going to tell you. I frightened the vixen, she ran around naked and also didn't put her eyes back in.

Miti said:

—Eh, it's all you Kutkh, all. I never hear from you anything sensible! You only play rough tricks and never do anything good. I'm ashamed to live with you.

—Ah, Miti, when a vixen runs around naked it just makes you laugh! But don't be angry anymore. When the snow starts falling, she'll crawl in her burrow and then I'll bring her to you for a nice fur collar.

56. How Kutkh Made His Wife Miti Work

Narrated in 1965 **by** L. N. Tolman, age 61. Recorded and translated into Russian by N. Starkova.

Kutkh lived with Miti. Miti was very lazy, but Kutkh was very hard working. Kutkh always went hunting and without fail he killed something: here a duck, there a deer or a bear. He fished and he also killed seals. He would come home and ask for food. And Miti always fed him with the same *yukola* [dried fish]; she never cooked anything. She just slept a lot.

When one day Kutkh returned from the hunt, Miti again fed him with *yukola*. Kutkh said:

—Today I'm not going to eat. I ache all over. My belly hurts very much. Now I'm going to die.

Miti cried a little:

—How am I going to live without you?

And Kutkh answered her:

—I'll tell you what to do: when I die, dig a shallow grave for me. Put a lot a grass in the grave and don't cover me with soil but with cedar chips. And every day bring me *tolkusha*,[42] *kirilka*,[43] *sarana*;[44] make cutlets with *sarana* and *kimchuga*;[45] provide me with *chaga*,[46] and brew some tea. All of this bring to the grave. Put everything down and leave. Don't look back or you'll die too!

And so Miti got up early, went to the forest, dug up much of the *sarana* and *kimchuga*, and picked all kinds of berries. She returned home, prepared the cutlets, made the *tolkusha* and *kirilka*, brought the teapot to a boil, prepared the tea, and carried all of that to Kutkh. Kutkh ate it all and gained much weight. And Miti cooked from early morning to late evening and also went to the woods. Finally Kutkh saw that Miti had become a good worker. Promptly he got up. He ferried across the river, where their house was; he came out and called loudly:

—Miti! Cross over here!

And Miti went to the river and saw a very fat man standing there. At first she didn't recognize him. The voice was that of Kutkh, only Kutkh was very thin. Then Kutkh said:

—Don't you know me? I'm Kutkh!

Miti became very happy. She asked her son Ememkut to ferry Kutkh across the river. She asked of Kutkh:

—How did you come back to life?

—Well, God said: "Your wife has become a very hard worker, and so I decided to return you to life. Go and live with her!"

From then on everything started anew: Miti cooked all the time, went to the woods, and became a very good worker.

---

[42]*Tolkusha* — a meal prepared from chopped tubers and stalks of a number of edible plants mixed with fish, blubber, berries, and other ingredients.

[43]*Kirilka* — local Russian. A traditional Itelmen meal. It consists of boiled brains or fish (more recently of potatoes), fresh crowberries, and rendered seal blubber.

[44]*Sarana* — local Russian. Tubers of the red lily. In the past they were used by the peoples of Kamchatka as food. The tubers were eaten raw, but when they dried they were ground into flour.

[45]*Kimchuga*, also *kemchuga* — an edible root.

[46]*Chaga* — a brown mushroom used by the Itelmens for a brew.

57. The Faked Death of Kutkh

Recorded in 1910-1911 in Khayruzovo *rayon* in Kamchatka *oblast* by W. Jochelson. Published in *Kamchadal Texts*, Worth 1961, no. K2. p. 151. Translated from the Itelmen language into Russian by A. Volodin.

Kutkh lived with his wife Miti. They had children: Ememkut and Sinanevt. Ememkut lived by himself. He fed his father badly. Kutkh thought a bit and said to his wife:

—Miti, my time is getting near. Tomorrow I'll die. Once you've taken care of me, ask Ememkut for a pouch of blubber and meat. Then you, Miti, put everything in the grave—the willow herbs, a small basket of crowberries, a mortar and pestle, a sieve, an oil lamp, water, firewood, and a fire place.

Miti began to get Kutkh ready. She said:

—Kutkh, you're talking idly, you're not going to die!

—Yes I am; I'm really going to die!

So Miti cooked the meat, made the *tolkusha*, prepared the meals to observe Kutkh's death. Kutkh had a glorious meal. After it he promptly washed and sat down. The whole family was looking at him. Suddenly Kutkh's eyes closed. Kutkh fell down and died. The dwellers of the house were frightened. Ememkut dug a large pit and covered its top. They carried Kutkh from the house to the pit. In the courtyard Kutkh could not hold back and smiled. Sinanevt saw it and she said:

—Look, Kutkh is smiling!

Miti told her:

—Your brother has gotten hold of you! Since when do the dead smile?

They pushed Kutkh into the pit. They covered all of the food and the top of the pit with grass and made a hole in the cover. It became dark. Kutkh lit the oil lamp and started a fire. He began to grind the *tolkusha*. Sinanevt went out and saw the fire in Kutkh's pit and heard the pounding of the pestle in the mortar. Right away she returned and said:

—Miti, there's a fire burning in Kutkh's pit and there's a pounding, like in making *tolkusha*.

Miti said:

—Well, there you go about your brother. How could a dead man make *tolkusha*, you dummy?

Kutkh began to live in the pit. He ate well. In the evening he cooked food, and made *tolkusha*. He ate all of the supplies. Then he came out of the pit and went to the house. He entered. The dwellers became frightened. The children promptly ran away. Kutkh said:

—Don't be afraid. I've returned because they wouldn't let me into the other world. Miti, call the children back!

Miti invited all the children back. They came in. Kutkh told them:

—Ememkut, god ordered that you are to feed me well, take care of me and live with me.

Ememkut began to take good care of his father and he fed him well. Kutkh lived to a great age, not in want of anything.

58. How Kutkh Died

Narrated in 1969 by an inhabitant of Tigil village V. Ponomareva, age 60. Recorded and translated into Russian by A. Volodin.

Well, there lived Miti. She did not want to do anything; nothing pleased her. She got lost in her thoughts and did not cook anything for Kutkh. Kutkh always wandered in the forest, he would come home and there wasn't a cooked meal. Miti would give him hard, very hard, *yukola*. He would eat a little, then, hungry, he would lie down to sleep. In the morning he would again go somewhere. When he came back there would again be on the table *yukola* that had turned sour, covered with worms. He hardly ate at all. He lay down and thought: "What's wrong with Miti? What should I do to bring back the way it used to be?"

He went to the forest and thought to himself: "I'm going to tell Miti that God came down from heaven and wanted to take me away."

He came home and again Miti gave him *yukola*.

—Miti, listen to what I'm going to tell you.

—What's wrong with you? Well, speak.

—Today God came down from the sky right where I was standing. He came down and told me: "I want to take you Kutkh, I want to take your soul. Let them place you in a pit. Only you tell Miti to make me a very good meal and bring it here to the pit for you." You see, Miti, I will now die. Put me in the pit, but don't cover it. And also remember, Miti, that the meal must be brought every day at the same time, just when the sun has set. God will not come during the day. Well, now I will die.

Kutkh fell down and died. Miti started to bustle about and started to bury Kutkh. She laid him down in the pit but did not cover it. Kutkh lay in the pit. Miti put the food there and went off. Kutkh said to himself:

—Now I'm going to see how far she went.

He looked and he could not see Miti. Kutkh promptly sat up and began to eat. He filled himself well.

—Well, I'll go and walk a little.

Whenever the sun set, Kutkh quickly came to the pit and stretched himself out. And Miti brought the food. To be sure, God wanted to eat. She put the food down, sat down and cried. She stopped crying and said:

—God has eaten all the food. Tomorrow I'll cook something even better so that they will not burn or torture Kutkh in the other world. His soul is with God.

And Kutkh heard what Miti was saying. She took the dirty dishes:

—I'll clean them very well and tomorrow I'll bring more food for God.

Miti left, crying and sobbing. As soon as Miti vanished, Kutkh promptly climbed out and began to eat. He ate everything; he filled himself perfectly. He walked around all-night and roamed until midday. As soon as the sun began to set Kutkh quickly arrived and stretched out in the pit. Miti came and again began to cry:

—O-oy, Kutkh, Kutkh! If you would now come back to life, I would become cheerful; I'd do anything for you.

And for Kutkh that was enough. Miti went home. Kutkh climbed out of the pit and after he ate he said:

—Well, now I'll go to Miti as if God did not accept me. As if God had said: "Your Miti cries so much, don't stay here anymore." And he gave me my soul back. And I'm going to tell her just that.

So Kutkh went home. Miti saw him and said: "It looks like my Kutkh is coming here!" She did not recognize him but Kutkh, who had become fat, went straight to her. Miti recognized him and became very happy:

—Oy, from where did you come to me, Kutkh?

—Well, God did not accept me; he saw that you were suffering very much. He gave me my soul right away and sent me off. "Go home, —he said, —live like you did before, well and truly."

139

59. Kutkh and Miti

Narrated in 1929 by an inhabitant of Utolok village in Tigilsky *rayon*, M. Zayev. Recorded and translated into Russian by E. Orlova.

One day Kutkh said to Miti:

—Miti! Let's go and pick nuts. I've seen a lot of nuts in a grove there.

They quickly got ready and went after the nuts. As soon as they arrived they started to pick nuts.

Kutkh was very apprehensive. He agreed with Miti that without fail they would keep in touch. They were to pick nuts and keep in touch by calling out: "Kutykhe! Mitykhe! Yakhakha-yakhakha!"

They picked many nuts over a long time. It was bothersome for Miti to cry out, and she did so in a more and more quiet voice and then she became altogether quiet. And Kutkh cried out all the time:

—Mitykhe! Yakhakha-yakhakha! Where are you?

Kutkh became very scared. What was he to do? He thought: "Maybe the bears have eaten Miti!"

Suddenly Miti called out:

—Kutkh, Why are you crying out so?

Kutkh became frightened, changed into a raven and flew to the forest. He sat on some kind of *balagan* [wooden booth] and began cawing like a raven.

60. How Kutkh and Miti Picked Nuts

Narrated in 1965 by an inhabitant of Tigil village T. Bragina, age 59. Recorded and translated into Russian by N. Starkova.

Kutkh and Miti were husband and wife. One day Kutkh said:

—Let's go to pick nuts!

They got ready and went. They began to pick nuts. Kutkh suggested:

—Miti, let's call to each other, because there're bears around here. You call to me and I to you.

They collected nuts and called out. Miti called: "Kukeve!" and Kutkh called: "Miti! Mitive!"

They collected nuts and all the time they were calling to each other. It was bothersome for Miti to call and she became quiet. And Kutkh thought: "No doubt, a bear ate Miti." He became frightened, he felt sorry for Miti.

And Miti thought to herself: "Now I'm going to frighten Kutkh." She crept up to Kutkh and yelled out:

—Ya-kha-kha-kha, Kutkh!

Kutkh was very much frightened; he changed into a raven and flew off. And Miti was left by herself.

Kutkh flew and flew. Then he saw a *balagan* and a grass-covered house [*shalash*] Two young girls lived in that house. They were sisters, very beautiful, skillful seamstresses and workers.

The older sister went out to throw away some rubbish. The raven saw her. The girl threw away the rubbish. Kutkh flew near her. The sister thought to herself: "No doubt that's Kutkh teasing." She threw some rubbish at him and went inside. She told her younger sister:

—Go to the *balagan* and bring some replenishments!

The girl went out climbed on the *balagan* and the raven promptly flew there and sat down. The girl saw the raven and said:

—Where did this raven come from? I live here with only my sister; I've never seen anybody else; only the forest.

The girl was happy; she fed the raven to satiety with different berries. And Kutkh thought to himself: "What a good-looking girl. Maybe my Ememkut would marry her."

The girl finished feeding the raven and she said:

—Fly to our place.

She went home. And at home the older sister became angry and spoke to the younger one spitefully:

—To be sure, that must be Kutkh playing his pranks again!

And the raven flew to the dwelling, turned around three times and again became Kutkh. At this time Miti was sitting at home and crying. She felt sorry for Kutkh.

Kutkh came in. Miti was happy and she asked him:

—Kutkh, where have you been?

—I've flown far, saw a house in the forest, and in that house lived two sisters: One was evil, the other—beautiful.

And Ememkut, their son, was lying down and he heard what Kutkh was saying. He listened and listened and then he said:

—I would visit there but I don't know how to get there.

Kutkh suggested:

—Take my raven parka, fly in that direction; you'll see a house in the forest. That's where the two girls live.

Ememkut put on the raven parka and flew off. He flew far. He saw the house and at once sat on it. The older sister came out and said to the raven in anger:

—That Kutkh is again having his fun!

She threw rubbish at the raven, went in, but told her sister nothing.

The younger sister went out, saw the raven and said:

—The raven has flown to us again.

She climbed onto the *balagan*; the raven also flew there and sat at the entrance. The girl said to the raven:

—My sister and I live in the forest; we never see anybody. It's good that you've come!

She began to feed him but the raven would not eat. The girl told him:

—The raven who was here a short time ago ate quite a bit, and you don't want to.

Then she added:

—Stay here and live with us!

Promptly the raven became Ememkut; he embraced the girl, and there and then a child started to cry. The girl became frightened and also cried:

—Now, how am I going to show myself to my sister?

Ememkut calmed her:

—Don't be afraid! We'll go together!

They let themselves down from the *balagan* and went in the house. Her sister said in anger:

—Didn't I say the truth that Kutkh was having fun? And you're here with a child!

Ememkut told her to calm down. The older sister stopped being angry. She began to get her younger sister ready to go. She asked:

—And on what are you going to travel?

Ememkut went to the forest and whistled three times. Right there reindeer appeared. They got ready and left. As they were nearing the village, a snowstorm drew near. Kutkh came out of the house and said:

—Miti, there is a snowstorm coming!

Miti came out and replied:

—That's not a snowstorm. It's our Ememkut returning with his wife.

Kutkh said to her:

—Our house is tight, Miti! Kick it a little! [Native expression for luck and hopeful wishes].

Miti kicked the house and it became wider. In no time they set out various kinds of food and they invited all the animals and birds. They made merry for a long time, and Ememkut is alive to this day.

61. Kutkh and the Vixen

Recorded in 1910-1911 in Khayruzovo *rayon* of Kamchadalsky *oblast* by W. Jochelson. Published in *Kamchadal Texts*, Worth 1961, no. K2. p. 11. Translated from the Itelmen language into Russian by A. Volodin.

Kutkh lived with his wife Miti. Kutkh said:

—Miti, I'm going to build a fish-trap across the river.

He went fishing. He placed the fish-trap. King salmon and various other fish began to get trapped. Kutkh went to take the fish out of the traps. At that time the vixen Petenga came by. Promptly she enticed Kutkh. He separated the fish heads for the vixen Petenga and carried the headless fish home. He told his wife:

—The bears marred the fishnets and bit off all the fish-heads!

He then added:

—Miti, I'm going to go to the fish-traps during the night.

Miti said:

—Very well, Kutkh, go there during the night!

Miti did not know that her husband was a cheat! And Kutkh slept with the vixen Petenga, loved her as a woman. He would get up and promptly go to the fish net. He would give all the fish heads to Petenga, and carry the headless fish to Miti. As soon as he arrived he said, as always:

—Here Miti, the fish!

Miti looked at them; again they were headless.

—Kutkh, why do you bring me fish without heads? Is it possible that you eat all the heads by yourself?

—No, Miti, the bears do that. They damage the fishnets and eat the heads off.

Kutkh stayed home a while and then left. Miti began to have her doubts.

—What kind of habit has Kutkh fallen in? Is it possible that he's tricked me?

In the evening Miti went to see Kutkh. She came there and saw Kutkh lying down with the vixen Petenga, talking together. Miti saw this, looked again and went home. She now knew where and how the fish-heads disappeared. She sharpened a long stake and tied a fish spine to it. In the evening she again started out and took the stake with her. She got there. Kutkh was already lying there with the vixen Petenga. Miti thrust the stake into the vixen's buttocks. The vixen began to groan:

—Oy, oy, it hurts!

Kutkh asked:

—What's with you, Petenga?

—My tail hurts!

The vixen jumped up, saw Miti and ran into the forest with the stake and the spine tied to it and bumping behind her. Miti said:

—Eh, Kutkh, what a liar you are! And I really thought that you were guarding against the bears. And you've fooled me!

Kutkh said:

—Well, enough of that, Miti, let's begin to live together again in a friendly way!

And they began to live well again and made merry.

62. Kutkh, the Vixen and the Wolf

Recorded in 1910-1911 in Khayruzovo *rayon* of Kamchatka *oblast* by W. Jochelson. Published in *Kamchadal Texts*, Worth 1961, no. K2. p. 22. Translated from the Itelmen language into Russian by A. Volodin. This tale adopts the subject matter of two tales about an old man tricked by the vixen, and about the wolf who at the instigation of the same vixen lets his tail freeze in an ice hole. Kutkh plays the role of the tricked fisherman here. The same tale, in different variations, is found among the Asiatic Eskimos and Chukchi. In this tale the influence of Russian folklore is evident.

Kutkh lived with his wife Miti. Kutkh blocked the small river with netting to catch salmon. He began to fish for salmon. Then one day the vixen decided to trick Kutkh. She lay down on the path pretending to be dead, as if she had frozen to death. Kutkh came by and saw the vixen lying there. Kutkh rejoiced. He loaded the salmon onto the sled. And he tied the vixen loosely onto the back of the sled. And he started for home. The vixen started to throw the salmon from the sled and then she jumped off. And Kutkh didn't notice that the vixen had run away. He arrived at the house and went in:

—Hey, Miti, put away the salmon and take the vixen!

Miti went out. There were a few salmon. She took them but she could not find the vixen anywhere. Miti entered the house and said:

—Kutkh, there's no vixen!

—What do you mean by that? She's lying at the back of the sled!

—Kutkh, you don't know the vixen. She's a trickster!

Kutkh went to the river again. Again he found a frozen vixen, took her and tied her very fast to the sled. He loaded the salmon and started for home. Again the vixen threw off the salmon but she could not jump off herself; Kutkh had tied her up tightly. Kutkh arrived at home and he said:

—Miti, go and collect the salmon and take the vixen. Put her on the stove and let her thaw out!

Miti carried the vixen in the house and put her on the stove. Kutkh fingered the vixen; she was frozen, she had not thawed out yet. Kutkh began to sharpen a knife; he was getting ready to disembowel her. The vixen saw that she was in big trouble. Kutkh fingered the vixen again—she had thawed out. As he was ready to disembowel the vixen, she jumped up and put out the fire [oil lamp]. Kutkh and Miti became frightened and the vixen ran to the courtyard and began to laugh. Kutkh said:

—Ah, you vixen, had I known that you were going to trick me, I would have disemboweled you right away, I wouldn't have waited until you thawed out.

The vixen left. She began to pick up the salmon. She gathered all of them. She began to eat. A wolf arrived and asked:

—Vixen, where have you caught so many salmon?

—Oh, I've put my tail in an ice hole and the salmon have stuck to my tail.

The wolf said:

—Ehe, vixen, teach me!

—Go over there and put your tail in the ice hole.

The wolf put his tail in. He became very cold. The wolf's tail froze to the ice.

—Hey, vixen, I'm going to take out my tail!

—Take it out!

But the wolf's tail was frozen to the ice. He couldn't pull it out. The vixen laughed, but the wolf became very angry:

—Now look here vixen: when I free myself, I'll kill you!

The vixen ran off and hid in a burrow. The wolf tugged and ripped off his tail fur almost to the bone. He ran after the vixen. He came to the burrow and yelled out:

—Vixen, are you there?

The vixen answered:

—I'm here, but my eyes hurt, I'm going nowhere! Not long ago I went outside and saw the vixen run past and hide herself in a nearby burrow.

The wolf said:

—Come here, show me where that burrow is; I'll go with you.

The vixen came out and said:

—As soon as I yell out, you promptly put your head in the burrow. If the burrow is tight shove your head in anyway! That's where she is, the trickster!

The vixen dove into the burrow; she yelled out, she began to make noises:

—Hey, wolf, shove your head in. There's your trickster!

The burrow was tight and his head got jammed in it; he couldn't pull it out in any way. The vixen chuckled again. The wolf got very angry. And the vixen ate all of the wolf's supplies, only the bones remained, and she ran away.

She ran and met another wolf on the path. He asked her:

—Where are you running to, vixen?

—I'm running to the forest, to my burrow!

Somehow the wolf pulled out his head from the burrow. Again he chased after the vixen. On the path he saw his friend, the other wolf. His friend looked at him and asked:

—Where did you lose your tail fur and snout?

—The vixen did this to me! My friend, have you by chance seen that vixen?

—I did, she hid in that burrow over there.

—Let's go and kill her!

They came to the burrow. The wolves began to yell:

—Are you there, vixen?

The vixen did not answer. The wolves again yelled out:

Are you there, vixen? The vixen yelled back:

—I'm here and my eyes hurt!

—Well then, come out vixen!

—I'm not coming out; my eyes hurt, I can't see anything!

The wolves said:

—She's harmful. Now let's dig out the burrow!

They began to dig. They dug up the burrow, pulled out the vixen, and tore her into small pieces.

63. Kutkh and the Crab

Recorded in 1910-1911 in Khayruzovo *rayon* of Kamchatka *oblast* by W. Jochelson. Published in *Kamchadal Texts*, Worth 1961, no. K2. p. 12. Translated from the Itelmen language into Russian by A. Volodin.

Long ago there lived Kutkh with his wife Miti. Kutkh was getting ready to go to the cape. He said:

—Miti, will you give me my cap, mittens and belt!

Miti said:

—If you want to, Kutkh, go right now!

Kutkh went to the cape. He got there. All the sea animals that he met, he kicked with his foot and said:

—That's how you must be treated!

He walked farther and saw a crab sleeping. He started to waken the crab. But the crab was deep asleep.

—Hey crab, wake up! The crab opened his eyes and said:

—I want to sleep Kutkh, don't bother me!

Kutkh said:

—All right crab, get up, you've slept enough!

The crab got up and Kutkh told him right away:

—Hey crab, take me for a ride!

Kutkh sat on his back, and the crab entered the sea. And Kutkh sang a song:

—I'm riding over the water. For you, Miti, it's better to sit at home.

The crab started to roll him. Kutkh cried out:

—Hey crab, if you let me go, I'll drown!

The crab said:

—Kutkh, why did you wake me? But now, don't be afraid!

He took Kutkh to the middle of the sea. And in the middle of the sea there was a big round boulder. He left Kutkh on that boulder. Kutkh settled down, he sat there, and the waves rolled over the boulder and splashed over Kutkh. Kutkh hid his face in his parka and heard people talking under the boulder. Suddenly a big wave rolled in and threw Kutkh under the boulder.

He went down a staircase and there the sea people met him. They received him well. They fed him with dry-cured meat. They began to put themselves to sleep. The sea lads hid all the water and dried out the river. Kutkh awakened during the night, he wanted to drink, but could not find any water in the house. He went to the river. Even the river was all dried up. He started to think about those that he had left at home, his wife, his small children. He called all of them by name. Kutkh said:

—Miti, you and the little ones drink water, but here I am dying of thirst!

The sea lads heard this but did not get up. Kutkh began to think about his older children, the girls:

—Sinanevt and Anaraklnavt, you are drinking water and your father is dying of thirst!

The sea lads then got up as if it was only then that they heard how Kutkh was lamenting, and they said:

—The women have tormented our guest! They did not give him water to drink.

Immediately water appeared. Kutkh began to drink. The lads filled a whole *baydara* with water. Kutkh drank it all. He went to the river. There he started to drink again. He drank and he quenched his thirst. He drank away [promised in marriage] his daughters. Their suitors took Kutkh home in a boat. Kutkh told his wife all that had happened to him.

—Miti, —he said, —tell our daughters to get ready, let them marry; I drank them away!

So his daughters got married. They began to live a happy life.

146

64. The Egg Maidens

Narrated in 1929 by an inhabitant of Utkholok village in Tigilsky *rayon*, M. Zayev. Recorded and translated into Russian by E. Orlova. About the transformation of Kutkh's daughters Sinanevt and Amzarakchan into animals, see also the variant of this tale, no. 80 in this edition.

Kutkh lived with his wife. They had an only son Ememkut. They lived well.

One day Kutkh and Miti went onto the spit to gather eggs. They arrived there. Miti began to gather large eggs of swans, geese, eagles, and sea gulls. But Kutkh gathered the smallest: those of the sandpipers, small ducks and various small birds.

Kutkh came up to Miti, saw that she had gathered large eggs, and he said:

—Why are you gathering large eggs and I only small ones?

Then they started to argue. Miti became angry and went home and Kutkh was left by himself.

He gathered many eggs, large and small. Then he built a *balagan* [temporary shelter] and a small house by the sea. Later he made from the eggs two girls and sat them on the bench in the *balagan*. And he went home.

After that he did not go out for a long time.

And Ememkut, his son, always went into the forest and killed many animals and birds.

Then one day Kutkh had the thought of taking a walk on the spit. He started. As he walked on the spit he found a spotted seal. He put her on the grass and walked farther. Then he saw a *balagan* and a small house. He thought: "Who could live here? Nobody ever lived here. Let me take a look!"

Kutkh went to take a look. The girls saw him and became very happy.

They went to meet their father and they said:

—Oy, oy! Our father is coming! We missed you so much! We thought you'd never come to see us. Father, we'll feed you well. We'll cook a lot of *sarana* [tubers of the red lily], we'll prepare a good *tolkusha*, and we'll serve berries!

They entered the small house. The girls bustled about the house. And Kutkh fell asleep. The sun started to set. The girls awakened Kutkh and fed him well. And when it became completely dark, Kutkh started for home. He did not remember about the seal. He walked fast.

He came home. He began to tell his wife:

—I walked on the spit and saw a small house and a *balagan*. I went to take a look. Two girls came out of the house and were very happy about me, as if they had met their father. They said that they yearned for me. I became frightened—could these be my children? Then they gave me a hearty meal. They said: "Father, come again any time, we'll feed you well again. We'll cook all sorts of food!"

The next day Kutkh went to the girls again and they received him very well.

Kutkh began to go to them every day. Then Miti became jealous and told him:

—Kutkh, you always go to the forest! Have you found something sweet there?

But Kutkh did not hear Miti; he went to the girls anyway.

Then, one day Kutkh invited Ememkut. Ememkut came in. Kutkh said:

—Ememkut! There, on the spit live two beautiful girls. They would be nice brides for you. Tomorrow I'll go there and arrange a marriage for you with one of them.

The next day Kutkh went to arrange a marriage for his son.

Again the girls were very happy and again they fed Kutkh very well. He could not tell them anything so he went home without making arrangements.

The next day Kutkh told Ememkut to go and make arrangements himself for a marriage. He said to him:

—I can't arrange for anything. You know, they take me for their father. Go and try yourself!

Ememkut went there. And the girls were very happy about him too. Again they wanted to cook much savory food and feed him well. Ememkut refused to eat anything. But he could not say anything. Yes, and how would he be able to utter such words? So he went home having said nothing.

And the girls, Sinanevt and Amzarakchan, had already guessed that the father and son had come for a definite reason. Sinanevt said:

—We've got to get away from this place. And for some reason father has taken to visit us very often. Let's get ready for the road, prepare the food. And we'll use the whale to take us.

The girls went to work. They prepared willow herbs, dried *yukola*, and sewed parkas, capes, and mittens. They finished it all, prepared everything and carried all of it outside. They burnt the house and the *balagan*.

They walked on the spit, called the whale, entered it and it swam into the sea.

The next day Ememkut and Kutkh again went to arrange a marriage. They came to the place where the girls had lived but there was nobody there. They decided to follow their footsteps, and these led to the sea. They thought: "Where did the girls go? No doubt they drowned!"—and they went back home.

And the girls were in the swimming whale for a long time. The younger, Amzarakchan, slept all the time; she never got up, she never did any work. The older sister did all the work.

Then suddenly the whale stopped swimming. Sinanevt thought: "Have we arrived at land? I'll make a small hole with a needle!"

Sinanevt made a small hole and through it saw land. She went out. She descended to a very nice place. Cloudberries grew there, and nut trees, and *puchki*,[47] and willow herbs. Sinanevt walked about with pleasure and ate to satiety. She picked a bunch of *puchki* and took it to the whale's house.

And the younger sister slept all the time. Sinanevt put the *puchki* on her headboard, then awakened her and asked her:

—What did you see in your dream?

—I saw nothing. I'm so bored. We haven't seen land for a long time! I'd like to find myself on land just now!

Sinanevt said:

—And today I saw in a dream that *puchki* were put on our headboard.

—And now, you take a look!

The younger sister went to the headboard and the *puchki* were really there! She was very happy and she thought: "Where did these *puchki* come from? Is it possible that we've come to land?

They then gathered themselves and left the whale's house. They went directly to the forest. There they again built a little house and took to working. They prepared a big lot of willow herbs.

They lived this way for a relatively long time. Then they thought that they should get married. With the willow herbs they made a bear and a deer. The younger sister took the bear, and the older one, the deer. One of them tried to turn into a deer, the other into a bear.

First the deer walked a little. The older sister told the younger one to see how she was going to walk. She walked like a real deer, jumping as she walked. She then returned.

The bear, the younger sister, went next. She also walked like a bear, holding her head close to the ground.

Sinanevt told her sister:

—Now I'm going to look for a husband. I'm telling you: "Don't go for a handsome husband. Go after a plain one. Then when you see my husband, yours will become like him."

Then Sinanevt transformed into a deer and Amzarakchan into a bear. Sinanevt immediately chained the bear and as a deer she went into the tundra. The bear started to yank at the chain.

The deer glanced back and looked at the bear. Sinanevt was sorry for her sister, she would return to her but then she would go to the tundra again. She looked back, she could not go on and she pitied her sister. Sinanevt returned to her sister three times. Then, the deer went to the tundra, and the bear was left alone.

---

[47] *Puchki* — bunches of hollow, sweet tasting grass.

The deer went directly to a hunter. The hunter saw the deer, stole up to it close, shot and killed it. He ripped open its belly—and a beautiful maiden came out of it. The hunter married her and they returned home. So they began to live together.

Sinanevt yearned for her sister very much. She told no one about it. The mother of her husband saw that Sinanevt was suffering outside the house. She began to question her but Sinanevt did not tell her a thing.

Sinanevt came in and again her husband's mother started to question her:

—Sinanevt, what are you so miserable about? Could it be that somewhere it's something about a relative of yours?

At first Sinanevt said nothing but the mother sensed that she was hiding something. Finally Sinanevt admitted:

—I have a sister far off in the forest. She's there straining at the chain. My sister is very dreadful. Nobody can kill her.

Sinanevt's husband gathered the people, they mounted reindeer and left. They traveled fast; they wanted to arrive there as soon as possible.

In that village there was a man by the name of Sysylkhan. He had no reindeer, no dogs, not even a sleigh. Slowly he began to prepare for the road. He was in no hurry in picking out his [sled] dogs-mice. He went to the burrows and holes, and invited the mice. In place of a sleigh, he took a trough in which pickled fish were kept; in place of a braking pole, a poker from the wood stove. He harnessed the mice to the trough and started out. On the way the mice ran into a burrow here, into a hole there. Those who waited for him had already used all of their arrows by the time he drove up. His bow was made of switches, his arrows of twigs and his arrow points of alder wood tips. His companions asked him to hurry:

—The sooner you get there, the sooner you'll shoot at the bear.

Sysylkhan drove up and released an arrow right away. The arrow had not reached the bear as yet when he promptly fell down. They opened the bear's belly and a beautiful maiden came out of it. She was perspiring all over—she was chained for a long time.

The hunters started to invite her to their sleighs, but she would not sit with any one. She said:

—I'll sit with the one who freed me.

The hunters said:

—Why would you want to sit with him? Look, his sleigh is a trough in which pickled fish were kept!

Yet, she did not sit with any of them. She went over to Sysylkhan and sat on his sleigh—the trough.

They went on very quietly. Over the low mounds Sysylkhan pulled the sleigh himself. At a certain place Sysylkhan went into the forest. He called to a deer. He entered one of its ears and came out the other. Immediately he became a very handsome man. Next to him stood fine reindeer and an elegant sleigh. He sat on the sleigh and drove to his wife. His wife did not recognize him:

—You're not my husband! My husband is altogether plain!

Her husband told her:

—I am indeed your husband. Come, sit here!

They drove on. They drove very fast. Suddenly a big snowstorm arrived. They drove toward the house; they saw the house from the distance.

They began to live well. The next day the sisters saw each other. Sinanevt said:

—Remember Amzarakchan that I forbade you to marry a handsome man. You did right to listen to me. Now look, your husband is more handsome than mine. May I wish you a good life! It's not necessary to lead a bad life!

And so the sisters began to live well.

65. The Fight of Kutkh with Ememkut

Narrated in 1929 by an inhabitant of Utkholok village in Tigilsky *rayon*, M. Zayev. Recorded and translated into Russian by E. Orlova.

There lived Kutkh and Ememkut. Kutkh stayed at home all the time; he never went anywhere. From lying around even his head hair became slightly rotten.

But Ememkut always went to the forest. He hunted for many kinds of animals and birds. And he always went to the same place. There many animals were to be found.

Then one day Ememkut decided to take a rest. He sat next to the forest. Suddenly he heard that somewhere somebody was singing very beautifully. Ememkut listened and thought: "Who could it be that sings so well? I'll go and see!"

He went in the direction from which the singing could be heard. He walked and the singing became louder. Ememkut's heart was also singing happy. The singing one was coming directly toward him. Ememkut hid in a hollow. And the singer was close by. Ememkut was trembling. Suddenly he saw the singing Iyanamltsyakh[48] appear. As she came closer to Ememkut, he jumped up from the hollow and embraced her. He then married her and promptly a child was born.

Iyanamltsyakh said to Ememkut:

—You have taken me, but you know, I am a forest being. How can we live in your house? You know that I have nothing. I'm getting married with absolutely nothing.

Ememkut could not say anything. His wife was so beautiful. He only said:

—It's now time, let's go home. I don't need anything of yours. And don't be sad. I forbid you to be sad.

Ememkut and Iyanamltsyakh went to Kutkh. They arrived and Kutkh, as usual, was lying on the bed. Ememkut and his wife entered the house. Kutkh became very frightened and he said:

—Ememkut, where did you get such a beautiful woman?

Ememkut told him:

—I found her in the forest.

To Kutkh, Iyanamltsyakh was the cause for his recuperation, as if his ailments were smitten away by a hand. Immediately he threw his bedding outside. And he started thinking as to how he could take Ememkut's wife from him.

"Very well, —he thought, —we'll send Ememkut after the bears."

Evening arrived. Kutkh said to Ememkut:

—Ememkut, tomorrow we'll go after bears. Over there in that forest I've seen a bear's den.

The next day they went after the bears. When they came to the forest, Kutkh started to tremble all over, and he said to Ememkut:

—Now then, you go first!

Ememkut, not suspecting anything, went on. He walked and Kutkh followed on his heels. Ememkut with stealth approached the den. When he was already at the very den, Kutkh shoved him into it.

Kutkh fell among the bears and they accepted him fully. A she-bear told her relatives:

—I forbid you to touch that man! People wanted to kill him because of his beautiful wife. Cook some bear meat for him! Then feed him well.

They met Ememkut nicely. They fed him with bear meat to satiety. Then they told him to go to sleep. Ememkut slept thoroughly.

And Kutkh came to Iyanamltsyakh. He told her to bed down with him. Iyanamltsyakh did not agree. He undressed completely and lay down next to her. But Iyanamltsyakh put on a prickly night-gown

---

[48]Iyanamltsyakh — lit. "raspberry" [the princeling's daughter].

150

woven with stinging nettles and lay down in it with Kutkh. Kutkh pressed himself against Iyanamltsyakh and his body began to itch very strongly. Kutkh said:

—Why is your body like pins and needles? How do you sleep with your husband?

Iyanamltsyakh told Kutkh:

—He cuddles up to me very nicely! Why did you throw my husband to the bears? Now you have to sleep with me!

Kutkh could not stay with Iyanamltsyakh; he was in much pain. He got up and told Iyanamltsyakh:

—Iyanamltsyakh, you'll be lost anyway. Ememkut is not going to return. The bears have torn him to pieces.

He had not even finish talking when Ememkut appeared. His wife was very happy. But Kutkh became very frightened. He went outside. He even slept overnight outside.

Only after a few days did he return home. He began to invite Ememkut to go fishing. He told him:

—Ememkut, let's go fishing! Over there, in the creek, I've seen many fish! Let's go there!

Ememkut agreed. They started after the fish. When they came to the river, Kutkh again told Ememkut to go first. When they arrived at the bank, Kutkh sneaked up to Ememkut and shoved him into the water. Then he went home right away.

Ememkut fell in with the salmon. They accepted him very well. An old salmon said:

—Children, do not hurt that man! People wanted to kill him because of his beautiful wife. Cook for him a lot of salmon.

They greeted Ememkut very well and fed him to satiety. Ememkut slept over and then returned home again.

Even this time Kutkh could not make out with Iyanamltsyakh. Again Ememkut found him in the bed of his wife. And again Ememkut did nothing to Kutkh. Ememkut was a good man, not a bad one.

Again Kutkh went somewhere in the forest. He did not return for several days. Ememkut started to think: "Where did Kutkh disappear to? Could it be that somebody killed him?"

Kutkh returned after some days and began to invite Ememkut to go after sables:

—Over there on that volcano I saw many footsteps of sables.

Again Ememkut went—he was afraid of nothing! When they arrived at the volcano, Ememkut again went ahead. He walked and came to a pit. And the pit was cleverly covered; it looked as if there was no pit below it. And Ememkut fell into that pit.

Quickly Kutkh covered the pit again and set a stick in the ground so that he could later find the place.

He returned home and again began to bother Iyanamltsyakh. She put on the nightgown with nettles—and so they began to live that way. They spent several days together.

But Ememkut did not die. He dug into the ground for some days, he wanted to get out of the pit. The pit was deep. Ememkut was very tired but after all he did get out. He went home. Before he arrived at the house, he fell to the ground. Nobody saw him. So Ememkut lay there all day. It was only the next day that Ememkut got home. He came in and saw Kutkh lying down with Iyanamltsyakh. Ememkut said:

—What are you doing there, Kutkh? But now, put on your clothes, we're going to the forest! You could not kill me, although you've tried several times. You've shoved me down to the bears, but the bears received me very well. You've pushed me into the water but the salmon met me like one of their own and fed me with fish until I was full. And you've caused me to fall in a deep pit where I almost died of hunger and yet, I returned home. Now we're going to the forest. I've always listened to you. Whenever you invited me, I went right away.

Ememkut and Kutkh went to the forest. They didn't go far. Ememkut called forth three bulls and four bears and told them to form a circle. They did so. And they stood Kutkh in the center.

Ememkut commanded the bears and the bulls to tear Kutkh apart.

They tore Kutkh into small pieces.

Ememkut began to live well again.

66. Nyaa—the Daughter of Kutkh and Miti

Narrated in 1969 by an inhabitant of Tigil village, V. Ponomareva, age 68. Recorded and translated into Russian by A. Volodin.

Kutkh and Miti lived there. Kutkh never went anywhere; he sat at home all the time. Suddenly Kutkh said:

—Miti! I'm going to take some air. I'm not going to go far. I'll just walk around.

—Go ahead. But see to it that you don't play any rough tricks!

—I will. Miti!

Then Kutkh put on his parka, tightened his belt and went out. He walked and saw that in the courtyard there sat an old grandmother-mouse.

—Hi there, granny!

—Hi there, Kutkh! Where are you going?

—Oh, just to get some fresh air.

—Sit down. Do you have children?

—There are none, granny. I have no daughters, only a son. Miti and I live together.

Kutkh did not tell the old woman anything about the children. The old woman said:

—Come in, if you want to and have some tea.

—Eh, let's go and have some tea together!

They went in. Right away the old woman told her grandchildren-mice:

—Now listen. Feed him with something salty so that he'll want to drink; and hide the water.

Kutkh started to eat and he ate well. He said:

—Now boil the tea!

—We can't heat the stove, grandpa; the wood is raw.

It then became very dark in the house. Kutkh wondered:

—What is this? It was so light here.

—You know, the sun has set. Where would you go in darkness? Sleep here. Soon the teapot will be boiling.

Kutkh lay down, and all the mice lay down, but the old woman did not sleep. Kutkh's throat was tingling with dryness; he could not sleep, and his soul had dried out. He got up and searched for water. He found none. Anyway he had stood his ground and did not admit that he had daughters. He felt worse; his throat was on fire. Kutkh sang out:

—Sinanevt, you've already carried the water away in a *chuman* [birch-bark vessel]!

And the mouse opened her ears wide: there is one girl. Then Kutkh again sang out:

—Oh you, Anoraklnavt, you're carrying water in buckets! How I would like a drink!

The mouse again spread her ears wide: he gave away his second daughter. Kutkh again sang out:

—Mrot, by now you've probably poured water in the *chuman*!

The mouse listened even more attentively: there is even a third girl.

Then Kutkh spoke very quietly:

—But Nyaa, my last one, I will not give you away for anything.

He suffered, he suffered, he did not have the strength to suffer any more and he wanted to drink so much! He began to sing very quietly:

—Nyaa, my little one, no doubt, you look at water like in a mirror!

At that the old mouse got up and said:

—No doubt you want to drink very much. Here, drink!

Kutkh gulped down the first mug of water as if he felt nothing. The mouse asked:

Do you really have children?

—Yes, I have children, four of them.

—Let my son marry your youngest daughter.

—Eh, let them marry, —Kutkh said, —Now let's boil strong tea; we'll drink a lot of it.

—Very well, grandpa!

Kutkh said:

—I'll leave your place first and you will come later. Only don't say that I was at your place.

—I won't betray you, —the old woman-mouse said.

The Kutkh drank of the tea and left. He came home.

—You've already got here? —Miti asked.

—Yes, I have. I've had a very nice airing.

—Sit down; eat!

—I won't, I do not feel well. I'd better lie down. Don't disturb me. If somebody comes, don't disturb me either. I'm very sick.

At that time Nyaa came in the house and said:

—Ma, there're a lot of mice coming here, they are loaded with something; they are pulling a sled with something on it.

Kutkh heard this and he began to moan:

—Oh, oh, Miti, tie a kerchief around my head! I have a splitting headache; no doubt it'll split altogether!

—Is it that bad, Kutkh?

—It's true Miti. Don't let anybody come to me!

The mice arrived. They brought a lot of food. They gave it to Miti and she said:

—Why have you brought so much to me?

And in the house Kutkh hollered loudly. The mice asked:

—Miti, who is screaming in your house?

—Well, Kutkh became sick, he has a splitting headache.

—Oy, Miti, how so? He was at our place just a while ago. He had some tea and he ate fully.

—So, he was at your place?

—Yes, he was. And we have come here. He promised us his daughter. Your little Nyaa suits us very well. She'll be a good wife to my son.

Miti stood there and swooned. She went in the house:

—Get up, you lousy creature! Whenever you leave the house you make a mess of things!

—O-oy, Miti, my head hurts so much.

—Get up, you glutton! You can never eat enough. You've given away my little daughter for a cup of tea!

—But, Miti, I had to drink something; my innards were so dry!

—Shut up, you greedy glutton!

—Where are the mice?

—They're in the courtyard.

—Let them come in!

The mice entered. They brought all sorts of cooked roots of herbs. And for Kutkh that was enough:

—Miti! Mother, sit down and eat of the rootlets!

Miti said:

—Gorge yourself, gobble it up and stuff your belly!

Nyaa burst out sobbing, threw herself on the floor, she did not want to go with the mice. Kutkh said:

—Don't be a crybaby! You'll have all kinds of plant roots to eat; you'll sleep on a feather bed.

—Just the same I'm not going with the mice, I'd rather sleep on a hard bark-bed!

—Listen to me Nyaa. If you don't obey me, I'll no longer be your father!

Her mother and sisters cried for her, but Kutkh took to eating the herb roots. The mice then said:

—Will you prepare your daughter? We want to take her with us now!

Nyaa even kicked them with her feet; she didn't want to go. But even so the mice took her away.

153

The mice awakened in the morning and said to Nyaa:

—Come with us, we'll get some *kimchiga*.[49]

From where the stores of it were, the mice began to carry *kimchiga* in their teeth to their homes. But Nyaa started to collect the way people collected: she took a sharp-pointed digging stick and started to dig the earth with it. Whenever the *kimchiga* started to make a crunching sound, she dug up the entire plant and put the *kimchiga* in a bag. The mice ran to the old woman complaining:

—She's such a good-for-nothing. She digs with the digging stick in the ground and disturbs all of our storehouses.

The old woman said:

—Do I hear that something's rustling in the ground? She is herself so wonderful; she is so different.

Nyaa came in, bringing the *kimchiga* in the bag. She cooked the *kimchiga* but the mice would not eat it.

—We're not going to eat that *kimchiga*; you've cooked it without *markasha*.[50] You eat it yourself!

They started putting themselves to sleep. The mice climbed into their feather beds but Nyaa made herself a bed of hides. The mice angrily mumbled:

—When our brother returns, we'll tell him all about you. Why do we have to put up with such a clumsy person?

In the morning the old woman got up and said:

—Well, now take her to the tundra and let her dig for the *kimchiga*.

They left. The mice started to dig for the *kimchiga* in their own way, but Nyaa began to use the digging stick again. The mice had already brought in half of their supplies, and she was still digging. The mice went home and again started to complain to the old woman:

—O-oy, granny; we all have a bad headache. All day she digs and digs with a stick in the ground and the ground trembles. Let us send her away; she really doesn't know anything. Why do we have to put up with her? We'll tell our brother all about her.

Two children were born to Nyaa, a boy and a girl. The old woman-mouse finished eating in the evening, found a dog's tail somewhere, all tangled up. She quietly put the tail in Nyaa's bag in which she kept her belongings. The mice took their own bag and started rummaging in it.

—Uh-uh, granny, our otter's tail is missing!

—Stop teasing me!

—It's true, granny, it's true.

And Nyaa did not know of any of this, she sat there spinning yarn. The mice asked her:

—Where is your bag?

—What do you want it for?

The mice threw themselves at her, grabbed Nyaa's bag, and took out from it their dog's tail:

—Granny, here's our dog's tail! She stole it!

—You've concocted this! —Nyaa said.

All of them shouted at her:

—Thief!

And Nyaa said:

—Why would I have a dog's tail, why would I keep such tails?

The mice scolded her anyway. Then their brother came in. They began to complain to him. He became angry and threw Nyaa out of the house. She went wherever her eyes took her. And the children

---

[49] *Kimchiga* — a small wild potato, which was collected with a sharp stick (i.e. a *tychka* [digging stick]). With this stick the women probe the ground in order to discover the "storehouses of the mice" in which the mice put *kimchiga* for future use. In one such storehouse there may be up to half-a-bucket of tubers. Such a mode of collecting made for effective removal of the tubers from beneath the separate bushes.

[50] *Markasha* — an edible root with a tart taste.

remained in the house. They cried day and night, they wanted their mother. Again the mice started to grumble:

—They cry day and night!

Their brother came in. The mice started complaining to him and again they made him angry. So he threw out the children too. The little children went, they did not know where. Then they came upon a little house, which was in bad shape.

—Little sister, let's live here.

They lived there and their mother looked at them from the garret. In the morning the children awakened, went to the courtyard to catch flies. They fed themselves with flies. And their mother was looking at them from the garret and she cried. Her tears fell on the children. The little boy said:

—Sister dear, it's raining! Let's go in the house!

Much time went by. Nyaa lay down and slept as if forever. And the little children had grown and began to run everywhere to filch a meal. They even stole something from Kutkh. Kutkh said:

—Who's making it a habit to steal things from us! When I learn who it is, I'll not hang him, I'll personally choke him to death.

And the little children walked and walked—and they found their mother.

—What is this? —they asked each other.

Then they started looking her over.

—The mouth—that will be the kettle, the ears—the ovens; it'll be possible to make a fire in them, and here are the nostrils—smoke will come out of them.

Then they saw her eyes.

—We can take out these little lakes and make little bowls out of them.

Again they went to filch something from Kutkh. Kutkh came out and chased after them. They ran away but he saw where their traces led. Suddenly he saw smoke. He went right in the direction of it. He saw Nyaa lying there. On one side of her was the boy, on the other, the girl. They made a fire in each of Nyaa's ears; they were roasting flies. Kutkh yelled out:

—Why are you playing rough tricks here?

The little ones became frightened and ran off. Kutkh went home and said to his wife:

—Miti! I'm going to tell you about something very bad.

—Well, what's wrong, Kutkh?

—Our Nyaa is lying over there dead. And some kind of little children are taunting her, they lit fires in her ears.

—What are you talking about, Kutkh? Now I'm going to run over to the old woman, the shamaness.

The old shamaness sat there twisting thread [yarn]. And the thread became all knotted, very knotted.

—Eh, something's happened. Who is thinking of me? No doubt Kutkh has again made a mess of something.

Miti came in:

—Hello, granny.

—Every time you come to me it means that something happened.

—Granny, some misfortune has happened to my Nyaa.

—Well, let's go and see.

They got there. Nyaa was lying with her arms and legs spread out.

—E-eh, very well, I'll try, —the old woman said.

She took a bit of water and talked to her:

—Nyaa, Nyaa, forget your past miserable life!

She sprinkled a little of the water on Nyaa. They looked—and Nyaa yawned.

—Now, Nyaa! What's with you? That's enough of sleep; get up! Come back to life!

Nyaa got up. Granny told her:

—It's because of your father that you've gotten to be so miserable. But you'll never have to live like that again. It was decided for you beforehand. Hey, Unyanyaskh, bring her little children here!

They brought the children to her.

—Now we shall go to Kutkh.

They arrived at Kutkh's. Kutkh was happy; Nyaa had returned. But with his grandchildren he was very angry:

—They look very much like mice. Their snouts are just like those of mice. Nyaa, you live here, but I don't need them.

What kind of mother would throw out her children? It would hurt her soul so! Nyaa said:

—I'm not going to throw out my children, no matter how they look! It is you who made such a miserable life for me. It'll be better if you don't ever see me again.

And Nyaa disappeared to somewhere. Miti became very angry with Kutkh. She became angry for good. She never did anything for him and she stopped preparing his meals.

67. The Children of Kutkh and the Wolf Family

Recorded in 1910-1911 in Khayruzovo *rayon* of Kamchatka *oblast* by W. Jochelson. Published in *Kamchadal Texts*, Worth 1961, no. K2. p. 10. Translated from the Itelmen language into Russian by A. Volodin. The subject matter of this tale is analogous to the Koryak tale no. 25 in this edition "How Rera Lost Her Bear-Bridegroom" [*Kak Rera poteryala zhenikha-medvedya*], in which in place of wolves, the bears are the actors. In the text that follows the double transformation of the principals is described: the wolf-suitors in pursuit of Kutkh's daughters change into bears, and from the bears slaughtered by the sons of Kutkh, Ememkut and Sisilkhan, there arise suitors in human form. In place of the Koryak Rera (the daughter of Kuykynnyaku), here we have Sirim (the daughter of Kutkh). The names of the other children of Kutkh and Kuykynnyaku have only a phonetic differentiation. In this tale, as in the Koryak variant, the motif of the good, sensible, resourceful Sinanevt, and the evil, obstinate Sirim, is preserved.

Long ago there lived Kutkh. He had two sons, Ememkut and Sisilkhan, and the daughters Sinanevt and Sirim. One day Ememkut began to make arrows in the courtyard. He told Sinanevt:

—I'm going to make arrows; don't look at me!

Sinanevt looked at Ememkut. Promptly, all of the arrows broke. Ememkut became very angry with Sinanevt. He went in the house, put Sinanevt's hand on a stone, and hit it with his fist, breaking the bones of her hand. Sinanevt cried and went out to the forest. She found a small lake, sat on its shore, and cried. And at that lake there lived the old mother of wolves.
Sinanevt cried and the granddaughter of the old one said:

—Granny, it's raining!

—Go and bring the bedding inside before it gets wet through!

The granddaughter went out to the courtyard and saw a beautiful girl there. She returned to the house and told her grandmother:

—It's not raining, there is a beautiful girl crying!

Grandmother told her:

—Let her come in here!

The granddaughter went out and said:

—They said for you to come in!

Sinanevt went in and sat down. The old one told her granddaughter:

—Feed her salmon *yukola* and give her a cup of blubber!

The granddaughter brought in a batch of *yukola* and a cup of blubber. The old one said:

—When you are eating, blink!

Sinanevt ate a little, blinked, and put her broken hand in the cup.

—Ay, the blubber spilled!

Her broken hand healed right away. Sinanevt prepared to go further on. The old one instructed her:

—Whatever you find, don't ever take it. If you find boots, put arrows on them. If you find tendons, spin them into thread. Then hang it up.

Sinanevt started out. On the path she came across a *balagan*. In it meat and blubber were hanging. She walked past it. She went farther and saw boots. She put arrows on them. She walked farther. She saw tendons, spun them into thread and hung it up right there. She went farther and saw a small house. The old wolf's sister came out of it. She grabbed Sinanevt with her teeth, threw her up in the air, then cought her with her teeth. She stopped throwing her and asked:

—My playmate. I didn't hurt you, did I?

—No, you didn't hurt me!

—I'm always so happy.

She fed Sinanevt. She then gave her boots to repair. Sinanevt repaired them very nicely. The wolf's sister told her:

—My dear friend, I'm going to hide you! I have brothers; they'll come any minute.

She hid Sinanevt. The brothers arrived and started sniffing.

—It smells like a man, sister!

—There's no man around here. You walk all around and so there's a smell of man that stays in your nostrils. Then you come home and you sniff it here.

—You're right, sister!

The old wolf told her younger brother to lie down to sleep at the edge:

—Don't lie down in the middle next to your older brothers.

They were getting ready to go to sleep. The younger brother said:

—I'm going to sleep in the middle!

—Why do you want to sleep in the middle?

—You jostle so much during the night!

The younger brother lay down at the edge. All fell asleep. The girl-she-wolf got up during the night and awakened Sinanevt:

—Hey, playmate, get up and run home fast!

Sinanevt got up and promptly started running home. And the she-wolf woke up her younger brother, turned him into a bear and told him:

—Now, you catch up with Sinanevt!

The younger brother started running after Sinanevt. She looked back when she was fairly close to her house; she saw the bear, and she yelled out:

—Ememkut, come out quickly, a bear is chasing me!

Ememkut came out, shot at the bear and killed him on the spot. They started to dress the bear, cut open his belly and out of it walked a nice lad, handsome and stately. He promptly married Sinanevt. They began to live well.

They gave all of the bear meat to Sisilkhan. Then Sisilkhan also went to the courtyard to begin making arrows. Sisilkhan said:

—You, Sirim, don't you look at me!

But Sirim looked at him and all of the arrows broke. Sisilkhan became angry, went in the house and broke Sirim's hand bones. Sirim began to cry and yelled out:

—Oy, oy, it hurts, he broke my hand!

She went out of the house and took the same path as Sinanevt did. She came to the small lake, sat on its shore and began to cry. The old she-wolf said to her granddaughter:

—It's raining!

—Go out and take the bedding in; it's going to get wet!

The granddaughter went to the courtyard and saw an ugly girl. She went back and told her grandmother:

—There's an ugly girl crying!

—Tell her to come in!

The old she-wolf's granddaughter went out and said:

—They told me that you could come in!

Sirim promptly went in and sat down. They began to feed her. The old she-wolf told her:

—When you eat the *yukola* and the blubber, blink your eyes!

Sirim began to eat, blinked her eyes, and put her hand in the cup. The hand healed. Sirim went on farther right away. She did not ask permission to leave; she did not inquire about anything. She walked and there was a *balagan* on the path. In it there hung meat and blubber. She ate all of it, and took the tendons and boots with her. Finally she came to the little house. A she-wolf came out of it. She began to throw Sirim in the air with her teeth and then she caught her with her teeth. Finally she stopped throwing her and asked:

—My playmate, did I hurt you?

Sirim told her:

—You sure did!

The she-wolf began to feed Sirim. They emptied the plate. The girl told her to cook more meat. Sirim started to cook. And the girl said:

—I'm going out for a little while; you keep cooking!

She had decided to secretly look at Sirim. She went out and looked through a little hole in the wall. Sirim took out the meat and ate it.

—Eh, the poor girl, —said the she-wolf.

She went in the house and told Sirim to repair the boots. Sirim started to repair the boots but she did a poor job. Then she said:

—Playmate, hide me, I'm afraid of your brothers!

—It's not necessary to hide you!

And Sirim wanted to get married. The she-wolf hid her. Her brothers arrived and again they began to sniff:

—What smells here like a man?

—There's no man here!

The wolves began to dress and saw that the boots were badly repaired. Then they lay down and fell asleep. During the night the she-wolf awakened Sirim:

—Now, get up, run home, and I'll wake up mine and they'll chase after you!

Sirim got up and ran off. The she-wolf woke up her brothers:

—Do any of you want to chase after the ugly girl?

Nobody wanted to. They released their shaggy dog.

The dog chased after Sirim. Not far from her house Sirim saw that a dog was chasing her. She yelled out:

—Hey, Sisilkhan, come out fast, a shaggy dog is chasing me!

Sisilkhan came out, shot, and killed the dog on the spot. Sirim was happy. They started to clean the dog. Sirim said:

—Careful now, my bridegroom is in there; don't hurt him.

They cut open the dog's belly. Nobody was in it. Sisilkhan became angry and threw Sirim into the forest. And there she withered.

68. Kutkh is Sewing

Narrated in 1929 by an inhabitant of Utkholok village in Tigilsky *rayon*, M. Zayev. Recorded and translated into Russian by E. Orlova. In the folklore of all of the peoples of Chukotka and Kamchatka the magical tale about stealing by harmful beings of people and mice is widespread. A giant spirit-*kele*, a wicked old man, the cannibalistic Mayyrakhlak, and others represent the harmful beings. In the majority of Itelmen variants on this theme, the thief is Kutkh. Only in one of the Itelmen tales (no. 85 of this edition), the role of the thief is acted by "a long-legged little old man."

Kutkh lived in his house. He sewed all the time. One day Kutkh was sitting next to a window. He was sewing fur breeches for himself.

Suddenly somehow the light was blocked. Kutkh did not look at the window. He thought: "What could be blocking the light. No doubt it is my nose. I'll have to cut it off."

He cut his nose off and once more began to sew. Again something blocked the light. "It's become dark outside again. Could it be that my cheeks are blocking the light? I'll have to cut them off!"

So Kutkh cut his cheeks off. He sat there and sewed. He hacked up his entire face: he cut off his nose, cheeks, lips, eyebrows, and eyelashes. Kutkh's face was burning with pain. It hurt so much that he began to groan. Then he looked at the window and saw that the mice were sledding. He said:

—So it's you who darkened the light here. And because of you I've marred my whole face.

Kutkh took his breeches and went out. He went to the mice and said:

—My grandchildren, are you sledding here, below my window?

The mice came to the window and Kutkh stretched out, opened the breeches and said:

—Look here, grandchildren! Slide into the breeches, sledding is so good in there!

The mice told him:

—We're not going to slide in your breeches because you will capture us!

Kutkh began to talk to them affectionately. He convinced them and they slid directly into the breeches.

As soon as the mice were in the breeches, Kutkh tied them and went to the forest. He arrived there and started to look for the best tree. Finally he found one.

Kutkh said to the tree:

—Tree, tree, bend down! Tree, tree, bend down! Tree, tree, bend down!

The tree bent down. Kutkh hung the breeches on its very top and again said to the tree:

—Tree, tree, straighten up! Tree, tree, straighten up! Tree, tree, straighten up!

The tree straightened itself up and Kutkh went home.

And the mice yelled out so loud that a vixen heard them and went in the direction of their voices. She came to the tree and asked:

—What are you mice doing up there?

The mice told her:

—Kutkh hung us up here!

—How did he hang you at the very top?

—He said: "Tree, tree, bend down! Tree, tree, bend down!" And the tree did bend down.

The vixen said the same words and the tree bent down. The vixen took down the breeches, untied them, and let out the mice. Only a very small mouse had suffocated, but all the others came out. The vixen told the mice to gather birch bark and to put it in the breeches. The mice gathered birch bark and filled the breeches with it. They put the dead little mouse on top and hung the breeches again on top of the tree.

The vixen asked of the mice:

—What did Kutkh say for the tree to straighten up?

The mice told her:

—Kutkh said: "Tree, tree, straighten up! Tree, tree, straighten up!"

The vixen said the same words. The tree straightened itself and the mice and the vixen went to the vixen's house.

The vixen told the mice to strip bark of an alder tree and prepare with it red water that looked like blood.

On the third day Kutkh went to take down from the tree the captured mice. He arrived and commanded the tree to bend down. The tree immediately bent down.

Kutkh untied the breeches from the tree and went to the side. He sat down. He closed his eyes tight, tucked up his sleeves, ground his teeth, opened the breeches and put his hand in. He grasped the little mouse, didn't look at it, shoved it into his mouth and ate it.

Kutkh uttered:

—Ah, how tasty! Uh-uh!

And right away he put his hand in the breeches again. He tried to find other mice. He found nothing; there was only birch bark in the breeches.

Kutkh became very angry. He thought: "Probably that thieving vixen did this! Now I'm going to go to her! I'll kill her for this."

Kutkh went to the vixen's house. He arrived there. And the vixen was very sick. She was groaning loudly.

Kutkh told her:

—It is probably you who stole my fermented meal!

The vixen said:

—Oy, godfather of my child, you've thought of me by mistake. I've been sick for several days now. Look over there; I'm also passing [urinating] blood and you're saying that I stole your meal. You, godfather of my child, are good and nice! Will you empty that basin in the river!

Kutkh was sorry for the vixen; he took the basin and started to go to empty it.

And the vixen called after him:

—Only, godfather of my child, don't look back. If you do, something very bad will happen!

As he walked, Kutkh thought: "Why did the vixen tell me not to look back? I'll turn around anyway!"

Kutkh looked back. He saw a beautiful rowan tree. He thought: "When I go back, I'll pick some rowan berries for the vixen."

He went on farther. He came to the river and began to empty the basin in it. The vixen stealthily sneaked up behind him and pushed Kutkh in the river. Kutkh drowned.

69. Kutkh and the Mice

Narrated in 1964 by an inhabitant of Kovrai village in Tigilsky *rayon*, P. Shadrin, age 69. Recorded and translated into Russian by N. Starkova. [Compare with Menovshchikov 1974, nos. 38, 196; Dolitsky and Michael 2000, no. 38 and no. 85 of this edition, and Jochelson 1908, nos. 88, 130]. Tales about a simpleton who jumps in an ice-hole after his own image, which he thinks is a woman, are widespread also among the Evens and other small groups of native peoples in the Russian Far East. [Compare with *Evenskiy folklor*, Magadan 1958, pp. 73-75; Jochelson 1908, no. 130 (Kuykynnyaku jumps after his image into a river and dies)].

Kutkh and Ememkut lived with their wives. They lived in a house. One day Kutkh said:

—I'm going to go and see how my grandchildren mice are doing!

He arrived at his grandchildren's place and was very pleased. The grandchildren called out:

—Taste our cooking, taste our *sarana*!

The grandchildren prepared *sarana* and *kemchuga*. Kutkh finished eating and said:

—And now, my granddaughters, catch the lice in my hair and kill them.

Kutkh said this and promptly fell asleep. And the mice took the bag with his belongings and sewed it on his back just below his spine. Kutkh awakened and said:

—Now, granddaughters, it's time for me to go home.

He walked, and he needed to relieve himself, and he relieved himself into the bag with his belongings. He went on and all he time there was a stench behind him. Kutkh did not know that it was from his own droppings that the stench came.

He approached the house and called out to Miti:

—The Koryaks are after me!

Miti came out, looked around—there was nobody there. She went in the house and asked of her husband:

—What is it that makes such a stench?

Promptly she discovered the bag with the droppings.

Kutkh said:

—Tomorrow I'll kill all the mice that made a laughing stock out of me!

He lay down to sleep, woke up, and again went to the mice. Miti told him:

—See to it that they don't make a laughing stock out of you again!

He walked to his grandchildren. The mice saw him and cried out:

—Taste our food, taste our *sarana*!

But Kutkh said:

—Just the same I'll kill all of you afterwards!

The granddaughters cooked the food, and fed it to Kutkh. Kutkh finished eating and the mice again began to seek lice in his head hair. Kutkh went into a deep sleep right away. And the mice took something red and sewed it over his eyes. Kutkh awakened, went home, and saw that his house was all red. He came to the house and yelled out:

—Oy, Miti, the house is on fire!

Miti looked at Kutkh and saw that there was something red sewn to his eyelids. Miti told him:

—It's because of where you go! And the mice played their tricks again!

Kutkh went to the grandchildren again. Miti called out after him:

—Don't go there, they're going to make fun of you again.

Kutkh told her:

—I'll kill all of them with the plowshare [cleaning] stick!

He came to the grandchildren. They said to him:

—Taste our food, taste the *sarana*!

Kutkh said:

—Very well, my granddaughters, feed me.

162

They put berries in front of him. Kutkh finished eating and became sleepy. He said:

—I'm going to lie down and sleep a little!

Kutkh fell asleep and the mice reddened his face with something. Kutkh awakened and went home. He arrived there and he said:

—Wait Miti, I'll go and get some water!

He went to the ice-hole, bent over it, saw his face in the water and exclaimed:

—It seems that some beautiful girl lives there! Right now I'll bring her a stone pestle, a wooden pestle and a trough.

He brought the trough, sat it on the water and said:

—Take it!

The girl did not take the trough. Kutkh thought: "She probably has a trough."

Then he placed the wooden pestle in the ice-hole. Again he said:

—Here, take it!

And the pestle floated on the water, and again nobody took it. Kutkh thought: "No doubt she has a wooden pestle too." Then he shoved the stone pestle in the water. It went to the bottom right away. Kutkh said:

—She doesn't have one since she took it so quickly!

Then he jumped in the ice-hole saying:

—Look, take me!

And he went under the ice. He called and called. And so he drowned.

70. Sinanevt and the Little Bear

Recorded in 1910-1911 in Khayruzovo *rayon* in Kamchatsky *oblast* by W. Jochelson. Published in *Kamchadal Texts*, Worth 1961, no. K2. p. 19. Translated from the Itelmen language into Russian by A. Volodin. In this tale the mythical powers of transformation and creation are possessed not only by Kutkh, who compels Miti to give birth to a bear, but also by his children—his daughter Sinanevt and son-bear who adopt a part of their father's magical abilities.

Once there lived Kutkh with his wife Miti. They had children: Ememkut and Sinanevt. Ememkut used to go hunting throughout the fall. Kutkh became bored and started to collect firewood. One day he said:

—Miti, I'm going after firewood, and you, give birth to a little bear!

—Eh, Kutkh, how stupid can you get; what are you blabbing about now!

Kutkh went after the firewood. And Miti gave birth to a little bear just then. She saw it and became frightened. She covered the bear. Kutkh came back and said:

—Uh, I'm tired. Just take this, Miti, this bundle of firewood!

—You carry the wood, Kutkh! I've already given birth to a bear, a terrible one!

They lived on. The little bear grew up. At all times he wanted to suckle her breast and he howled like a bear. Kutkh and Miti became frightened. Kutkh said:

—Miti, let's get away from here when the children fall asleep; things are so strange here!

And the bear slept alongside Sinanevt. He slept very soundly. Kutkh and Miti ran off. They abandoned their children. The children awakened and saw that their father and mother had gone away somewhere. Sinanevt lived on and brought up her brother. Her brother grew up. He became a big bear. He told her:

—Well sister, let's go somewhere; we'll look for a river with fish in it!

They gathered things and left. In places where there were rapids, the brother carried his sister over on his back. Finally they found a river with fish in it. They started to live there. They stocked up *yukola*. The bear made a den and they stored all of the *yukola* in it. The bear crawled in the den and said:

—Sinanevt, I'm going to go to sleep. Don't be afraid of me! In the winter, in the middle of the month, I'm going to turn over on my other side, and I'm going to yell. Don't be afraid. After the ice crusts, the snow people will come; they will shoot at me and kill me. They'll come in the den, but they won't be able to pull me out: I'll become very heavy. Then you grab my ears and pull me outside. They will try to disembowel me. Their knives will break right away. Then you cut me up and hang my head on a tree. And when you're about to be married, don't eat my flesh; don't eat even the smallest piece. If you eat a piece, you'll forget me right away [you'll kill me].

They began to live in the den. The bear went into deep sleep. Sinanevt ate the *yokula* all the time by herself. Even if she just looked at her sleeping brother, she began to cry. So, in this way Sinanevt spent the winter. During the winter, in the middle of the month, the bear howled and began to turn from side to side. Sinanevt was frightened. When a crust of ice formed on the snow many people came. They began to shoot and they killed the bear. They went in the den and couldn't pull him out. Then Sinanevt grasped his ears and pulled him out. They began to disembowel the bear. Everybody's knife broke. They did not know how to dress the bear. Sinanevt cut up the bear all by herself and hung his head on a tree. She told them:

—Don't you touch that head!

Sinanevt got married. They took her to her husband's home. They celebrated the wedding and cooked bear meat. Then Kutkh, and Miti, and Ememkut arrived. They began to eat. Kutkh said:

—Eh, if Sinanevt were alive, she would also want to marry!

But Sinanevt did not reveal herself to her father and mother. And she did not eat the bear meat. All were calling out to her:

—Eat at least a small piece!

Sinanevt could not hold back and she ate a small piece. She killed her brother immediately. They began to live on. After some time Sinanevt suddenly remembered her brother and she said:

—I'm going to take a short walk!

She walked and she found that tree. And the head had already fallen to the ground. She lifted it and blew on it and suddenly a handsome lad was standing next to her. He said:

—Sister, you've killed me! You know I forbade you to eat my meat!

They went home. Kutkh recognized his children and was very happy. The children said:

— And you, father and mother, had ran away from us!

They began to live well and in good cheer.

71. The Wolf and Sinanevt

Narrated in 1965 by an inhabitant of Tigil village, T. Bragina, age 59. Recorded and translated into Russian by N. Starkova.

Kutkh and Miti lived together. Kutkh was very hungry and he said:

—Miti, make some *tolkusha*!

—From what can I make *tolkusha* for you?

—Long ago when I was young, I killed a seal. What did you do with its blubber?

—It's gone long ago!

—Then when I was still young, I killed a big wild deer. What did you do with its fat?

— I've saved it!

Kutkh politely asked Miti to prepare *tolkusha*, but Miti became lazy and invited Sinanevt:

—Come over to our place and make *tolkusha*. Kutkh is very hungry.

Sinanevt began to make *tolkusha* from the very old, overly old rancid fat. She breathed in the noxious smell, fell asleep and died.

Kutkh and Miti saw that Sinanevt had died. Kutkh became very frightened and said:

—Miti, let's run away from here!

They ran off and Sinanevt was left in the house—dead.

A wolf passed by and he thought: "Why did Kutkh stop living in his house? I'll go there and look." He went in and saw nobody. Only Sinanevt sat there, bent over the trough. Then the wolf said to himself:

—I'm going to eat that girl. Really, I'm not going to eat her here, I'll carry her over to that mountain.

He dragged her to the mountain, he got there and thought: "Should I eat her here in the lowland? I better drag her higher." He dragged her up the mountain, sat down and began to look all around. He thought: "It's necessary to look to see if anybody is looking at us." As he was looking to the sides, Sinanevt rolled down the mountain, became alive and sat down. The wolf saw that Sinanevt was alive. He said:

—I'll carry her to my house and I'll marry her. And he brought her home.

Sinanevt became very frightened—there were so many wolves around! She thought to herself: "They're going to tear me to pieces now!" Night arrived. Sinanevt became even more afraid.

Ememkut returned from hunting. He went in and saw that nobody was home. He saw the traces of the wolf and followed them. He came to the wolf's house and saw his sister. He thought: "How could this be? Then he spotted an old wolf, killed him, removed his fur hide and put it on. He then climbed out the mountain and called out:

—Children, carry me down, I can't walk!

The wolves took him below and carried him in the house. He saw Sinanevt and asked:

—Where did you get this girl?

The biggest wolf answered:

—I've found her and brought her here!

—Let her lie next to me to sleep, I'm the oldest one here!

Sinanevt became even more frightened and thought: "Do I really have to sleep with that decrepit, terrible wolf?"

As soon as they lay down Ememkut whispered:

—Don't be afraid, it is I, Ememkut! Let's run away from here!

And they ran away. They ran, they had already come far when suddenly they heard the wolves catching up to them. Ememkut threw a piece of flint in their direction—it burst into large flames. While the wolves were going around the fire, Ememkut and Sinanevt ran farther yet. And again the wolves were about to overtake them. Then Ememkut spat and a very large river started to flow. It was difficult for the wolves to cross the river. Again Ememkut and Sinanevt ran farther.

It was not very much farther to the village but again the wolves were catching up with them. Then Sinanevt threw her comb at them. A wall-like dense forest rose up behind them. As the wolves strayed in the forest, the brother and sister reached their house. And in anger the wolves tore each other into shreds.

72. Ememkut, Chichkimchichan and Porkamtalkhan

Recorded in 1910-1911 in Khayruzovo *rayon* of Kamchatka *oblast* by W. Jochelson. Published in *Kamchadal Texts*, Worth 1961, no. K2. 25. Translated from the Itelmen language into Russian by A. Volodin.

Long ago there lived Kutkh with his wife Miti. They had children, Ememkut and Sinanevt. Ememkut went hunting and killed many animals. Chichkimchichan, who was already married, asked for Sinanevt in marriage. Kutkh not knowing that Chichkimchichan was married accepted him and promised to give him Sinanevt in marriage.

Chichkimchichan invited Ememkut to hunt with him. Ememkut did not want to go with Chichkimchichan; he wanted to hunt alone. Chichkimchichan went home. At Ememkut's he took meat and brought it to his wife. He stayed a while at his house, to seem as if he was hunting, ate the meat, and again went to Kutkh's house. He said:

—Uh, I'm tired! I can't kill animals in any way!

Chichkimchichan took his boots off:

—Here, Sinanevt, dry the boots!

Sinanevt hung up the boots. Soon Ememkut returned with a good number of killed animals. Chichkimchichan said:

—And yet I can't kill any animals at all!

Ememkut went hunting again. And Chichkimchichan went to his own house. And again he brought Ememkut's meat to his wife. Again he stayed for a while. And Sinanevt went to the seashore to gather edible grasses and plants. Suddenly she heard somebody singing not far away. It was Porkamtalkhan floating to the sea in a small kayak. Sinanevt listened to him; he sang beautifully. She became pregnant right away. From one song only, Sinanevt became pregnant!

She came home. Miti told her:

—Sinanevt, it seems to me that you are pregnant!

—I'm not pregnant, I haven't lived with anybody; I can't understand it myself!

Then Porkamtalkhan came to them. He was a very handsome fellow. He married Sinanevt at once. Ememkut began to hunt with his brother-in-law, earning a living with the animals. They lived well. Chichkimchichan came again and said:

—Uh, again I can't kill anything!

Promptly he took his boots off.

—Here, Sinanevt, dry my boots!

Sinanevt told him:

—Chichkimchichan, you hang them yourself!

—Why are you angry Sinanevt? I haven't killed anything and you're cross with me!

Sinanevt slapped the child and the child cried a little. Chichkimchichan promptly said:

—Hey, Sinanevt, you've already given birth. My child has been born and all the same you're angry with me!

Then Porkamtalkhan came. Chichkimchichan looked and said:

—Sinanevt is already married! Sinanevt, let me help you to take the night pot outside!

Sinaevt said:

—I can cope very well by myself.

Porkamtalkhan got ready to go to his house. All started out: Kutkh, Miti and Ememkut. Chichkimchichan also intended to go and he tied up his bundle. They started to load the boat. They finished loading. They tossed Chichkimchichan's bundle into the grass. Ememkut asked:

—And where is your bundle, Chichkimchichan?

—I thought it was right here, — Chichkimchichan said. —But I must have left it in the house. I'll run and get it; wait for me!

He ran quickly into the house. And the others started off right away. Chichkimchichan returned and saw that they had left. He cried and said:

—If I had only known, I would have killed all of you!

Chichkimchichan went home. He got there and beat up his wife thoroughly. He said:

—Because of you I've lost a beautiful woman!

Porkamtalkhan came home. His father and mother were happy. They received Kutkh well. They lived a prosperous and merry life.

73. Ememkut, Kotkhanamtalkhan and the Cannibals

Recorded in 1910-1911 in Khayruzovo *rayon* in Kamchatka *oblast* by W. Jochelson. Published in *Kamchadal Texts*, Worth 1961, no. K2. 4. Translated from the Itelmen language into Russian by A. Volodin. In this tale, the son of Kutkh, the giant hunter Ememkut, uses his magical forces in fighting evil beings.

Long ago there lived Kutkh with his wife Miti. There were children—Ememkut and Kotkhanamtalkhan. They went to the forest to hunt animals. One day Kutkh thought and thought and then commanded his sons to stay home:

—My little children stay home; don't go hunting.

Ememkut said:

—If it's to be your way, father, won't we have to feed you with yesterday's food?

They went hunting. They walked all day and found nothing. They walked until it got dark. They came home in darkness. The next day they went hunting again. They saw two paths. Kotkhanamtalkhan stopped and waited for his older brother. Ememkut came up. Kotkhamantalkhan said:

—Well, my older brother, which path should we take?

Ememkut said:

—Why can't we kill any animals? Let's take the left path!

They walked and passed by hills. And on one of the high hills there lived a family of cannibals. The cannibals said:

—Ah, Kutkh's children came by themselves!

They started to sharpen their knives right away.

Ememkut said:

—Maybe you could eat us tomorrow? It would be better tomorrow morning when we get up!

The cannibals said:

—All right, we'll eat you tomorrow!

Ememkut was very smart; he knew everything. Kutkh's sons lay down to sleep. Ememkut told the cannibals:

—Don't you worry; we're in your hands, we're going nowhere!

The cannibals tied their dog Lala to the door. They lay down next to the door and fell asleep. But Kutkh's sons did not sleep. Ememkut had lulled the cannibals to sleep. When they fell asleep they could not hear anything. During the night Kutkh's sons got up. Ememkut told his younger brother:

—Well Kotkhanamtalkhan, we'll go now! You go first, but carefully, don't step on the dog Lala's ears!

Kotkhanamtalkhan jumped outside without touching the dog's ears. Ememkut followed him. He trod on all of the cannibals. He trampled them but they did not waken. He trod on the dog's ears, but the dog kept sleeping; the cannibals did not waken. He went out to the courtyard and said:

—Well, let's go home!

They started for home and always looked back. They stopped half way home. But the cannibals had awakened and heard the dog Lala tearing at the leash. They got up right away and saw that Kutkh's sons were not there. The cannibals said:

—Ah, Kutkh's sons are very smart; they know everything! Well, we too know everything! Hey, let the dog Lala loose. She'll catch up with Kutkh's children and hold them and we'll follow her traces. And take your knives with you!

They unleashed the dog Lala and she promptly followed the traces of Kutkh's children. With her snout to the ground, her tongue twirling from side to side, froth formed on her tongue. She almost caught up to Kutkh's sons; they already came into sight! Ememkut said:

—We'll have to ambush her on the path. We'll go back and hide along the path; you on one side, I on the other.

They hid and held their spears at ready. Ememkut told his younger brother:

170

—See to it that she doesn't pass by, hit her as soon as possible!

The dog Lala ran up to the place where the brothers were hiding. They immediately thrust the spears into her from both sides, killing her. They cut off her head, hung it with the muzzle facing the direction of the cannibals, ripped open her belly and let the guts fall out. They left the dog Lala there and went home. The family of the cannibals came and saw what Kutkh's sons had done. The cannibals said:

—Ah you, Kutkh's children, have already killed her!

They came closer and saw the head of their dog Lala hanging there. They said:

—Yes, Kutkh's children are very smart; they know it all! They killed our dog. And we hoped for so much from her.

The cannibals turned back. Kutkh's children came close to their house. They stopped and did not enter the house. Miti saw the children and said to here husband:

—Kutkh, the children are here but they are not coming in the house. They're standing in the courtyard.

Kutkh immediately understood what the matter was and he said:

—Something has happened to them!

Kutkh went out to the courtyard and lit a fire on each side of the path. His sons came on and walked through the fire. They began to live anew and were merry. They didn't need anything else.

74. Ememkut, Maroklnavt and the Geese

Recorded in 1910-1911 in Khayruzovo *rayon*, Kamchatka *oblast* by W. Jochelson. Published in *Kamchadal Texts*, Worth 1961, no. K1. p. 24. Translated from the Itelmen language into Russian by A. Volodin. In this tale the themes of magic, reincarnation, and a marital union of a woman and bird are intertwined in a miraculous fashion. The harmful old woman Kamankhnavt in this tale is somewhat similar to the harmful rogue of Eskimo and Chukchi tales who in the form of a little old woman appears as an antagonist of the hero.

Long ago there lived Kutkh with his wife Miti. Ememkut, Kotkhanamtalkhan, Sisilkhan, Sinanevt, and Sirim were their children. For the entire fall Ememkut and Kotkhanamtalkhan went along a flowing river. They began to hunt for all kinds of animals. Ememkut could not hunt down a single animal. He went again and again to hunt but he never was able to kill anything. Ememkut became weak; he was lying down all the time. Then again they went hunting. Ememkut said:

—Kotkhanamtalkhan, let's hunt apart!

They left singly. Ememkut went to the forest. In the depth of the forest he found many edible plants of bear's garlic. He pulled them out, with the roots, took them to the low ridge surrounding the house and put them in the *balagan* so that they could make soup later on. Kotkhanamtalkhan came in; he had not gotten anything. Ememkut told him:

—Light a fire.

Kotkhanamtalkhan did so. Ememkut said to him:

—Up there on the ridge I've put some bear's garlic plants in the *balagan*. Go and get them.

Kotkhanamtalkhan went and climbed to the *balagan*. There he saw the beautiful girl Maroklnavt combing her hair. There were no bear's garlic plants. He was embarrassed by the girl, went back immediately and said:

—Ememkut, I could not find the garlic. The only one there was a nice girl combing her hair. She is very beautiful!

Promptly Ememkut went out to the courtyard. He went to the *balagan*, climbed up and saw a beautiful girl. He married her right off. Maroklnavt gave birth right away.

Kotkhanamtalkhan became uneasy. He went home. He came home. Kotkhanamtalkhan told his father and mother:

—Ememkut got married to the beautiful girl Maroklnavt.

Sirim began to tell everybody:

—Ememkut got married. His bride Maroklnavt is very beautiful; Kotkhanamtalkhan said so.

Ememkut began to live there. At one time Maroklnavt had a bad dream. She didn't want her husband to go hunting. She told him:

—Ememkut, I've had a bad dream—don't go hunting!

Ememkut said:

—I'll not go far. Are you going to eat yesterday's already eaten food?

—All right then, go!

Ememkut left. As soon as he left, the old woman Kamankhnavt[51] came in. Maroklnavt said:

—Sit down, old woman!

I don't want to sit down, —the old woman said, —Maroklnavt, take off your clothes; I'm going to try them on.

Maroklnavt said:

—Old woman, I never undress!

—Take your clothes off!

—I'm not going to; better that I bring you some other clothes!

—The clothes you're wearing, those are the ones I want to try on.

---

[51]Kamankhnavt — an evil old woman-lizard, the negative adversary of Itelmen tales.

They began to fight: the little old woman threw Maroklnavt down. She stripped her and pushed her into the courtyard. She put on Maroklnavt's clothing and tied a cloth around her head. Then she lay down as if she were sick.

Ememkut arrived and saw his wife.

—Hey, what's with you? It seems you've changed!

Kamakhnavt said:

—A while ago I told you not to go hunting; that's why I got sick!

They lay down to sleep. They slept soundly. Maroklnavt came in the house, fed the child, and cried a little. She could not awaken her husband. First she covered him with kisses, then the child. She put the child to sleep and went to the courtyard.

In the morning Kamankhnavt said:

—Ememkut, there's something bad in this house, let's leave it!

They left the house right away; they walked off. But Maroklnavt, when she had been there during the night, took Ememkut's knife. On the way Ememkut's sledge runner broke. Then he saw that his knife was missing and he said:

—Eh, I left my knife in the house!

He ran to the house. He began to search for his knife. Maroklnavt called out:

—Ememkut, your knife is here!

Ememkut said:

—Ah, it's you, Maroklnavt! Your voice sounds like it did before!

Ememkut did not guess that it was his wife. He took the knife and left again. He walked home and reached his father and mother. They met. The local people saw that Ememkut's wife was a bad, wicked woman who made nobody happy. But they all loved the child. And Kamankhnavt seemed to be sick all the time. She bandaged her feet, but when food was offered, she ate it all.

And Maroklnavt started to live by herself. She went away to a warm place. From grass she made herself a parka, boots, and all other clothing. She also built a house. She began to live in it. In the spring geese flew in and said:

—Who has taken our place?

One of the geese promptly married Maroklnavt. They began to live well. Again, Maroklnavt gave birth. In the fall it became cold. The other geese flew away. Maroklnavt's husband also was getting ready. How could he take his wife with him? With a small strap he tied her to his neck. He could not lift her. The goose said to her:

—Maroklnavt, you stay here, winter here. I'm going to fly off; I don't want to freeze and die.

The goose flew off, looked back, and again came back to his wife and cried. He flew off again and left his wife. Maroklnavt began to live well; she lacked nothing. Her son went hunting and brought back little birds.

But one time he killed a young deer. His mother was happy. In the spring the geese flew in again. The son of Ememkut killed the gander, the husband of Maroklnavt. The other geese became angry with Maroklnavt and said:

—Her son killed our companion; let's go and kill Maroklnavt!

They came. Maroklnavt quickly went to the courtyard and crawled in a fur sleeping bag. The geese started to beat on the sleeping bag with their wings. They finished beating on it and said:

—We've killed Maroklnavt!

The geese went away. Maroklnavt again went in the house and started to work. Her son went hunting. He killed a large deer.

Ememkut's son arrived, became angry and said:

—You're driving away all the animals! I'm going to kill you!

—That's not necessary, friend. Come here; let's eat together!

They met and began to eat. They finished eating. The son of Maroklnavt said:

Friend, I'm going to play [mussel]-shells, and you look.

He began to play shells. He showed everything: how Maroklnavt lived before, how she gave birth to the son of Ememkut. The son of Ememkut understood everything immediately. He cried a little and said:

—Are you really my younger brother?

—Yes, true, I'm your younger brother; we have the same mother. Well, let's go to mother!

Then the son of Ememkut said:

—I don't want to!

He was ashamed. His clothing was too tight and too old. He grew up in the same clothes that his mother put on him long ago. All the seams pulled him to his mother!

They started out to their mother's and they arrived there. The son of the goose went in and said to his mother:

—My older brother came here.

—Where is he?

—He stayed in the courtyard.

—Let him come in!

He went out right away and said:

—Older brother, mother says that you should come in!

But he would not come in; he was embarrassed. Maroklnavt came out herself, saw her son, cried a little, led him in the house, took off the breeches, parka, boots—she took off all his clothes and put on him another parka, breeches and boots. He became a handsome lad. They began to live well. Maroklnavt said to her son:

—You, who had killed the goose, go and bring here all of his bones!

He promptly went home to his father's place. He arrived there and asked:

—Kamankhnavt, you ate the goose. Where did you put his bones?

—Over there are his bones!

The boy gathered all of the bones and went to his mother. He gave her all the bones. Maroklnavt took all the bones, blew on them—and promptly a goose appeared. They got ready and went to Ememkut. They arrived there.

They were greeted readily. They were happy. Kamankhnavt became frightened. She said:

—I'm going to the courtyard to urinate!

She wanted to run away but they would not let her. Maroklnavt hit her head with a knife at where her hair parted and she immediately became two women: one side for Ememkut and another for the goose. They prepared a feast, invited everyone, cooked meat and made *tolkusha*. Ememkut heated over the flames of a stone basin; the basin became as red as the fire. Kamankhnavt groaned:

—Oy, oy, I can't stand this anymore; I've got to go to the courtyard!

Ememkut became angry, grasped Kamankhnavt, dragged her to the kitchen [cooking fire] and put her in the heated stone basin. Then he threw her in the courtyard. She was covered with *tolkusha*. Like that she went to her granny. She came to her and said:

—Here's a little bit of *tolkusha* for you!

The old woman said:

—Why for me? Eat it yourself!

Ememkut and the gander started to live well and they were happy.

75. Kamankhnavt

Narrated in 1926 by an inhabitant of Khayryuzovo village in Tigilsky *rayon*, A. Shadrina. Recorded and translated into Russian by E. Orlova.

Two of Kutkh's sons, Ememkut and Kotkhanamtalkhan, went fall hunting while their family stayed with kin in the winter camp. The hunt went well—they saw an animal and they got it. Suddenly misfortune befell them. They walked in the tundra all day but everything ran away from them. It came to the point that in order not to perish from hunger they had to eat "old food."

Ememkut lay down on the sleeping bench and Kotkhanamtalkhan began to cook. The next day they decided to split: one would go to the tundra, the other to the birch forest.

In the birch forest Ememkut found a long bear's garlic plant. He pulled it out with the root to make soup. He brought it home, climbed in the *balagan,* put the plant in a bin, and lay down to sleep. He told his brother to cook soup.

Kotkhanamtalkhan got the firewood and water ready and went for the plant in the *balagan*. He climbed up and entered it. The bear's garlic was not there, but only a girl was sitting there. She sat there combing her hair. He became embarrassed—the girl was very beautiful—and quickly ran away.

His brother asked him:

—Why didn't you bring the bears' garlic? How are you going to make soup?

—There was no bear's garlic. There was a girl sitting in the *balagan* combing her hair. She was beautiful—a pleasure to look at! I was afraid to look at her.

Ememkut heard this, jumped up from the *polog* [sleeping bench] and ran to the *balagan*. He saw Maroklnavt, married her promptly, and right then a son was born.

Kotkhanamtalkhan embarrassed, ran to his father and told him how beautiful his brother's wife was.

Ememkut began to live with his wife. One day in the morning his wife would not let him go hunting:

—I had a bad dream.

—I've made up my mind; I'm going! —Ememkut answered her.

—It's going to be bad, don't go, —his wife begged him.

—Don't be afraid, I'll be hunting nearby.

And he went off.

Kamankhnavt overheard what they said. As soon as Ememkut was out of the door she was already on the way. She came in.

Maroklnavt stood there not saying a word. She became frightened; she knew that something bad was going to happen.

—Well, sit down granny! —Kamankhnavt said.

—I'm not going to sit down!

—Give me your breeches!

—I will not!

They started fighting. Kamankhnavt bested Maroklnavt and took off her clothing. Ememkut's wife became embarrassed because she was naked. She went out, sat in the courtyard and cried. She covered herself with grass.

Kamankhnavt sat on the *polog*, tied a cloth around her head, moaning as if she had a headache.

Ememkut returned from the hunt and did not recognize his wife: she became as black as coal. And Kamankhnavt said to him:

—Why did you go away? You know, I said that things are not going to be right, that I had a bad dream.

Ememkut stayed with his black-as-coal wife-lizard and his real wife sat naked in the courtyard crying, grieving.

Night came. All in the house fell asleep. Maroklnavt came in the house, fed her son and covered him so he'd be warm. She kissed Ememkut and returned to the courtyard. On the way out she took Ememkut's hunting knife and put it on top of the *balagan*.

In the morning Kamankhnavt got up and said to Ememkut:

—Let's get away from here; your house is dirty.

And the poor wife of Ememkut was hiding. She was ashamed; she was naked.

On the way the sled's runner broke. Ememkut wanted to repair it but there was no knife.

—Why did you stop? —asked the evil old woman.

—The runner broke; it has to be repaired. I've forgot to take my knife; I'll go home after it.

The bad old woman-lizard became frightened:

—Wait a bit; it's probably in the bag!

She searched and searched but did not find it.

Ememkut ran home, began to look for his knife but could not find it. Maroklnavt looked through a window and called out:

—The knife is on top over there.

—What happened to you? You're like you were before!

And she could not answer; she could not come out and show herself. She was ashamed because she was naked. She ran from the window and hid. And Ememkut found the knife and went to the sled and the black old woman.

Maroklnavt went in the house and cried. She wiped her face with the child's grass clothing.

Ememkut and Kamankhnavt went home to his father. His parents saw that somebody was arriving; they guessed who it was and came out of the house to see the beautiful wife of their son. They looked and saw that she was as black as coal. Ememkut told them all that had happened.

Maroklnavt, his real wife, prepared for herself bedding of grass, hung it up in a birch grove, made herself clothing of grass and started to live there. In the spring the geese flew in.

—Why have you hung up that bedding in our place?

—I'll go away. I didn't know it was your birch grove.

And she wanted to leave. A gander flew at her, married her and a son-goose was born.

In the fall the geese got ready to fly south. Maroklnavt held onto her husband-gander with a leash but alas, he flew off.

—Let me go, in the spring I'll fly in again! —begged the goose.

She felt sorry and she let him go. She was exhausted. Her son-goose was comforting. He hunted down a fawn here, a wild duck there.

In the spring the geese flew in again. Maroklnavt met her husband-gander again. They started to live together. And their son already was big.

One time the older son of Ememkut, and Maroklnavt, went hunting and killed a gander, the husband of his mother. Kamankhnavt, the evil old woman-lizard ate it, collected its bones and kept them. The geese became angry and decided to kill Maroklnavt.

One day Maroklnavt was sitting and sewing. And near her the spider Sikukechkh was meddling. She threw him off.

—I'm sewing and you're confusing me! —she said.

—Better hide yourself in the sleeping bag and go to the courtyard, —Sikukechkh said.

She listened to him, went to the courtyard, got in the sleeping bag, covered herself from head to toe, lay down and waited. The geese flew in and began to beat her. They thought that they killed her and they flew away. And she returned to the house, sat down and started to sew.

The lad, the son of the gander, became a young man, but he did not wear the same kind of clothing that people did. His clothing was made of grass; he slept on grass bedding. As we know people sleep on deer skins and walk around in parkas!

One day the lad went hunting. At first he decided to go in what he wore at home but then thought things over and put on his best parka that his mother had given him. The son went hunting far away from the house and killed a wild deer. Suddenly he saw a man walking toward him. It seemed that his clothing grew into his body—the same clothing that his mother put on him long ago. This was the elder son of Maroklnavt and Ememkut. His brother-gander invited him:

—Come and eat with me!

—No, I can't, —the other one answered.

—Why not?

They began to talk.

—You have a beautiful parka, but my clothing has grown into my body. He thought he was a stranger.

They began to eat and they talked some more.

—Yes, you are my brother born of the same mother! —said the brother-gander, when he figured it out for himself.

They both cried in happiness. They went together to their mother. One walked boldly, the other in shame; his clothes were so unsightly.

And mother waited for her son for a long time.

—Did you go far? —she asked.

—Yes, far. But I didn't come back alone. My older brother stays in the courtyard; he's ashamed to come in. He's poorly clothed; his clothing is as if it had grown into his body. He wears the same clothing that you put on him.

The mother went in the courtyard, recognized her son and cried:

—Oh, my poor, unhappy boy! You've worn the same clothing that I put on you.

She then took off his grass clothing, put a parka on him, and he became handsome to look at! She fed him and then told him to go home to Kamankhnavt and bring back the bones of her second husband. Her son left.

Kamankhnavt saw him, became frightened and wanted to run away. She said to her husband:

—I'm going to the courtyard.

Ememkut guessed that his real wife was alive. He did not let Kamankhnavt, the evil old woman-lizard, leave the house. He was afraid that she might do some mischief. He gave his son the bones of the gander, sent him to his mother, and told him to tell his mother to come home. The son ran to his mother and gave her the bones of the gander. She blew on them—and there was a live gander.

Maroklnavt parted her hair in the middle, prettied herself and went to her first husband—Ememkut.

Kamankhnavt, seeing a pretty woman coming to the house, tried to break away to the courtyard, but they did not let her go.

Maroklnavt came in Ememkut's house, hit herself on the forehead below the pared hair, and divided in two parts: one part went to the gander the other to Ememkut.

Ememkut sent for the frying pan and heated it red hot. He stripped Kamankhnavt naked, gave her a shove and put her in the red-hot frying pan, and went to the yard to fry the fatty meat.

They were all happy. They began to eat, drink, make merry, and then they lay down to sleep.

And Kamankhnavt fried to death in the pan.

76. Revne

Recorded in 1910-1911 in Kharuzovo *rayon* in Kamchatka *oblast* by W. Jochelson. Published in *Kamchadal Texts*, Worth 1961, no. K2. p. 38. Translated from the Itelmen language into Russian by A. Volodin. In this tale Ememkut appears not as a brother of Sinanevt but as her bridegroom. The daughters of Kutkh, portrayed in Itelmen tales as human beings, enter into marital unions most frequently with animals. This is conditioned by the fact that they themselves were born of animals—the raven Kutkh-Kuykynyaku and the magpie's daughter Miti.

Long ago there lived Kutkh with his wife Miti. Their children were all daughters: Sinanevt, Anaraklnavt, Naa and Sirim. At that time there also lived Revne, a male partridge. He decided to ask Sinanevt to marry him. One day Sinanevt went to gather nettles. And Revne followed in her steps. Revne said to himself:

—Sinanevt already went off; I'll go and catch up with Sinanevt.

Revne went and built a fish fence across a small river and took out the trapped fish. Sinanevt sang a song. Revne heard her and followed her voice. He saw Sinanevt and flung himself at her. Sinanevt pushed Revne away and said:

—What's with you? I don't want to marry you; your eyes are red.

They turned around and came to the river. Revne said:

—Sinanevt, let me carry you across!

Sinanevt said:

—I can go across by myself very nicely.

Revne said:

—Sinanevt, you'll spoil my river!

But Sinanevt made up her mind and crossed the river by herself. They went farther. They went in Revne's house. Revne told Sinanevt:

—Repair my parka! I'll go and get same fish heads.

Revne left. And then Ememkut came, took Sinanevt and married her. They left. Revne came back and Sinanevt was not there; she had left him by himself.

The next day Anaraklnavt went to gather nettles. Revne followed in her footsteps and said:

—Aranaklnavt already went off. I'll go too and I'll catch up with her.

Revne went off. He came to the little river, looked at the fence-trap—and it was full of fish. Anaraklnavt sang. Revne heard her; he went and threw himself at her. She pushed him away:

—What's with you, Revne? I don't want to marry you; your eyes are very red!

Revne was embarrassed and went off to the side. He begged Anaraklnavt to allow him to carry the nettles:

—Eh, Anaraklnavt, let me carry your nettles!

Anaraklnavt said:

—I'll carry them very nicely by myself!

They went on and came to the river. Revne said:

—Eh, Anaraklnavt, let me put you on my back and carry you over!

Anaraklnavt said:

—I can cross it by myself very nicely!

Revne said:

—You're going to spoil my little river; nobody has ever crossed it.

But Anaraklnavt made up her mind and crossed by herself. Revne led her to his house. They entered the house. Revne said:

—Anaraklnavt, you stay with me, repair my parka, and I'll go and get some fish heads.

Revne left. Ilvimtalkhan, the wild deer, arrived right away and asked through the little window:

—Anaraklnavt, are you marrying Revne?

—No!

178

—Are you repairing his parka?

—No!

Then he promptly took Anaraklnavt and led her away.

Revne returned and Anaraklnavt was not there.

—Don't think that I don't know who took you away? Ilvimtalkhan!

Then Naa went to gather nettles. Revne went out to the yard. He followed her, gave chase. Naa sang. Ravne heard Naa singing. He came to her. Although he wanted to throw himself at her he suddenly became embarrassed because his tail always pointed upward. He overcame his embarrassment, threw himself at Naa and married her right away. Naa cried. Revne said:

—Now, stop your moaning! Let's go home!

Revne took the nettles and carried them. They walked. They came to the river. Revne said:

—Hey, Naa. Let me put you on my back, I'll carry you over.

Naa said:

—I can cross that little river by myself. I'm heavy; you couldn't lift me.

—Heh, just sit on my back!

Naa did. Revne crossed the river with her. All his joints began to crackle. Naa asked:

—What is that crackling?

Revne said:

—The stones under my feet are clattering.

They crossed over and went home. They entered the house. Revne said:

—Naa, you repair my parka!

Revne left. He went to get fish heads. And right then Zusch, the lizard, came in. He called out:

—Naa, have you already married Revne?

Naa said:

—Yes, I did!

—Are you repairing his parka?

—Yes, I am repairing it!

Zusch left. Revne came back with the fish heads. They began to eat. They finished eating. Revne said:

—Well, now we'll go to your father and mother!

Revne went out to the yard, blinked at the sun—and what a different fellow he became! Very handsome! He went in the house and Naa saw him. She began to laugh:

—Ay, now my husband has become very handsome!

They went to Kutkh. He met them. Kutkh promptly rushed to Revne and pushed his older sisters-in-law away. They did not look at Revne; they were ashamed. Sirim said:

—Ehe! And Naa's husband is very handsome!

Revne started back for his house. He took Kutkh and his family with him. The older sisters-in-law stayed back. They did not look at Revne. They were ashamed.

Revne began to live well, he was merry; he was not in need of anything.

77. Ememkut, Anaraklnavt and Valen-Sinanevt

Recorded in 1910-1911 in Khayruzovo *rayon* in Kamchatka *oblast* by W. Jochelson. Published in *Kamchadal Texts*, Worth 1961, no. K2. 2. Translated from the Itelmen language into Russian by A. Volodin.

Long ago there lived Ememkutkh with his sister Anaraklnavt. Ememkut would go hunting and kill all sorts of animals. One day Ememkutkh pretended to be sick. Anaraklnavt started for the hills herself, passed by them and went to the seashore. She found a high cliff, climbed down to the seashore and there she saw Valen-Sinanevt[52] floating on the sea in a skin boat [*umiak*]. The *umiak* was well loaded with bearded and ringed seals. Sinanevt began to dress the animals, took some of the kill, and then went the shore to gather seaweed. Suddenly she saw Anaraklnavt.

—Oh, is it you?

—Yes, I thought you were a boy, that's why I hid myself.

—Very well, let's go to my house!

At home Valen-Sinanevt began to host Anaraklnavt with all she had. Valen-Sinanevt said:

—No doubt you have a brother? Don't be afraid, I'm not going to give you to my brothers, and you will not give me to your brother. All of my brothers went to hunt mountain sheep.

Valen-Sinanevt's brothers came home and asked:

—Sister, did anybody come here? Tell us!

—Nobody came here. I've just come from the seashore.

The next day Valen-Sinanevt's brothers again went mountain sheep hunting. Anaraklnavt said to her friend:

—My brother is sick; I should go home!

Valen-Sinanevt started to fit out her friend Anaraklnavt for the trip. She gave her everything: Brains, marrow and meat. Valen-Sinanevt said:

—Your brother is sick; you're going to be hungry. Take a good supply of food!

Anaraklnavt started for home. She came home and her brother was very sick. Ememkutkh began to ask his sister for something to eat. She brought him meat but he said:

—No, I want something else!

At this Anaraklnavt became angry with her brother. She told him:

—I'm going to leave you forever!

Anaraklnavt left. Ememkutkh got up, put on his sister's parka, became a raven and flew off. He flew to Valen-Sinanevt, sat on the *balagan*, hopping about.

Valen-Sinanevt came from the seashore, saw the raven sitting on the *balagan* and began to throw stones at him.

—You thieving raven!

Ememkut became embarrassed and flew off to another place. He became a man again. He went to Valen-Sinanevt, threw himself at her, seized her. Valen-Sinanevt became frightened, she recognized him. Ememkut married her and they went home. They began to live well and were happy.

---

[52]In this story Valen-Sinanevt is not Ememkutkh's sister Sinanevt but a sister of brothers who were hunters of mountain sheep.

78. Chelkutkh and the Maidens-Mushrooms

Recorded in 1910-1911 in Khayruzovo *rayon* in Kamchatka *oblast* by W. Jochelson. Published in Worth 1961. Translated from the Itelmen language into Russian by A. Volodin.

Long ago there lived Chelkutkh.[53] He asked for Kutkh's daughter Sinanevt in marriage; he worked for her, and brought in much firewood. Eventually he married Sinanevt. They began to live together; they were merry. Sinanevt gave birth. A son was born. Chelkutkh went to the forest, found the beautiful [deadly] mushroom maidens[54] and remained in the forest with the girls, having forgotten his wife.

Then Sinanevt began to worry waiting:

—Where is he? No doubt they killed him!

And an old woman lived with them. She was her aunt, Kutkh's sister. She told her:

—Sinanevt, stop waiting for your husband, he's been with the toadstool maidens for a long time. Send your son to his father.

The boy went to his father. He sang a song:

—My father is Chelkutkh, my mother is Sinanevt and my father has forgotten us.

Chelkutkh heard what his son was singing and he said:

—Go and burn him with smoldering pieces of wood. Tell him that I am not his father.

The girls took smoldering pieces of wood, burned the child, and burned his small hands.

—It burns! Mama, they're burning me—he cried out.

The little boy went back to his mother. He came home and she asked him:

—Well, what did father say?

—He said: "I'm not your father." He told the toadstool maidens to burn me with smoldering wood; they burned me all over my hands. It burns; it hurts! I won't go to father tomorrow because they will burn me again with smoldering wood.

The next day the old woman again sent him to his father:

—Go there once more, sing again and tell him this: "Father, tomorrow we'll leave with all our property; you'll be left in the forest, with the toadstools. All of you will then be hungry."

Chelkutkh heard what his son was singing and he became angry:

—Go girls and lash him with a strap as befits him and burn him with fire. Then maybe he'll stop coming here!

---

[53]Chelkutkh — the raven, a tale personage, in Itelmen folklore the opponent of Kutkh. With the present-day knowledge of Paleoasiatic languages we cannot etymologize the names Kutkh and Chelkutkh. What seems obvious is that Chelkutkh is derived from Kutkh. It may be surmised that the word *kutkh* means "raven" and originated in one of the ancient Paleolithic languages or related dialects of the Itelmen language which died out in the far past (compare the present Itelmen *fe'klkh*—[*kutkh*],"raven").

[54]Mushroom maidens — in Itelmen folklore they are the mythical forest, beautiful, hostage-taking, maidens, who lure hunters into the depths of the forest with their charms. The myth of deadly mushroom maidens can be traced to the ancient custom of the Paleoasiatics of Kamchatka and Chukotka to use the [poisonous] toadstool to bring on a stupefying, hallucinatory condition. "The toadstool *vanak* is used as an intoxicating substance by the Koryaks, but among the Chukchi it is found rarely, particularly so in Kolymsky *kray*, where toadstools do not grow" (Bogoras 1900, p. 57, footnote).

The myth about women-toadstools luring men into a magical world is expressed in the petroglyphs in the rocky mountains Pegtymel in the most northerly petroglyphs found by Soviet geologists and archaeologists in 1965-1966. These petroglyphs picture a dance of toadstools, and on one of the fragments, the luring of hunters by women-toadstools (cp. Dikov 1969, pp. 219-221). Evidently, the subject matter of the petroglyphs and the tale under discussion are traceable to a single mythological source.

The girls took fire, took a strap and began to lash him, to burn him. Then they chased him away. The boy cried out, went back to his mother and he came burnt all over. His granny breathed on him and all his ills promptly passed away. And she said:

—Well, Sinanevt, let's get ready; we're going to the forest!

They started to get ready. They invited all the animals and took all of them along; they did not leave any back. They went to the forest, arrived there, chose a high mountain, climbed to its top, poured water on the mountain—and there was an ice-mountain.

Chelkutkh went to the forest. He did not kill one animal; all traces of them were gone. Chelkutkh and the girls began to starve. There was nothing to eat. Chelkutkh remembered his wife and son. He went to his house. He came home and found neither wife nor son. Chelkutkh moaned:

—To where have all of mine disappeared? I'm hungry, Sinanevt, I want to eat. Where have you and my son gone?

He followed his wife's traces and came to that high mountain.

—How can I get to the top?

It was very slippery. He called out from below:

—Sinanevt, lift me!

Sinanevt lowered a thong and called out:

—Hey, Chelkutkh, grasp the thong!

He grasped the thong. She started to lift him to the top of the mountain. It was already close and he even put one foot on the top. Then she cut the thong with a knife. Chelkutkh flew down, fell, fainted, came to, and called out again:

—Sinanevt haul me up, I'm dying of hunger!

—Why don't you go and live with the toadstool wenches? Why don't you go live with your toadstools? Why did you come here to us? You're doing very well! You've almost tortured your son to death; so now take what you deserve!

—Sinanevt, stop being angry, haul me up, I want to eat.

She lowered the thong again.

—Very well, grasp it; I'll haul you up.

Chelkutkh grasped the thong and she hauled him up. Not far from the top she again cut the thong. Again Chelkutkh flew down, fell, fainted, lay there for a while and came to. Again he called out:

—Sinanevt, stop being angry!

—If I haul you up here will you then do the same thing all over?

—No, Sinanevt, I won't. I'll not do that again.

She threw down the thong and hauled him up. He dried himself, was happy, began to eat and finished eating. They began to live again as before, with much merriment. And the toadstool maidens dried out and died.

79. How Sinanevt Was Jinxed

Narrated in 1969 by an inhabitant of Tigil village V. Ponomareva, age 60. Recorded and translated into Russian by A. Volodin. This is a tale about marital unions of Kutkh's daughter Sinanevt with a pink salmon, wooden ring, dog, and a corpse.

Long ago there lived Sinanevt and Ememkut. They lived well; they lacked nothing. Then something happened to Sinanevt. Disfavor fell on her; she was always thinking and thinking about something. Her brother questioned her but she never answered:

—What's wrong with you?

—Don't ask me anything. It's very tiresome for me to live.

Sinanevt went out somewhere. Suddenly she saw *gorbuscha* [pink salmon] in the river. She took one of the salmon and said:

—You're going to be my husband!

The salmon fluttered in her hands. Sinanevt said:

—Oh-ho, my husband is very playful!

She went home right away, climbed into the attic and she laid down there with the salmon. The salmon flapped and to her it seemed funny:

—Yes, it will be ticklish to you!

All night Sinanevt screeched and giggled in the attic while lying with the salmon. She disrupted Ememkut's sleep all night. In the morning Sinanevt said:

—Now, you can sleep. I'll cover you, and I'll go and gather berries.

Sinanevt left. Ememkut climbed up to the garret and saw the *gorbuscha*. He grabbed it and took it to the river. Sinanevt saw this and promptly sang out:

—The-y threw my lit-tle hus-band in the river!

She felt sorry for her husband. She went home and took for a husband a wooden ring for extracting blubber.[55] She laid down with it, and the ring even spoke to her:

—Shi shshe shishu shisheshi, shi shshe shushyy shisheshi.[56]

Sinanevt asked:

—What's with you? May I give you a kiss?

And the ring said:

—Shi shshe shishu shisheshi, shi shshe shushyy shisheshi.

Sinanevt asked again:

—May I embrace you?

Again the ring said:

—Shi shshe shishu shisheshi, shi shshe shushyy shisheshi.

In the morning Sinanevt said:

—You go to sleep, I'll cover you, and I'll go and pick berries.

As soon as Sinanevt left, Ememkut climbed up thinking: What was Sinanevt screeching about? He saw the ring. He took it, started a fire in the yard and threw the ring in it. Suddenly Sinanevt saw smoke rising and she sang:

—My-y lit-tle hus-band is in the fire; he's bu-r-ning. Thick smoke is ri-sing! Ememkut bu-r-ned him.

---

[55]Raw seal blubber cut into small pieces was put in a seal bladder for preservation. To extract the blubber from the bladder a special stick with a ring was used.

[56]In the original, a purposely distorted language. According to the narrator, Sinanevt and the ring talked in their "wood" language, not understanding each other. More of this later in the story.

Sinanevt went home. Suddenly she saw a shabby dog. She took it and said:

—You'll be my husband.

The dog began to growl at her. Sinanevt said:

—Why are you laughing? Let's go to the attic, we'll go to sleep.

She put the dog to bed and he snarled all the time. Sinanevt laughed.

—And why are you laughing—she asked the dog. —Because I'm beautiful? Yes, I'm really beautiful.

Again, Sinanevt screeched and giggled all night. Because of this Ememkut did not sleep all night. In the morning Sinanevt said:

—You go to sleep now and I'll go after berries.

Sinanevt got ready to leave. She wanted to kiss the dog. The dog bit her. Sinanevt said:

—All right, all right, I won't go far. Oh, come on, do you always bite when you kiss!

Sinanevt left. Ememkut went to the attic right away. He was very angry. He pulled the bedding off and saw the dog. He grasped it by the neck, lowered it from the roof and hung it. Sinanevt saw the dog hanging. She sang out:

—My-y lit-tle hus-b-and ha-ngs up there, with his tongue hanging out so far, my lit-tle hus-b-and was always ready to smile! Ay, ay, ay, Ememkut!

Sinanevt walked home. She started towards the house and found a dead man. The lower half of his body was eaten away by dogs. She took him, lifted him to the garret and put him down to sleep with her. They lay down and began to talk to each other. The dead one said to her:

—Sinanevt!

—What is it?

—Dy bedya podizhe poshupay [distorted and incoherent language, see footnote 56].

—What are you saying?

—Da du zhe, dy bedya podizhe poshupay.

And Ememkut saw her take the corpse up to the attic and thought to himself: "Life is going to become very difficult now."

In the morning Sinanevt went after berries. She had covered the corpse with a blanket. As soon as she left Ememkut climbed up to the garret. He saw the corpse, became frightened, covered him, and let himself down.

Sinanevt returned and laid down next to the corpse right away. And that one said to her:

—Bedya dvoy bdat didel.

—What is it; did I do something wrong? —Sinanevt asked him.

—Bedya dvoy bdat didel.

—Are you telling me that I'm going to get rid of you? No, I'm not going to get rid of you, —Sinanevt said.

—Bedya dvoy bdat didel.

And Ememkut said to himself: "It'll be better if I burn the house down and go away from this place."

He put the house on fire and left. And Sinanevt and the corpse burned to ashes.

80. The Marriages of Sinanevt and Anaraklnavt

Recorded in 1910-1911 in Khayzurovo *rayon* of Kamchatka *oblast* by W. Jochelson. Published in *Kamchadal Texts*, Worth 1961, no. K2. p. 8. Translated from the Itelmen language into Russian by A. Volodin. The tale is about Kutkh's daughters creating a whale and being transformed into a wild deer (Sinanevt) and a bear (Anaraklnavt). In the other variant (no. 64 of this edition) there is no mention of a "sea" Kutkh, and the daughters of old Kutkh, created [born] of birds' eggs, and floating on a whale's back to an unknown country. Later in the story, the subject matter is in agreement. However, the name of the second daughter of Kutkh does not agree in these two variants. In no. 64 of this edition her name is Amzarakchan.

Long ago there lived Kutkh. He had two daughters—Sinanevt and Anaraklnavt. Kutkh treated the children badly; they did not live well. Sinanevt thought and said to Anaraklnavt:

—Let's go to the sea, our father is treating us so badly!

They went to the sea. They started to pick all sorts of berries, then with the berries they began to make a fancy whale. They finished making the whale. They sat inside it. They started out for the "sea" [sea-dwelling] Kutkh. The whale dove, came to the surface again, and the air came out of him as smoke. They came to the "sea" Kutkh. He received them very well. The "sea" Kutkh asked them:

—Where are you going?

—We came here to live with you!

They began to live there and were very happy. They wintered there not wanting in anything. In the spring they started back to their own land. "Sea" Kutkh loaded them with meat, blubber, and hides; he provided them with everything. Suddenly the whale stopped. Sinanevt awakened and said to herself:

—Why is the whale not moving?

She went out and saw that all around the land was green. She jumped onto the land. She gathered bunches of grass, shrubbery and bead-ruby, returned and put all under the pillow at the head of the bed. Anaraklnavt was sleeping. She awakened. Sinanevt asked her:

—Did you dream about anything?

—No, I didn't!

Sinanevt said:

—But I did dream that we were already on land and I was gathering grass, shrubbery and bead-ruby. Won't you look, there really could be bunches of them under my pillow!

Anaraklnavt looked under Sinanevt's pillow. She found the grass, shrubbery, and bead-ruby. Anaraklnavt said:

—Sinanevt, you're fooling me!

Anaraklnavt went outside and saw the land. They both stepped on the land and left the whale behind. Sinanevt said to her younger sister:

—Anaraklnavt, I'll transform you into a deer, and I'll become a bear! You're going to run around the forest and I'll tie myself to a post with a thong!

She turned Anaraklnavt into a deer and Anaraklnavt started to walk like a real deer. Sinanevt became a bear herself and she tied herself to a post with a thong. She became a terrifying sight.

Sinanevt said:

—Anaraklnavt, you run around in the forest. It may be that somebody will then marry you. Only take care not to speak about me to anybody!

Anaraklnavt went to the forest. She went and she left her older sister. She began to walk in the forest. She walked and walked.

Two friends were hunting in the forest. The saw the deer, sneaked up close to it, released their arrows and brought it down. They began to dress the deer. They slit its belly, and a beautiful girl walked out of it. The older one immediately married her. They took her home. They began to live well.

But then Anaraklnavt began to go to the yard at sun set. There she cried thinking of Sinanevt.

An old woman lived there. She heard how Anaraklnavt was remembering Sinanevt. Anaraklnavt came into the house and the old woman asked her:

—Whom are you thinking about?

—I'm not thinking about anybody, —Anaraklnavt said, —I have an older sister, Sinanevt. She is there, at the sea. She has made herself into a bear and she is terrifying.

The hunters began to prepare themselves for the road; they began to make arrows. Kechi also began to make arrows; he made them of the branches of willow bushes. They went after the bear. Kechi also went with a sled made of twigs to which mice were harnessed. His companions laughed at him:

—Where are you going, Kechi?

—I'm traveling simply; maybe I'll eat just a small piece of meat!

The two friends arrived and they shot and shot again at the bear but could not bring her down. The bear broke the arrows with her teeth; she broke all of the arrows. At that point Kechi arrived. The companions began to ask him for arrows. Kechi said:

—I'll shoot him myself!

Kechi shot, hit him, and the bear fell to the ground. They began to dress the bear and slit its belly. Sinanevt walked out of it. The companions began to envy Kechi. They all started for home. Kechi also was taking his wife home. They went on and then saw that Kechi was not there. And they had stopped on the road. Kechi said:

—You stay here. I'm now going a short distance away. Don't be afraid!

Kechi went to his granny. He arrived and he said:

—Granny, I've married Sinanevt, but my wife is freezing on the road!

Granny whistled. Two reindeer with a sled appeared. In the sled there was a parka. Granny was very happy that her grandson had married. Kechi went to his wife. She did not recognize him. Kechi told her:

—Come here and sit down!

Sinanevt said:

—I'm not going to sit down. I have a husband and he will be here shortly!

Kechi said:

—I am your husband and I've gone to my granny!

Sinanevt sat on the sled and they went on. Soon they caught up to the companions and overtook them. The companions saw Sinanevt. There was a handsome man driving her. To them it meant that somebody had already stolen Kechi's wife. Kechi began to live well and was happy.

81. The Marriage of Ememkut

Recorded in 1910-1911 in Khayruzovo *rayon* of Kamchatskaya *oblast* by W. Jochelson. Published in *Kamchadal Texts*, Worth 1961, no. K2. p. 5. Translated from the Itelmen language into Russian by A. Volodin. In another variant of this tale (no. 60 of this edition) Kutkh and Ememkut, in running away from Miti and Sinanevt, turn into ravens. This is not stated distinctly in the text that follows.

Long ago there lived Kutkh with his wife Miti. They had a son Ememkut. They lived well; they lacked nothing. Ememkut decided to go and seek a girl—he wanted to get married. He started out for the search.

Kutkh and his wife went to the pine forest to gather pine kernels. Kutkh said:

—Miti, let's call out to each other; you know the bear comes to this pine forest!

They began to call out to each other. Kutkh would call out, and his wife would call back:

—Miti-i!

Miti would call back:

—Akh-akh-yakha-kha!

Then Miti would call out to her husband:

—Kut-khe-e!

And Kutkh would call back:

—Akh-akh-yakha-kha!

Again Kutkh would call out to his wife:

—Miti-i!

Miti would call back:

—Akh-akh-yakha-kha!

Miti would call to her husband:

—Kut-khe-e!

Kutkh would call back:

—Akh-yakh, yakha-kha!

It became boring to Miti; she stopped calling out. Kutkh said:

—Where did Miti go? She stopped calling!

Again Kutkh started to call out:

—Miti-i, Miti-i!

Miti called out very loudly:

—Akhakh, yakhakha!

Kutkh became intimidated and at once went after the sound. He found a nice *balagan* and house. He sat on the *balagan*. A girl came out to the yard, saw that Kutkh was sitting on the *balagan*, and she asked:

—What have you come for? You'll only spoil the food in the *balagan*.

She started to throw stones at him. Kutkh was not afraid of the stones. A younger girl came to the yard. The older one told her:

—Look, he's sitting there. Of course you'll take pity on him.

The younger girl climbed up to the *balagan* and started to feed Kutkh with all sorts of food. But Kutkh hid all of the food in his parka. At that time Miti came home. Kutkh was not there. Miti cried:

—Where is my Kutkh, where did he go?

Kutkh came home; she saw him. She was happy. Kutkh brought with him good food. Miti asked him:

—Kutkh, where were you?

—You frightened me, and I went after your sound!

Ememkut came back. He had not found any girls. He thought so much about ir that he became sick and stopped eating. Then he asked his father:

—Father, when you were walking in the forest did you see any girls?

—I did not; I don't go anywhere, I'm always at home, and I only carry the chamber pot out.

And Kutkh had altogether forgotten about the girls; he could tell Ememkut nothing. But Miti remembered about them and she said:

—Kutkh, you had told me that you saw girls somewhere!

Then Kutkh also remembered:

—You're right Miti. Be quiet, I'll tell him myself. Listen Ememkut; I did see girls in another place [another world or in the sky]. I saw two girls. Don't marry the older one; marry the younger girl. Tomorrow go to the pinewoods with your sister, call out to each other. Your sister will frighten you; you will become frightened. You will not recognize yourself, and you will follow my path. You'll see a house and a *balagan*. Sit on the *balagan*. Just then the older girl will come out to the yard and will start throwing stones at you. That will tell you that she is the older one. That's the one you don't marry. Then the younger sister will come out. Without delay she'll climb up to the *balagan* and she'll feed you. Here's my parka for you, take it. When you get married bring it here, to us, right away.

Ememkut went with his sister to the stony pine forest. They started calling to each other. As Kutkh and Miti had called out to each other, so did they. Sinanevt got tired of calling; she was quiet for a while, and then she called out again. Ememkut became frightened, promptly followed Kutkh's path and came to the other place. He found the *balagan*. He sat on the *balagan*. The older girl came out to the yard. She started to throw stones at him and said:

—He's come again; he's getting in the habit of coming here!

The younger girl came out to the yard. She climbed to the top of the *balagan* and began to feed Ememkut. Ememkut did not eat anything.

—Why aren't you eating? —asked the girl.

Then Ememkut embraced her. He married her and she became pregnant right away. The girl cried. Ememkut said:

—Now, stop crying, you'll stifle the child!

The older sister heard that the younger one was pregnant and she became angry:

—When my brothers come back, I'll tell them about you!

Her brothers arrived and the older sister promptly went out to meet them and she said:

—Do you think that our younger sister lives well? She has already married and is pregnant!

Her brothers said:

—You know, it's a very good thing to get married!

They began to live together. Ememkut and his brothers-in-law went to the forest to hunt, to kill animals. Then Ememkut began to make sleds—a large one and a small one. He finished and he told his brothers-in-law:

—Well, tomorrow we're going home!

Ememkut whistled. At once a large herd of reindeer appeared. All of the reindeer were motley-colored. He whistled again. Again a herd of reindeer arrived. All of the reindeer were white. He puffed at the motley ones and they left.

His brothers-in-law were very happy. This was the first time they had seen such a herd. Ememkut began to harness the reindeer. He harnessed them. He plucked a single hair from his wife's head and with it he tied the house of his brothers-in-law to the last in line sled. He started with his wife for home. The brothers-in-law saw this and they said:

—Look at that! Ememkut is going nowhere; he stays in the same place!

They did not know that the house was tied to the sled and that Ememkut was pulling them, his brothers-in-law, to his home. Ememkut's brothers-in-law looked again and said:

—What is Ememkut doing? He's not moving; he's sitting in the same place!

Ememkut drew near his house. He stopped short of it and went farther on foot. He left his wife on the sled. He came to his mother and told her:

—Cast everything we have on the path: hides, sewn things, sable furs, fox furs.

188

He went to his wife and they started out again. Ememkut's wife saw that beautiful hides, sewn things, sable and fox furs were scattered everywhere. Ememkut's wife asked:

—Who has thrown out such beautiful hides, sewn things and sable and fox furs?

Ememkut told his wife:

—Kutkh and Miti wipe their back end with them!

They arrived. Kutkh and Miti were happy and had a good time.

82. Ememkut and His Wife Eltalnen

Recorded in 1910-1911 in Khayruzovo *rayon* of Kamchatskaya *oblast* by W. Jochelson. Published in *Kamchadal Texts*, Worth 1961, no. K2. p. 13. Translated from the Itelmen language into Russian by A. Volodin. This story reveals a clear breach of the tale tradition about the composition of Kutkh's family. Ememkut appears as the son-in-law (not the son) of Kutkh, who marries the daughter of the latter, Eltalnen. The name of the daughter is also mentioned for the first time. The tale concludes with an economic ending, which reflects the social aspects of the life of the Itelmens in the 19th century (e.g. the Russian Cossacks working for one's future wife).

Long ago there lived Kutkh with his wife Miti. With them lived a daughter Eltalnen and also an old woman, Kutkh's mother. Many suitors came. The old woman promptly ate all of them; she did not let anyone get to the house. That old woman was a man-eater. Ememkut also heard of the very beautiful girl Eltalnen. Ememkut got ready to go to Kutkh. He captured a wild deer. Ememkut started and took the deer with him. He got close [to Kutkh's house]. He drove the deer ahead. The old woman ate the deer right off. Ememkut slipped by; the old woman did not notice him. He came to Kutkh and asked him:

—Kutkh, where is your girl?

Kutkh told him:

—There's no girl here!

Eltalnen was in another house. Ememkut began to live there with Kutkh. To be sure he wanted to go to Eltalnen but she would not let him in. Ememkut thought and thought. Then he turned himself into an old woman and created a snowstorm. Again he went to Eltalnen and begged of her:

—Eltalnen, let me in, I'm freezing!

She let him in.

—There, old woman, you sit at the door!

Eltalnen did not recognize Ememkut and truly accepted him as an old woman. Ememkut lulled Eltalnen to sleep. Eltalnen fell asleep. She slept and felt nothing. Ememkut did what he wanted to do and left promptly. Eltalnen became pregnant right away. Eltalnen recognized that she was pregnant and she began to sew children's clothing. Miti went to her and said:

—Hey, Eltalnen, what are you doing? Are you thinking about something bad?

Eltalnen said:

—Yes mother, I am pregnant! Yet, I have not slept with anybody. Only when there was a snowstorm I let in an old woman.

Miti told her:

—Of course, that was Ememkut!

Eltalnen gave birth; she gave birth to a very beautiful child. Eltalnen said to her father and mother:

—Tell the suitor that Eltalnen said: "Of course I agree!"

To that Kutkh and Miti said:

—If you're agreeable, marry Ememkut!

Ememkut married her. They began to live well. Ememkut said:

—Now we're going to get ready to go home!

They started to get ready. Ememkut went to the yard and whistled. Immediately three teams of draught reindeer appeared. They started for home. Eltalnen's girl friends told her:

—You're fine now, but later on snot will drip out of your nose.

They arrived home. The ravens had befouled Ememkut's house with their droppings. Ememkut cleaned the house. He decided to give a feast and he invited all. The Russian Cossacks arrived. Chichkimchichan came and it seemed that he had eaten fly agaric. He said:

—Hey, Eltalnen, you urinate a bit in a horn ladle; I'll drink your urine so we can sleep together in one sleeping bag!

Eltalnen told him:

—You're the rudest thing, Chichkimchichan!

Ememkut became angry with his wife. He cancelled the feast. All of the guests went home before they started feasting. Ememkut laid down and he lay there all the time. He did not get up, he was angry with his wife because of Chichkimchichan. He did not even look at her. Eltalnen said:

—Ememkut, you're always angry with me, I'm going to go to my father!

Ememkut said:

—You can leave right now!

Eltalnen cried and went to the yard. She whistled. Promptly two harnessed deer appeared. She went back to the house again and said:

—Well, farewell Ememkut, I'm going now!

Ememkut grasped the edge of his wife's skirt, but he could not stop her. Eltalnen drove the reindeer and disappeared at once. She rode along the path and cried, and snot dripped out of her nose. She said to herself:

—Really, my girl friends were right!

She arrived at her parents' place. She began to live in their house again. The yard became warm; the sun heated it. Just then Sinanevt, the sister of Ememkut, said to her brother:

—Ememkut, the sun is glorious, I'll carry you out to the yard!

Ememkut did not want to go to the yard. All the same Sinanevt carried him out together with the bedding. Ememkut's flanks had become weak from his constant lying. He sat in the yard and he said:

—Sinanevt, get me my arrows; I'll count them. Maybe some of them were lost!

Sinanevt got the arrows. Ememkut started to count them. There was a blade of grass hanging from the arrows. He could not remove nohow. So he cut the blade off with a knife and threw it behind his back. From behind him somebody cried and said:

—Ememkut, I feel sorry for you and you cut me off with a knife!

Ememkut looked in back of him and saw an old woman-spider. She got up and ran around Ememkut three times. Ememkut got well right away. He became handsome. He became happy again. He remembered his wife. He went to his wife again. He got there and they would not let him see her. Ememkut began to live there. He worked for Kutkh for three years. But Kutkh would not give him his wife. Then Ememkut dug an underground passage to his wife. Through that passage, unknown to Kutkh, he made his way and slept with his wife. He did this for three years. They finally gave Ememkut his wife. Again they went home. They arrived there. Again they began to live well. They again prepared a feast. They invited everyone. Many guests came. And again the bad man Chichkimchichan came. Readily Ememkut seized him and threw him away somewhere. He began to feed his guests. They finished eating. They began to compete. Nobody defeated Ememkut; he threw everybody to the ground. They finished fighting. They started to wrestle each other on a hide. Again nobody could do anything to Ememkut; he brought down all the others. They finished wrestling on the hide. All started to urinate. Ememkut urinated very far. Nobody could cope with Ememkut; he defeated them all. Ememkut began to live well and be happy.

83. Sisilkhan and Ememkut's Wife Ayanomlkhchakh

Recorded in 1910-1911 in Sedanka village of Kamchatka *oblast* by W. Jochelson. Published in *Kamchadal Texts*, Worth 1961, no. K2. p. 26. Translated from the Itelmen language into Russian by A. Volodin. This story represents a much earlier variant of no. 65 of this edition. The subject matter of these two stories is in agreement. The difference is that in one of them the transgressor of family precepts is Kutkh who attempts to take away his son's Ememkut's wife Iyanamltsyakh. In the other story, it is the wife of Ememkut who attempts to possess his brother Sisilkhan. In these stories the name of Ememkut's wife may perhaps be dialectic variants of the same word. Thus, Ayanomlkhchakh, Iyanamltsyakh, lit."[Arctic] brambleberry."

Long ago there lived Kutkh with his wife Miti. Their children were Ememkut, Sisilkhan, Sinanevt and Sirim. One day Ememkut went to the forest. There he found Ayanomtalkhan and his daughter Ayanomlkhchakh. Ememkut asked for her in marriage. Ayanomtalkhan gave her away. Ememkut married her. They started for home. They arrived there. Sirim went to the yard, saw the wife of Ememkut, and said:

—She is very beautiful!

Sisilkhan became envious; he wanted to take Ememkut's wife for himself. He sent his sister Sirim to Ememkut.

Sirim said:

—Ememkut, Sisilkhan wants to take a look at the bears' lair! Do you want to go?

Ememkut said:

—I'll go; I'll take a look!

Ememkut went and looked in the lair. Sisilkhan instantly pushed him into it. The bears received Ememkut well. They fed him with meat. The bears knew who had pushed him in the lair. The bears said:

—Well Ememkut, go home. Sisilkhan wants to take your wife for himself.

They gave Ememkut bear meat. He went home. He got there, entered the house and asked of his wife:

—Did Sisilkhan come here?

Ayanomlkhchakh said:

—Just now he came!

Sisilkhan was sending his sister:

—Sirim, go and invite Ememkut's wife here!

Sirim went and said:

—Hey, Ayanomlkhchakh, Sisilkhan is inviting you!

Ayanomlkhchakh said:

—I'm not going; do you really want me to leave my husband?

Sirim looked around:

—Ah, Ememkut came back!

—Sit down Sirim; eat some meat!

Sirim sat down, ate well, finished eating, went home and entered the house. Sisilkhan asked her:

—Well, is she coming?

—She's not coming, Ememkut returned.

—You're fooling me Sirim!

—No. I'm not. He really came, gave me meat and I ate well.

Sisilkhan said:

—Is it possible that Ememkut will live forever?

Sisilkhan sent Sirim again:

—Go to Ememkut and ask him if he wants to go to the wolf's den tomorrow.

Sirim went to Ememkut. She entered and asked:

—Ememkut, will you go to the wolves' den tomorrow?

192

Ememkut said:

—I'll go!

Sirim went home, came in and said:

—He'll go!

They went to the wolves' den. They arrived there. Again Sisilkhan told Ememkut to look into the den. Ememkut began to look through a chink. Again Sisilkhan pushed him in.

The wolves received Ememkut well. They fed him meat. Afterwards Ememkut went directly home. He arrived and entered the house.

And Sisilkhan again sent his sister:

—Hey Sirim, go and invite Ememkut's wife here!

Sirim went, went in and said:

—Ayanomlkhchakh, Sisilkhan invites you!

Ayanomlkhchakh said:

—I'm not going; do you really want me to leave my husband?

Sirim saw that Ememkut had returned.

—Sit down Sirim; eat some meat!

Sirim ate her fill and went home. She entered and said:

—She'll not come, Ememkut returned!

Sisilkhan said:

—Why didn't the wolves kill Ememkut?

Sisilkhan sent off Sirim again:

—Maybe Ememkut will want to go fishing tomorrow for loaches in the ice hole?

Ememkut told her:

—I'll go!

Sisilkhan and Ememkut went to the ice hole. They saw many loaches there. Sisilkhan pushed Ememkut in the water. He went directly to the bottom. The loaches received Ememkut well; they fed him with fried loaches. They began to ask him to live with them.

Ememkut did not want to:

—I have a wife!

Ememkut went home; they had loaded him with loaches. He arrived at the house and entered.

Sisilkhan again sent his sister:

—Go and invite Ememkut's wife here! I've drowned Ememkut.

Sirim went, entered and said:

—Ayanomlkhchakh, we invite you, your husband will not come!

—What are you saying; my husband is sitting right here!

Sirim looked around:

—Ah, there's Ememkut!

—Sit down Sirim, eat some of the fried loach!

Sirim ate and went home. Sisilkhan asked her:

—Well, what's doing? Is she coming?

—No, she'll not come! Ememkut came back. He brought trout; I ate well.

Sisilkhan said:

—Eh, I can't get rid of Ememkut!

Then Sisilkhan dug a pit at the door that reached all the way to the underground country. He covered it with grass. Again Sisilkhan sent his sister:

—Go; invite Ememkut to eat with us as a guest!

Sirim went, entered and said:

—Ememkut, we're inviting you to eat with us!

—I'll go!

Ememkut went, did not see the pit. At once he fell through the pit to the underground. He found nice people there. They received him well and began to feed him. There were beautiful girls around. All the time they insisted that Ememkut should marry.

—I don't want to get married! —Ememkut said and he cried.

Sisilkhan finally brought Ememkut's wife to his place. Ayanomlkhchakh put on the prickly skin of a plaice. Sisilkhan said:

—Well, let's lie down!

They did. On purpose Ayanomlkhchakh began to embrace Sisilkhan. Sisilkhan began to moan:

—Oy, oy, why is your skin so prickly?

And Ememkut's wife began to embrace him even more intensely. Sisilkhan became angry, pushed Ayanomlkhchakh away and said:

—And I thought you were a beautiful woman!

Ayanomlkhchakh went to the yard. She fell in the pit. She met her husband. Ememkut had not looked at anyone there.

—Ememkut, I've come here, I am your wife!

He saw his wife; he was happy; he started to kiss her. They went back home right away. On the way Ememkut captured two old bears. They came home. At once Sirim came out to meet them. They told her:

—Go and bring Sisilkhan here!

Sirim went, came in and said:

—Sisilkhan, Ememkut is inviting you!

—Did he come here already?

—Yes, he did!

They went to Ememkut and saw two huge bears. They became frightened and called out:

—Ememkut, they're terrible!

Ememkut became angry and he seized Sisilkhan and his sister. They cried out:

—Ememkut, let us go, we're afraid!

Ememkut caught up with the bears and they took Sisilkhan and his sister to the forest forever. And Ememkut began to live well and he was happy.

84. Mechkhch, the Bear and Kutkh

Narrated in 1969 by an inhabitant of Tigil village V. Ponomareva, age 60. Recorded and translated into Russian by A. Volodin. In this story, Mechkhch ("The Skinny Man") turns to the all-powerful Kutkh for help against his oppressor, the bear. In this case Kutkh appears in the role of a protector of the harmed ones.

Long ago there lived Mechkhch. He fed himself with fish only. When summer came, he prepared *yukola*. He hung the *balagan* full of them and in the winter, being wary, he slept in the granary in which willow herbs were drying. In the fall somehow a bear got into the habit of coming to him. He ate and ate the *yukola*! But what could Mechkhch do about him? The bear was nearly finishing the *yukola*, and he grew fat. He came once more, finished eating the *yokula* and said:

—Well Mechkhch, I've finished the *yokula*. Now I'm going to eat you.

Mechkhch said:

—Eh, I'm sorry but I'm lean and tough!

Then how do you want me to eat you?

—It would be better if you boiled me!

—Well, then I'll boil you. We'll have to get firewood, —the bear said. —Make haste and drag in some wood. I'm going to lie down; somehow I got tired. But don't be away for long!

Mechkhch went to the forest and he cried as he sang a farewell song.

He brought in the firewood, put it down and said to the bear:

—I'll go out again; this will not be enough wood.

He went out again and sang his farewell song:

—For the last time I walk, soon I'll be eaten!

At that time Kutkh was walking in the tundra. He heard that somebody was singing a farewell song. At once he walked up to the singing voice:

—Look at you, Mechkhch! Why are you moaning?

—Eh, Kutkh, I'm walking here for the last time!

—How's that?

—Soon I'll be eaten. I'm carrying this firewood for my kettle; I'm going to be boiled.

—Who's going to boil you?

—The bear.

—What's wrong? Well, that's enough of crying! You go and take that wood there. Build the fire slowly. Don't hurry! In the meantime, I'll make myself a stout club. Then, as if by accident, you'll see me and you'll tell the bear: "Uh, what the devil is bringing Kutkh here!" You say this as if you were angry with me.

Mechkhch went home. The bear asked him:

—You've already come?

—Yes, I have.

—Well, build a fire!

Mechkhch sat down and slowly started to build a fire. Suddenly he called out:

—Ah, what the devil is bringing Kutkh here!

At once the bear said:

—Look here; don't you give me away. I'm going to curl myself into a ball. The bear curled himself into a ball and lay down. Kutkh arrived:

—Hello Mechkhch!

—Hello!

Kutkh went over to the bear

—And what sort of a thing is this lying here?

—Oh, that's my *selnitsa*.[57]

Kutkh began to look it over.

—Mechkhch, why does it have fur?

—That's because I took it and covered it with a fur hide!

—Mechkhch, why does it have legs?

—Oh, I just wanted it that way, so I made it with legs!

Kutkh walked to the head of the bear.

—Mechkhch, why does it have a head?

—Oh, I just made it with a head!

Kutkh carefully took aim at the bear's head so he would hit it for sure. And the bear lay there not even breathing. Kutkh grasped the club, took aim—and how he did strike the bear's head! The bear did not even move. Kutkh called out:

—Mechkhch, quickly rip open his belly, so he doesn't revive!

They had a busy day. They disemboweled the bear, cooked it and broiled it right away. Kutkh said:

—Now, Mechkhch, let's make bags out of the bear's hide and carry the meat to Miti!

—Oy, granny, you should take all the meat; you've kept me among the living!

They went to Miti's place. They arrived there. They climbed up to the entrance opening and called out:

—Miti! Come and take the load!

Miti jumped to the entrance.

—Oy, Kutkh, where did you get all this meat?

—Don't prattle too much, —Kutkh told her. —You should fix something tasty! And you, Mechkhch, don't go anywhere. Live with me as my son.

---

[57]*Selnitsa* — an elongated wooden trough for the preparation of *tolkusha* (q.v.).

85. Ivlikelkhen

Narrated in 1969 by an inhabitant of Tigil village, V. Ponomareva, age 60. Recorded and translated into Russian from the Itelmen language by A. Volodin. The tale about an evil being who devours anything living is widespread among the peoples of Chukotka and Kamchatka. In Itelmen folklore, the evil being is Ivlikelkhen, "the long-legged little old man." In no. 68 of this series, it is Kutkh, among the Chukchi it is the *kele*, among the Eskimos it is the giantess Mayyrakhpak, and so on. It should be noted that in the tales of the above-mentioned peoples, the monster who devours an animal's young ones is presented as a female. Thus, the presentation of Ivlikelkhen in the tale of the same name as a male appears to be the result of a change of the subject among the contemporary Itelmens, that is, from female to male. The variant of the tale in which Kutkh takes Ivlikelkhen's place is apparently secondary and very late. In this variant the mythical creator, the raven Kutkh, is demoted to a negative personage.

Long ago Ivlikelkhen lived in his little *yurta*. One time a bitch came to his place.

—Good day, grandpa [old man]!

—Good day, bitch!

—I've come to spend the night here.

—Well, do stay over!

And to himself Ivlikelkhen said: "Just the same, I'll eat you." Aloud he said:

—Bitch, you lie down over there and I'll lie down here.

The bitch said:

—Grandpa [old man], tell a story!

—I'll tell one, you just listen.

Ivlikelkhen started to say:

—Body, body, a whole one, whole one, much brain in the head, much marrow in the bones, let it grow. It will grow; it will be bigger yet.

And the bitch lay in the corner digging under—she wanted to dig a hole to the outside.

—Bitch! Are you digging something?

—I'm digging for mice. Grandpa, you just tell the story, I hear you well. I already want to go to sleep.

Ivlikelkhen again began to recite:

—Body, body, a whole one, whole one, much brain in the head, many kidneys, livers, let it grow. It will grow, it will be bigger yet . . .Bitch! What are you digging there?

And the bitch had already finished digging the hole. She answered:

—Grandpa, I'm digging between my feet. You tell the story to yourself. One of my eyes is already sleeping. Tell some more and all of me will fall asleep.

At once Ivlikelkhen began to narrate:

—Body, body, a whole one, whole one, much brain in the head, a tender neck, sweet ears, let it grow. It will grow, I'll eat my fill of you . . . Bitch!

There was no answer.

—She fell asleep. Oh, what a tasty meal I'll have now!

Ivlikelkhen got up and sought the bitch. He found the hole through which the bitch had run away. Ivlikelkhen became angry:

—Ah, you bitch, you bitch; just the same I'll catch up to you! Then I'll eat you alive!

He chased after her. The bitch ran and suddenly she saw a little bird. She took her and wrapped her up in her *kukhlyanka*.[58] Thus she promptly made a sort of cradle. She sat down herself, and rocked the bird, as if it were her child.

---

[58]*Kukhlyanka* — a long, pullover outer fur garment. The combination of inner and outer fur shirts has no appropriate equivalent in English. The term suggests a "cocoon," but this is too farfetched to apply to clothing of this type.

197

Ivlikelkhen arrived and asked her:

—Have you seen a bitch?

—My child is very sick. Whom could I have seen? Grandpa, you stay overnight here.

—Very well, I'll stay.

Then the bitch said:

—You lie down to sleep. I'll sit up with the child; he would cry all night.

And for herself she was thinking how she could get away. Night came. She called out to Ivlikelkhen:

—Grandpa, are you asleep?

He did not answer; he had fallen asleep.

Somewhere she found a piece of suede and she nipped holes in it so as to make stars in it. She put it over Ivlikelkhen's face. "Sleep Ivlikelkhen"—and she ran off.

Ivlikelkhen slept until daytime. He opened his eyes and before him he saw a darkened sky covered with stars. "Well, this is a long night indeed, —he thought, —and so clear, with so much starlight!" He started to turn on his other side and the suede slid off his face. He then understood what had happened:

—Bitch, I didn't know it was you. Well, I'll catch up to you in no time!

Ivlikelkhen started running and he began to catch up to the bitch. The bitch saw him. She set out to tease him:

—Grandpa, look at my legs!

— Your legs are like sticks, —Ivlikelkhen replied.

—Grandpa, look at my nostrils!

—Uh-uh-uh, your nostrils are like holes in a wall!

—Grandpa, my face is smooth as if it were licked clean, but look at my eyes!

—Uh-uh-uh-uh, your face is like a piece of smoked hide and your eyes are narrow as if slit with a knife. All the same I'm going to eat you!

—Take a look at me; see what a girl I am!

—You're no girl; you're simply a bitch!

Ivlikelkhen ran and ran after the bitch; his breeches tore; he could not catch her. He then said:

—It'll be better if I go home and repair the breeches.

He came home, sat down and prepared to repair the breeches. Then mice came and at once began to trundle all over his little *yurta*. All the time they trundled past the window and he said to himself: "What's darkening the light? No doubt it's my cheeks." At once he cut them off. Blood poured and the mice started trundling again.

—Yes, it must be my nose that's darkening it!

He cut off his nose. His whole face was hurting.

Ivlikelkhen thought to himself: "I'll go out to the yard and see what's happening."

He went out and saw the mice. He told them:

—Now you're not going to get away from me.

Quickly he ran in the house, tied the legs of the breeches to make a sack, went to the yard and said:

—And now jump in here!

The mice were obstinate, they didn't want too. A tiny little mouse pushed ahead and fell in the breeches. Ivlikelkhen spoke again:

—And now you jump in there quick!

All the mice jumped in the trousers.

—Now I'm going to make pickled meat.

Ivlikelkhen tied the breeches tightly and went to the forest. He found a straight tree and talked to it:

—Tree, tree, bend down! Tree, tree, bend down!

The tree bent down. He tied the breeches to its top and said:

198

—Tree, tree, straighten up!

The tree straightened up.

—Now I'm going to make very tasty pickled meat. Then I'm going to have a dainty dish.

Ivlikelkhen went to his little *yurta*. Then the fox ran through the forest and heard faint voices calling. It was the mice bitterly crying up there. The fox looked around and saw them. She asked them:

—Who hung you up there?

—Ivlikelkhen hung us up here so that he could make pickled meat of us.

—And as he was going to hang you what did he say?

—He said: " Tree, tree, bend down!"

The fox said those words and the tree bent down. She let the mice out and said:

—Quick, gather pieces of rotten wood.

The mice gathered rotten wood and filled the breeches with it. And the little mouse that was at the bottom and who had suffocated, they put on top—let it be pickled. The fox said:

—Now tell me what he had said to the tree when he hung you on it?

The mice said:

—Tree, tree, straighten up!

They hung the breeches to the top. The fox then said:

—Now come to my home. You'll make a trough and bring alder bark.

Ivlikelkhen stayed at home for some time and then he said to himself:

—It's time to go; there'll be some fabulous food for me.

He came to the forest.

—Tree, tree, bend down! Tree, tree, bend down!

The tree bent down.

—Now I'm going to eat my most pickled, most tasty food. My sweets I'll eat!

Ivlikelkhen shut his eyes, put his hand in the breeches, pulled out the little mouse and began to eat:

—Uh, how tasty; well, I'll feast on it!

Again he put his hand in the breeches, pulled out a piece of rotten wood and put it in his mouth. He became angry:

—It must be the fox that messed this up! So, now I'll go see her!

He started out. The mice saw him from afar; they said:

—Ivlikelkhen is coming!

The fox said:

—Quick, chew the bark!

The mice chewed the alder bark and filled the trough with it.

—Now, hide yourselves.

Ivlikelkhen arrived and said:

—Good day, fox.

But the fox lay there with her head wrapped.

—Is it you who stole my food? —Ivlikelkhen asked.

—Oy, grandpa, I've been sick for three months, — the fox answered.

—What ails you?

—Blood is flowing from my soul.

Look, the trough is full of blood. Yes, somebody should take it and pour it out. Grandpa, maybe you will go and pour it out.

—Very well, I'll go and pour it out. You really must be very sick, so much blood came out of you.

He took the trough and carried it. The fox told him:

—Only don't look back. Just pour it out from that cliff.

Ivlikelkhen carried the trough. He got tired and stopped. He wanted to look back but he remembered that the fox had told him not to look back. He started out again; the cliff was not far. He was very tired. He stopped, wanted to glance back but again remembered that the fox had told him not to look back. And the fox followed him by stealth. Then Ivlikelkhen came to the cliff and started to empty the trough. Just then the fox pushed him from behind and Ivlikelkhen fell down head over heels.

—Ah, you fox; I'm going to have you anyway!

What kind of fox is he now going to have? He broke into pieces—his head and hands fell here and there.

And the fox shouted with laughter. She had her laugh, went to the mice and told them:

—Now you can go home; don't be afraid of anything, and tell the bitch that she can live in peace—Ivlikelkhen is dead.

86. The Fight of the Two Kutkhs

Recorded in 1910-1911 in Khayruzovo *rayon* in Kamchatka *oblast* by W. Jochelson. Published in *Kamchadal Texts*, Worth 1961, no. K2. p. 24. Translated from the Itelmen language into Russian by A. Volodin. This is the story about the Sea-Kutkh (see also no. 78 in this edition). In it, the two Kutkhs, the sea and the terrestrial ones, are antagonists.

Long ago there lived Sea-Kutkh and River-Kutkh. River-Kutkh started out for the sea. Sea-Kutkh started out for the river. They met mid-way. At once they threw themselves at each other and started fighting. Neither of them won. Again they started to tear at each other: they scratched each other; they bit each other. Again they became weak. Lying on the ground they tore at each other. Blood started flowing. The ground became red. They tore at each other so much that they stripped all of their muscles from the bones. Suddenly an old woman came from somewhere. She asked them:

—Hey, what are you doing?

—Well, we've met here!

Sea-Kutkh said:

—I went to the river.

River-Kutkh said:

—I went to the sea. We met here. We fought; we tore at each other. We became weak and we lost our strength.

The old woman began to rub them with the palms of her hands, curing them. She blew on them and at once they mended themselves. With a staff the old woman smoothed the ground. At once they got up and thoroughly embarrassed for themselves, they went to their homes.

87. The Koryak and the Vixen

Recorded in 1910-1911 in Sedanka village, Kamchatka *oblast*, by W. Jochelson. Published in *Kamchadal Texts*, Worth 1961, no. K2. p. 30. Translated from the Itelmen language into Russian by A. Volodin. The allegorical form of this tale reflects the struggle of the reindeer herders to control their herds.

There once lived a Koryak. He had a herd of reindeer. Spring arrived. He drove the herd to the mountain range. A vixen came out of the range and said:

—Hey, Koryak, let's live together!

—Eh, vixen, did you know that the Koryak has a herd?

—Yes, Koryak, and I'll work with it!

—You don't have to do any work, just guard the herd with me!

Hearing those words, the vixen was happy. She said:

—Let's go and you'll look them over; maybe some of the reindeer got lost!

They drove the herd to the pasture. The vixen began to select the bulls, the fat ones. She ate all the meat under their hides. In that way she was finishing off the herd. The ones she ate she left standing. Those that remained alive she drove to the place where she had eaten the others. The vixen said:

—I'm going to bring the master here!

They came there and the master looked them over.

—How do you like that, vixen? You've become a master in pasturing. All the same, you've no doubt killed a few reindeer for yourself.

The vixen said:

—Why would I do that to my good companion? It'll be better if I go away; I'll go to my father.

The Koryak said:

—Vixen, take whatever you want.

The vixen said:

—I'll take nothing! Later I'll come to live with you again.

The vixen left. Suddenly a bad snowstorm blew up. The Koryak started out, got lost, fell into an abyss and died. The vixen came back and took the herd for herself. She was happy all the time.

88. Ikymtu and Ivyltu

Narrated in 1960 by an inhabitant of Palana village, M. Medveditsyn, age 54. Recorded and translated into Russian by A. Volodin. The subject matter of shamanesses bringing about better weather is known only among the Itelmens and is a relatively recent recording.

Sometime long ago there lived in that land two people. One of them was called Ikymtu,[59] the other Ivlytu.[60] At the time it was summer. Soon fall would come. Where were they to live? They decided to build a little house next to the birch forest. They cut grass, dragged in logs, and dug turf. They brought everything to one place and built a little house not giving any particular thought to it. And it was closer and closer to fall. Then all of a sudden the weather got bad. The sky could not be seen. The sun disappeared altogether; black clouds hung over the very land. Then suddenly it started to rain. It poured and poured! Again and again they would open the entryway and look outside. And it rained and rained. What were they to do? Then Ivlytu said to Ikymtu:

—Listen to what I've thought about!

—Tell me what you've thought about!

—I'm going to climb up to the sky. Maybe I can break up the clouds with my feet. You stay home and cook something to eat! I'm not going to stay overnight there; I'll come down.

Ivyltu went to the yard, turned around himself once and rose to the sky. As soon as he got to the sky he started to kick the clouds apart with his feet. Ivyltu kicked and kicked. And the sky darkened, night came. Just before daybreak he lowered himself to the ground. His companion met him and asked him:

— Well Ivyltu, what did you do?

—Ikymtu, I couldn't kick them apart! I'm tired. Feed me; let me drink some tea!

Then Ikymtu said to Ivyltu:

—You are Ivyltu [Long-legged] and I am Ikymtu [Short-legged]. I should climb to the sky. Somehow I'll try to kick the clouds apart.

Ivyltu said:

—Who do you think you are, Ikymtu? Do you really think you can? I am Ivyltu, and I couldn't!

—Anyway I'll try; I'll climb up!

Ikymtu got ready, put on his parka, girdled himself with grass and said:

—Well, now it's time for me to go.

He opened the door, ran around himself, spun like a whipping top and, as if somebody pulled him up, he raced toward the sky. He got near the sky, nudged the cloud just once, and made a hole in the sky. He nudged it two, three times more and at once the clouds began to sink down. Then a wind started blowing up and in no time the clouds were blown away. What else was there left for him to do? Ikymtu let himself down to the ground. He went to the house and told his companion:

—Come now, open the door! Look at the sky. The yard is now very beautiful. You see, the sun is shining. Come to the yard; let's roll in the grass. Listen to the birds singing. Do you hear the lark? Now, let's live in peace.

---

[59]Ikymtu — lit. "Short-legged."
[60]Ivlytu — lit. "Long-legged."

89. The Snail

Recorded in 1910-1911 in Nayruzovo *rayon*, Kamchatka *oblast*, by W. Jochelson. Published in *Kamchadal Texts*, Worth 1961. Translated from the Itelmen language into Russian by A. Volodin.

A snail came out of the sea and went to the forest. In the darkness she went to a house and asked from the yard:
—Are you sitting there with a light?
They answered:
—Yes we have light.
She called out from the yard:
—A family with a light!
Then she came to another house. Again she asked from the yard:
—Do you have light?
Again they answered her:
—Yes we have light.
—The snail called out:
—A family with a light!
She went farther, found a house, and asked from the yard:
—Do you have light?
They answered her:
—We don't have light.
The snail called out:
—A family without light!
But the people had covered the oil-lamp with a cup. The snail entered the house.
—Sit down, be our guest!
The snail sat down.
—Guest, will you treat yourself to some *yukola*!
—I don't want any; I just had some.
—Treat yourself to some berries!
—I don't want any; I've just eaten some berries.
—Well, how about nuts?
—Oh, I love nuts!
They gave her nuts. She tried to crack the nuts but she could not. Her mouth was watering. Then all sorts of sea animals started coming out of her mouth. The whole house was filled with animals. The people became frightened and uncovered the oil lamp. The snail saw the fire, became frightened, got up at once and cried out:
—A family with light!
And she promptly went into the sea.
And the people became rich; they did not lack anything.

90. The Bitch and Kekukemtalkhan

Recorded in 1910-1911 in Khayruzovo *rayon* in Kamchatka *oblast* by W. Jochelson. Published in *Kamchadal Texts*, Worth 1961, no. K2. p. 7. Translated from the Itelmen language into Russian by A. Volodin. This is one of the early variants of tales about evil monsters devouring children. As was mentioned earlier (see notes attached to no. 85 of this edition), this subject, in different variations, is widespread over the entire Kamchatka-Chukotka region.

Long ago there lived the bitch Eltkhekhenay. Her family was a large one. The children begged of her:

—Mom, tell us a tale.

—I don't want to tell one. It bores me. Invite the old woman Ivlikelkhen, maybe she'll tell you a tale.

They invited her and she came. The old woman Ivlikelkhen began to recite:

—I'll find many brains, livers, bone marrow, all soft. I'll eat well.

The old woman was telling tales only for appearance sake; after all she wanted to eat them all. The bitch with her children started to suspect that there was something wrong—the tale that Ivlikelkhen was telling was not a regular one. Eltkhekhenay became frightened and started digging a hole to the surface. Ivlikelkhen heard the digging and asked:

—What's that? It seems that somebody is scratching the soil, digging.

— No, I'm just scratching myself.

The old woman said:

—Oh, you're scratching yourself, and I thought you were digging.

Again the old woman sang out:

—I'll find many brains, livers, soft ones, and bone marrow. I'll eat well.

Then she asked:

—Are you already asleep, Eltkhekhenay?

—Not yet; only one of my eyes wants to sleep.

The old woman sang again and then asked:

—Are you already asleep, Eltkhekhenay?

—Not yet, but both of my eyes already want to sleep.

Then finally Eltkhekhenay finished digging a hole to the outside. Quietly she pushed the children out. One very small puppy did not want to crawl through the hole and cried out:

—I'm not going to crawl through the hole!

The old woman Ivlikelkhen heard this and said:

—Who doesn't want to crawl through a hole?

—Eltkhekhenay said:

—That's one of the children; she put her feet under the blanket of her older sister, and she doesn't want to crawl out!

Suddenly Ivlikelkhen saw light coming through the hole.

—What's that shining?

—The moon is shining through a hole; it's being covered with clouds.

The bitch shoved all of her children outside. She hid the little one with her body. She got to the outside herself. Ivlikelkhen asked:

—Are you asleep?

There was no answer. The old woman said:

—She must be sound asleep. Well, now I'm going to have my fill!

She stuck out her tongue, felt around with it, and her tongue found the hole. She realized that Eltkhekhenay had run away. The old woman said to herself:

—If I had known that this would happen, I would have eaten you and your whole family right away.

205

The old woman started to chase after them. The little puppy cried out:

—I'm here; mom hid me on this ridge!

Ivlikelkhen heard the puppy, turned around and went back. She started to search but could find no one.

The old woman said:

—Come to me, little child!

—You'll eat me!

—No, I'll not eat you; I'll take good care of you.

The puppy went to the old woman. They went home. The puppy lived well with the old woman. The old woman was very rich. She had all sorts of animals. She put them in bags. No one ever came to her grounds. She had all the sea animals—the house was full of them. Ivlikelkhen told the puppy:

—Don't touch the bags you see in the house, but eat to your fill. Don't fear; eat as much as you want.

The old woman Ivlikelkhen used to go to pick berries and she left the puppy at home. As soon as she left, the puppy would start running around and testing herself: She would run far and then run back.

The old woman would come back and ask:

—Well, have you touched anything?

—No, I've touched nothing.

The old woman went again after berries, and she went far off. The puppy had grown and become big.

As soon as the old woman left, the bitch said to herself:

—Why doesn't the old woman allow the bags to be touched? Well, I'll take a look and see what's in them.

She untied a bag and right off geese came out of it and flew away. She untied all the other bags—all the animals, land and sea, came out of them. The bitch herself ran off. The geese had flown directly to the place where the old woman was.

The old woman saw the geese and she said:

—I didn't put those in the bag.

Then she saw a herd of deer run by. She saw her basket on the antlers of one of the deer and she then knew what had happened. The old woman said:

—Aha, the bitch has let all of my animals loose.

She became angry and promptly went home. She saw that the animals had broken down the house. Right then the old woman started chasing after the bitch. The bitch sensed that the old woman was catching up to her. She took a young animal's hide and with her heels made a circle around it. Immediately a house appeared. She sat in it. A child was howling, crying. The old woman came there and asked:

—Have you seen a bitch running through here?

—No, I've seen nobody, my child is crying so loudly. I go nowhere, how could I leave the child? His father went hunting.

Then the bitch added:

—Old woman, stay with us overnight.

The old woman said:

—Very well, I'll stay with you overnight.

They began to get ready to lie down. The bitch said:

—Old woman, take your clothes off, sleep well, rest.

The old woman fell asleep. The bitch awakened and got up. She started to look for the old woman's cap. She found it and, cut off its brim and made in it the sky and the stars: the Great Bear, the Pleiades and Orion. The old woman slept on her back. The bitch put the cap on her face and ran away at dawn. She ran to the river and called out:

—Cuckoo Kekukemtalkhan; carry me across!

Kekukemtalkhan carried her across and promptly married her. The old woman slept for three days and three nights. She touched her face and realized what had happened. The old woman got up and said:

—Ah, that bitch, she fooled me again, and I thought that it was really somebody else.

Again she started chasing after the bitch. She came to the river and yelled out:

—Kekukemtalkhan, carry me across!

The bitch taught her husband how to answer:

—Tell her: "There are no boats!"

The old woman said:

—Then how did she get there?

Again the bitch taught her husband:

—Tell her: "She drank the river dry!"

Kekukemtalkhan called out:

—Grandmother, the bitch drank all the water from the river!

The old woman started to drink the water. She became sick but started to drink again. She drank the river dry. Then the old woman's belly burst. She died and floated downriver in the current. And the bitch began to live well.

91. The Mouse and the Raven

Narrated in 1929 by an inhabitant of Utkholok village in Tigilsky *rayon*, M. Zayev. Recorded and translated into Russian by E. Orlova. This is a variant about the stupid raven who is fooled by mice. (Cp. with no. 68 of this edition; see W. Jochelson 1908, pt. 3).

One day the mouse went to the sea to hunt; she killed a seal and at once started dragging it home. Unexpectedly a raven saw her and asked:

—What's that you're carrying?

The little mouse replied:

—It's a piece of wood I'm carrying.

The raven said again:

—That's not wood; look at that head dangling.

—You know, that's a knot!

The raven then became angry, took the seal, cut it into pieces and carried them to his house.

The mouse cried and went home. Her children wanted to comfort her, to please her:

—What happened?

The mouse told them how the raven had robbed her. The mice exclaimed:

—During the night we'll carry everything back here!

The raven cut the seal into small pieces and carried them outside so they would freeze a bit. Night came. And the mice took all the meat and carried it to their house.

The next day the raven woke up—and there was no meat. The raven then became angry, went to the mice, thinking: "Just the same I'll kill them all!"

When he came close, the mice cried out happily:

—Grandpa, grandpa, grandpa! We'll feed you with roots and we'll cook tubers for you!

The raven was happy and he praised the mice.

Then the raven finished eating and promptly fell asleep. The mice then sewed red rags to his eyelashes.

The raven awakened and started for home. His son came out to meet him. To the raven it seemed that his son was on fire. He grabbed him and began to bang him against the wall. And [in this way] he killed his son.

Then his wife came out and saw the red rags sewn to his eyelashes. She began to tear them off. The raven cried out:

—Yen-ne-nekh, yen-ne-nekh!

She tore them off. Again the raven went to the mice. The mice were again happy:

—Grand-pa, grand-pa, grand-pa! We'll fee-eed you with roo-oots! We'll coo-ook tu-bers for you!

Again they fed the raven to his fill; again he promptly fell asleep. Then the mice painted his face. When the raven was ready to leave, the mice said to him:

—Walk straight to the water!

The raven went to the water. He saw his reflection in the water and fell in love with it: "Ah, what a beautiful woman lives in the water!" He came home and said to his wife:

—I don't need you; I've found a woman who is far more beautiful then you!

Then the raven got his parka, boots, fur stockings and mittens and went to the river. He threw his parka and boots into the river. Then he jumped into the water and drowned—just like Kutkh.

92. The Brant Gosling

Narrated in 1954 by an inhabitant of Napana village in Tigilsky *rayon*, V. Ponomareva. Recorded and translated into Russian by E. Orlova. The contents of nos. 92-95 of this edition are a series of variants of the Itelmen tales about a wingless gosling that cannot fly with his parents to warmer country and is forced to spend the winter in a *polynya*.[61] In this tale the actors are both animals and people. Here the motif of maternal anxiety and friendly mutual assistance is presented with particular lyricism. The role of the positive characters is played by the traditional personages of Itelmen-Koryak folklore—the older children of Kutkh, namely Ememkut and Sinanevt. They protect the gosling from the cold, and the threatening vixen, and they fashion wings for it out of grass. In three variants of this tale Sinanevt makes the wings, and in one variant Ememkut makes them. In two of the variants the harmful creature is the vixen who in trying to get the gosling from the *polynya* dies from having drunk too much water. In the other two variants the vixen goes away. In the last variant, in gratitude for being saved, the goose gives her oldest son in marriage to Sinanevt. The cosmological images [beliefs] of the early Itelmens about the blood relationship of people and animals are spontaneously reflected in tales of similar type.

Long ago, somewhere, there lived geese. They flew in from far away, from warm places. They flew here in the spring. Snow still covered the edge of the tundra but in the middle it had already thawed out. The geese started to make nests. A goose laid a few eggs. Then the fledgling chicks hatched. Their mother started to feed them and they grew. Their mother began to teach them how to fly. One of the chicks could not fly; he did not grow wings. His mother and father started thinking. The frosts had already started and his wings had not grown at all. They thought for a long time: What were they to do? They could not think of anything. They decided to leave him by himself in the tundra.

The grass was drying, withering; dry leaves fell from the trees. The geese prepared for the long flight. They were ready to fly. Only one of the goslings sat on the sides looking at his mother and brothers.

—You'll stay here; you know you have no wings. It is time for us to fly away. We'll fly off tomorrow before dawn.

The geese awakened during the night, began to flap their wings, and flew off. Only the brant [wild] gosling was left by himself in the middle of the lake. She sat there and lamented:

—I'm a brant gosling, a brant gosling without wings! I'm very cold; I'm freezing!

And the geese were flying farther and farther. The mother heard the lamenting of her child and said:

—My child is lamenting mightily. My soul is sick, let's go back!

They returned. The brant gosling saw the geese flying in and became very happy. They stayed overnight with their brant gosling and admonished him:

—Don't complain! Are we to freeze with you also? What can we do for you?

They awakened before dawn and flew away. Again the brant gosling remained by himself in the middle of the lake. He sat there and cried:

—I'm a brant gosling, a gosling without wings! I'm very cold; I'm freezing! The geese had already flown out of sight, but his mother heard all that her child was lamenting about.

—The poor thing! Let's fly back! Better that we all freeze together.

But her husband differed with her:

—What are you doing? Do we have to freeze to death because of her? She was born that way!

Again they returned to the gosling. She saw her mother and father and was very happy. By this time off-shore ice was starting to form. The gosling came to her mother and said:

—Why did you return to me? Let me freeze to death by myself!

It is very painful to leave a child behind. The mother decided: "I'm going to go to Sinanevt and Ememkut and ask them if they will take the gosling as a child."

---

[61]*Polynya* — an unfrozen patch of water in the ice.

They came to Ememkut and said:

—We came to you. It's already become cold and we can't fly away!

—Why can't you?

—Our child is staying here; it doesn't have wings. It is crying! Take her to yourself!

Ememkut agreed to take the gosling to his place.

—I'll take him! When are you flying away?

—We'll fly away during the night, before dawn!

They went to the gosling and said:

—Tomorrow Ememkut will come to you. Go with him, he is going to bring you up. It's possible that somebody else will come, but don't go with him. Tomorrow we'll fly off. Even if you complain, we'll not return!

The geese flew away. In the lake the gosling started to complain again, but the lake was covered with ice all over. The gosling was freezing and complained:

—I'm a brant gosling, a gosling without wings! I'm very cold; I'm freezing!

—Our poor thing has been left behind! She's freezing, she's cold, —her mother said.

The geese flew very far but they still heard their child complaining. However, they did not return.

A vixen came out of her burrow and heard that somebody was complaining.

—Oho! What is this? Who's yelling so loud?

She ran out of the burrow and went to the little bird sitting on the lake.

—What are you doing there? Come to me and be my child!

But the gosling replied:

—No. I'm not going to go to you. You'll eat me!

—I won't eat you!

—No, you'll eat me!

The vixen got angry. She began to run after the gosling; she wanted to catch it. She could not. She became very tired. She rested and then she began to drink up the lake:

—Now I'm going to drink up the lake and I'll eat you!

She drank and drank; she could not drink it dry. Then her belly burst. She died right away.

Ememkut came to the lake and promptly threw a birch-bark vessel into it.

—Sit in it and float to me!

The gosling sat in the vessel and floated to him. Ememkut took her home and there they fed her and dried her out.

From that day on they thought as to how they could make wings for her. Sinanevt was good with fancy needlework. She began to weave grass blades. It was close to springtime. Soon the geese will fly in; without fail they'll fly in. Sinanevt made wings for the gosling. The gosling put them on and began to fly. She flew to the roof and could not fly any farther.

—How am I to fly with grass wings? They will not carry me high and far!

Sinanevt again sat down to do some fancy work. She wove another pair of wings.

Outside the snow was already thawing. The skylarks and ducks had flown in—and the wings were not ready. Finally Sinanevt finished the second wings. She fastened them to the gosling.

—Well, now fly and meet your parents!

The gosling flew off. She flew to a flock of geese and asked:

—When will my parents fly in?

—They're flying in the rear. They will arrive tomorrow.

She returned home very happy. She said:

—Tomorrow my relatives will fly in.

The next day the gosling got up before dawn. She put on her new wings. She flew to her mother's call. She flew to the flock, saw her relatives and was happy. In the beginning they did not recognize their child, but afterwards they started asking her:

—How did you stay alive? We thought that you had already died.

The geese started to think how they could reward Sinanevt and Ememkut—what kind of gift to give them. They thought it out: they killed the fattest goose. And they flew to Ememkut's house. The door was open. They flew to the house, called out, and then entered the house. Sinanevt and Ememkut were happy to see the geese. The geese gave them the gift and said:

—This is for you! And take the gosling, our child, for a helper!

But Sinanevt and Ememkut told them:

—We'll not take the gosling. Let her live with you. You know, she wants to live with her relatives.

The geese flew off. And the gosling flew with them.

They spent the summer there. The gosling lived with all of them and she's still alive. She flies over us in the spring.

93. Angaka-sisike

Narrated in 1965 by T. Bragina. Recorded and translated into Russian by I. Starkova. See introductory remarks to no. 92 in this edition.

The geese spent the summer on the lake. When fall came they began to get ready to fly off, but one of them could not fly. All of the others began to get ready and his parents asked him:

—Angaka-sisike, you poor fellow, how are you going to live without wings?

The geese flew off. Angaka-sisike was left by himself and he sang out:

—Angaka-sisike! All of the other geese flew away, and I don't have wings!

His parents heard what he sang and they returned. Angaka-sisike told them:

—Fly away; don't pity me!

His mother advised him:

—When you are left behind, a bright fur coat will come to you; don't go to her. When a light small fur coat comes, then go with her!

The geese flew away and Angaka-sisike was left alone on the lake. A vixen came by and began to entice him:

—Come to me and I'll give you shelter!

The gosling did not listen to her, did not go to her. The vixen became angry and told him:

—I'm going to eat you!

But she went away. The lake began to freeze. Angaka-sisike was frightened: "The vixen will come and eat me."

Then Sinanevt came to the lake to fetch water and she asked:

—Why haven't you flown away?

Angaka-sisike cried and said:

—I don't have wings; my parents flew away and left me here! The vixen invited me to join her but I didn't go. She wanted to eat me.

Sinanevt said:

—Come to me, I'll give you shelter!

Angaka-sisike agreed and went with her. Sinanevt took very good care of him. She dried him and fed him only tasty bits.

Toward spring things got better. Sinanevt made nice little wings for the gosling, put them on him and told him: "Fly!" The gosling flew a bit and returned. Sinanevt asked him:

—Well, how are the wings?

—With others I could really fly!

Sinanevt gave him another set of wings. Angaka-sisike put them on and flew wonderfully! He came to a flock of geese. He asked them:

—Did you see my parents?

—They're flying back there.

Angaka-sisike flew off to meet his parents and he was very happy. His relatives saw him and began to ask him how he kept living. The gosling then told them everything: how Sinanevt sheltered him and how she made wings for him. The geese were very happy, went to Sinanevt and treated her with all sorts of things: they brought with them a lot of food and gave it all to Sinanevt.

Angaka-sisike stayed with his parents and began to live very well.

94. The Gosling Without Wings

Narrated in 1966 by an inhabitant of Verkhnyaya Sedanka village in Tigilsky *rayon*, N. Fedotov, age 46. Recorded and translated into Russian by A. Volodin. See introductory remarks to no. 92 of this publication.

Long ago there lived a flock of geese. Fall arrived; all of the goslings grew up. Only one poor little gosling did not grow up. Her mother said:

—You stay there in that lake. The vixen may come to you and invite you. Don't listen to her; otherwise she'll eat you. You'll stay here and we're going to fly off. It's gotten cold and your little brothers and sisters would freeze. You stay here on the lake. And tomorrow we'll fly away.

The poor little thing said:

—Very well, mom, all of you go ahead and fly away and only I, without wings, will stay here!

In the morning the geese awakened and began to kiss the poor little one, asking her forgiveness. Finally they took off and began to circle over the lake. As soon as they took off the poor little one sang out, complaining:

—I'm a poor little one without wings; where are my friends? They have wings; they flew away and left me, the poor one, behind.

Her mother heard this and said:

—Let's go back! My heart hurts! How can I leave her by herself? After all, I'm her mother!

Their hearts bled for her. They sat on the lake. The wingless one said:

—Why did you come back, because of me? After all I am what I am. Leave me!

One of her little sisters cried:

—How can we leave her?

The wingless gosling said:

—Fly away tomorrow and don't return because of me.

In the morning the geese got up again, began to kiss her—in no way did they want to part. Finally they did fly off. Again the gosling cried, complaining:

—I'm a poor one, without wings. Where are my friends?

Again the geese settled on the water. What mother would cast her child away? Again the wingless gosling said:

—Why did you come back, because of me? You know, you'll freeze! You want to stay alive, and I'll die anyway. Fly away tomorrow and don't come back again.

And the water in the lake had already begun to freeze. The wingless gosling said:

—Don't come back! Fly away!

The geese took off, circled around the lake three times and flew away.

Soon the vixen came by. She immediately sensed that a gosling was left on the lake. She came there and said:

—Oy, you poor one, and what are you doing on the lake by yourself? Let's go to my place and I'll take care of you. Let's live together.

The gosling swam farther away from the shore and told her:

—I'm not going; it's better that I freeze to death here.

The vixen got angry and decided to drink up the lake. She leaned over the water and began to drink. She drank and drank and she drank so much water that her belly burst. All the time the gosling was floating. By the morning all of the lake was covered with ice. Suddenly Ememkut came from somewhere. He said:

—Gosling, what are you doing here? Let's go to my house, it's warm there.

—I'm not going; I don't have wings.

—Come anyway, I'll make wings for you.

He took the gosling and brought her home. He began to feed her and then began to make the wings. When it became warm again the gosling grew up. And by that time Ememkut made the wings. Then the geese were flying in. The gosling met them and asked:

—Have you seen my parents?

—They're flying there in the rear.

Again a flock of geese was flying in. The gosling met up with her relatives.

—Is that you? —the mother asked. —Let's go to the one who gave you wings.

The geese flew to Ememkut, landed and said:

—Thank you Ememkut for helping our daughter. Maybe some day we'll be useful to you.

The geese got up and thanked Ememkut. Then they said:

—Now we're going to fly away.

Ememkut told them:

—In the fall you'll fly, come to see us again.

95. The Wingless Gosling

Recorded in 1910-1911 in Khayruzovo *rayon* in Kamchatka *oblast* by W. Jochelson. Published in *Kamchadal Texts*, Worth 1961, no. K2. p. 6. Translated from the Itelmen language into Russian by A. Volodin. See also the introductory remarks to no. 92 in this publication.

There lived a goose Kysumtalkhan and his wife. His wife laid eggs; they hatched fledglings and brought them up. One gosling did not have wings. Fall arrived and it became very cold. Other geese had flown away. Kisumtalkhan thought: "How are we going to carry our wingless son?" The geese were clamoring—it had become very cold. One night the geese flew away and left the sleeping gosling. Dawn was near. The gosling awoke and said:

—My mother and father have flown away.

He cried, he yelled. He sang a song:

—Mom, mom, you've left me, the wingless one, behind!

The geese heard their son singing, honked, and returned. Their hearts were aching for their little son. They asked themselves: "How could they take him with them?" It became very cold. Again the geese flew away during the night and left the little boy behind. At dawn the gosling awakened again and started singing:

—Mom, mom, you've left me, the wingless one, behind!

The vixen heard the gosling singing. She came to the lake and started to invite the gosling to come to her:

—Come to me, I'll treat you well. The gosling said:

—I will not go to you; you'll eat me.

—No, no, I'll not eat you.

—Vixen, I don't want to go to you!

The vixen got angry and said:

—When the lake freezes over I'll come here and eat you all the same.

The vixen left. The gosling cried again and lamented:

—Mom, mom, you have left me, the wingless one, behind. Now I'm going to freeze on this little lake.

And all the time he was swimming around. At that time Sinanevt was walking nearby. Suddenly she heard somebody singing in a mournful, very mournful voice. Sinanevt followed the voice. She saw a gosling swimming on the little lake. She did not call to him but went home right away. At home she plaited a grass grating. She plaited three pieces; they made a very nice grating. She went to the lake. She arrived there. She began to invite the gosling, but he did not come. Sinanevt said:

—Come to me, you'll freeze here.

The gosling agreed. She sat him on the grating and brought him home. At home she made a small lake and put various kinds of food in it. The gosling wintered there.

Spring arrived. Sinanevt decided to make wings for the gosling. She made them and fastened them to him. The gosling flew far. He flew back. Sinanevt asked him:

—How are the wings?

—They're good; I flew far.

The next day Sinanevt fastened another set of wings on the gosling. Again he flew very far. He flew back. Sinanevt asked him:

—And how are these wings?

—Very good, I've flown even farther.

The third time she put on him very beautiful wings. Again she sent him to try out the wings. The gosling flew very, very far. He returned and she asked him again:

—Well, how are these wings?

—Just as if they were my own.

215

Sinanevt told him:

—Well then, now fly off and meet your father and mother.

The gosling Kisumtalkhan flew to meet his father and mother. He met some small birds, geese, and asked them:

—Where are my father and mother?

—They're in the rear; they're flying this way.

He flew farther, and met his father and mother. They settled down and asked:

—Where are you going?

—To meet you.

—Who are you?

—I am your little son.

—Why do you want to fool us? We've left our little wingless son behind.

The geese started to cry. The gosling told them:

—Don't cry. Now I'll tell you all about it. Last year you left me on the little lake. And I sang songs there. First the vixen came to me and invited me to come with her. Then Sinanevt came. She took me to her home. I wintered at her house. She looked after me very well. She even made these wings for me. The geese recognized him and were very happy. They said:

—Well, let us fly.

—The geese flew to Sinanevt. They gave her in marriage their oldest son. They began to live well and be merry. They lacked nothing. They lived well.

GLOSSARY

Agutag (Alaskan Yupik) An Eskimo dish, or so-called "Eskimo Ice Cream." This is an Eskimo word meaning "something mixed together" (e.g. seal oil, blueberries, Crisco oil, sugar, fish). It is also one of the favorite foods of the Eskimo people and is considered a treat.

Akiba (local Russian) Ringed seal (*Phoca hispida*). The most common and most widespread seal in the Arctic.

Alyut (Koryak) A river and locality in the Kamchatka Peninsula.

Alyutortsy (local Russian) A Koryak tribe.

Ambon (local Russian) A locality at the mouth of the Tigir River in Kamchatka.

Amek (Eskimo) Lit. "skin" in Siberian Yupik language.

Antchiny (Antchinveem) A river in Kamchatka.

Arakamchechen (Chukchi) An island in the Senyavina Strait of the Chukchi Peninsula [Siberian Yupik: *Kigi*].

Argish (Chukchi) A caravan of reindeer-drawn sleds in the northern reaches of the Chukchi Peninsula.

Artel (Russian) Russian term for a small commercial company or joint enterprise. Distribution of the product was allotted in proportion to the work performed by the members. By the 1920s there were more than 8,000 *artels* in Russia. As commercial enterprises they existed in Russia almost to the 1970s.

Autonomous oblast (Russian) This administrative unit is based on the nature of the economy and composition of native people of the unit. In the pre-*glasnost* period (before 1985), each *autonomous oblast* was represented in the Soviet of Nationalities of the Supreme Soviet of the USSR by five deputies. The executive, administrative, and judicial procedures within an *autonomous oblast* are carried out in the language of the local nationality.

Ayak (Eskimo) A small island in the northern reaches of the Bering Strait (presently belongs to the United States of America).

Balagan (local Russian) A light, temporary shelter made of branches and grass. In form it resembles a truncated pyramid.

Baleen (local Russian) The durable, elastic, hornlike material found in plates or strips in the upper jaws of whales.

Baydara (local Russian) An open skin boat with a light frame made of driftwood and covered with split walrus hides. [Eskimo: *umiak*]. *Baydara*s were the principal means of travel among the Coastal Chukchi. The large *baydara* with sails was used for open-sea hunting of whales and walrus and for carrying goods along the coast. The small *baydara* was used for short local trips, for instance, to check fishnets, to retrieve-killed seals, birds, and the like and in hunting from the edge of the ice during winter. Reindeer Chukchi who lived close to the coast used the same kind of *baydara* as the Coastal Chukchi. In the Chukchi language *baydara* is *lyg'ytv'et* or "real boat."

Botalo (local Russian) A clapper or rattle.

Beluga (local Russian) The *beluga* or white whale (*Delphinapterus leucas*) is a medium-sized cetacean belonging to the group known as *odontocetes* (toothed whales), which also includes sperm whales, killer whales, dolphins, and porpoises.

Cape Uyakakh (Eskimo) The present-day Cape Dezhnev.

Chaga (Itelmen) A brown mushroom used by the Itelmens for a brew.

Chauchu (Chukchi) A nomadic reindeer herder.

Chavchuveny (Koryak) Nomadic Koryak reindeer herders.

Chavicha (local Russian) King salmon (*Oncorhynchus tshawytcha*). A large fish of the salmon family frequenting the rivers of the Kamchatka Peninsula.

Chelovek obychayev (Russian) In Eskimo and Chukchi myths, a personage living in the "upper world" who rules over the actions of people on earth.

Cheremsha (local Russian) A species of wild onion.

Chirim (Itelmen) An alcoholic potion made by boiling fly agaric and bog whortle berries.

Chiruch (Koryak) A fishing trap.

Chizhi (local Russian) A fur stocking.

Chuman, chumashek (local Russian) A vessel made of birch bark.

Chuvantsy [pl.] (local Russian) One of the Paleoasiatic peoples, possibly an isolated group of Yukaghirs. The local inhabitants of the old Russian-Yukaghir-Chukchi settlements on the Anadyr, Belaya, and Anyuy Rivers.

Cossacks [pl.] (Russian) Free Russian peasants commonly recruited by the Tsar's government to serve in the army. Russian Cossacks also were among the first explorers of Siberia, the Russian Far East and North America in the 17th and 18th centuries. Aboriginal people of the Russian Far North and North America have been using this word to describe a white man.

Dozhdevik (local Russian) A cloak made of segments of the intestines of sea mammals by the Eskimos and Coastal Chukchi. It is worn to protect fur clothing from rain and dampness.

Drygalka (local Russian) A short, thick club used by Itelmens and Koryaks in hunting, self defense, and attack.

Egalitarian Society is one that gives equal rights to all people; it usually results in sharing and cooperation.

Evala (Itelmen) A fish spawning roe.

Golets (Russian) The arctic char (*Salvelinus alpinus Linnaeus*) is present in the polar regions in both the anadromous (seagoing) and the nonanadromous (freshwater) forms.

Gorbuscha (Russian) A pink salmon (*Onchorhynchus gorbuscha*).

Gyk (Eskimo) An encouraging exclamation.

Igra verevochkoy (local Russian) Finger string games among the Eskimos, which involved the formation of complex patterns by looping a string over the fingers.

Imaklik (Eskimo; lit. "Located in the sea"; the Chukchi adaptation is *Imetlin, Imeglin*). An island in the Bering Strait (Big Diomede Island or Ratmanov Island belonging to Russia). In the past the island served as a stopping point in the sea voyages of the Asiatic Eskimos and Chukchi to the Alaskan Eskimos, and for the latter when traveling to the Chukchi Peninsula.

Imeglin (Chukchi) See *Imaklik*.

Inalik (Eskimo adaptation of *Inetlin*) An island in the Bering Strait (Little Diomede Island, U. S.).

Inetlin (Eskimo) See *Inalik*.

Ira-ira (Eskimo) A war cry.

Irtyn (Chukchi) A Chukchi man's everyday outer clothing. An *irtyn* was a closed, broad, short garment, which consisted of two separate fur shirts, one fitted into the other.

Izmennaya (local Russian) A volcano in Kamchatka.

Kala (Kerek) The same as *kele* (q.v.).

Kalaus (Koryak) A container made from the bladder, stomach, or hide of an animal. The container was filled with rendered seal blubber.

Kale (Chukchi) Sea kelp.

Kamchadal (local Russian) Current self-designation, Kamchadal, is derived from an early Russian term for a native of Kamchatka.

An ethnographic group of Russians of mixed Russian and Itelmen origin. Few relatively pure Itelmen survive today. Although the Kamchadals speak Russian and consider themsleves part Russian, they maintain many Itelmen cultural elements. They live on the Kamchatka Peninsula.

Kamleyka (local Russian) An outer garment with a hood. Made of cloth and worn over fur clothing to protect the latter from rain and snow. It was made of *rovduga* (q.v.) or cloth and was of the same cut as the inner shirt, except that it was considerably longer and had a hood. The *kamleyka* was commonly used to protect the fur of the garment from snow or rain. Both men and women wore a *kamleyka*.

Kamus or kamos (Chukchi) The tough skin from the lower legs of reindeer or other animals. It is used in the northern regions principally for making footwear and mittens.

Kamus skis (Chukchi) The Siberian natives' term for the sliding surface of arched skis, and often of flat skis, that was fitted with fur coverings. The *kamus* skis also were called dragging skis or draggers, in contrast to bare (uncovered) skis. As a rule, *kamus* was used for the covering. It was fastened in a way that would not hinder sliding: by gluing, sewing, or nailing.

Kayak (local Russian) A closed canoe with a light wooden frame covered with the hides of sea mammals, principally walrus, and completely decked. The top is covered with hide except for a small circular opening, the hatch, in which the paddler sits. The hatch is tightened around the oarsman's body with a thong. The *kayak* was used for both hunting and transportation. The Chukchi word for *kayak* is *yanratvyk'ay*.

Kayugun (Eskimo) A transversal axe similar to a hoe. In antiquity it was made of stone, since the nineteenth century, of iron.

Kele (Chukchi) Spirit-werewolves with evil powers in Chukchi and in Koryak folklore. In Kerek folklore they are called *kala*.

Kemchuga (local Russian) An edible root.

Kerker (Chukchi) A woman's fur overalls, as pronounced by males, that are put on through a neck opening. Used over the entire area of the Chukchi and Kamchatka Peninsulas. The *kerker* consists of two separately sewn combinations that fited in one another and have fur facing in opposite directions. The combination has a trouser-like lower section that reaches to the knees.

Ketstsy (Chukchi) The Chukchi woman's clothing as pronounced by females. See *kerker*.

Khozyain morya (local Russian) [lit. "The ruler of the sea"]. In Eskimo folklore a mythical personage possessing all the riches of the sea and regulating the hunt for sea animals.

Kichiga (Koryak) An inhabited locality in the Koryak National *Okrug*.

Kigi (Eskimo) See Arakamchechen.

Kigmak (Eskimo) A cape in the Bering Strait near Naukan.

Kilykil (Koryak) A meal of cooked fish and berries.

Kimchiga (local Russian) See kemchuga.

Kirilka (local Russian) Traditional Itelmen meal. It consists of boiled brains, fish, or more recently potatoes, fresh crowberries, and rendered seal blubber.

Kopylya (local Russian) Struts uniting the runners of a sled with its top planks and also each other (i.e. horizontal or arched pieces uniting the struts or stanchions).

Kray (Russian) A large administrative and territorial unit which supersedes *oblast* and *rayon* districts. The literal meaning of *kray* in the Slavic languages is "edge," indicating the original pioneering nature of *krays*. There were nine *krays* in the territory of the former Soviet Union, six in Russia and three in Kazakhstan.

Kruglaya sopka (local Russian) A volcano in Kamchatka where according to Itelmen legends the great Tylval dwelled.

Kukashka (local Russian) See *kukhlyanka*.

Kukhlyanka (local Russian) A long, pullover outer fur garment. The combination of inner and outer fur shirts has no appropriate equivalent in English. The term suggests a "cocoon," but this is too farfetched to apply to clothing of this type.

Kukul (local Russian) A fur-lined sleeping bag.

Kulki (local Russian) A river in Kamchatka.

Kuspuk (Eskimo) An Eskimo woman's shirt or dress often made so that an infant may be carried piggyback-style inside. The *kuspuk* is made in lightweight fabric, typically calico, edged with furs and ribbons.

Kyflyavik (Eskimo) A mountain and locality of a former Eskimo settlement in the vicinity of Cape Chaplino.

Kygmik (Eskimo) A cape in the Bering Strait.

Lakhtak (local Russian) A bearded seal (*Erignathus barbatus*). The largest true seal normally found in the seas adjacent to Alaska, Kamchatka and Chukotka.

Lemeshina (local Russian) Chewing tobacco made of a mixture of *makhorka*, an inferior type of tobacco, and ashes of burned toadstools.

Letatelnye amulety [wing objects] Among the Eskimos wooden or bone figures of birds serving as amulets which help a person surmount great distances. In tales such amulets make it possible for a person to fly like a bird.

Lopatka (local Russian) A cape in Kamchatka.

Lorino (Russian) Russian adaptation of the name of a Chukchi settlement Luren.

Maktak (Eskimo) A word for whale blubber.

Makarsha (local Russian) An edible root with an astringent taste.

Mamrugagnak (Eskimo) A mountain in the Mamrokhpak *rayon* of the Chukchi Peninsula.

Mamrokhpak (Eskimo) A former Eskimo settlement and locality on the eastern shore of the Bering Strait.

Mamrugagnak (Eskimo) A mountain in the Mamrokhpak *rayon* of the Chukchi Peninsula.

Mangak (Eskimo) A mountain chain north of Sireniki on the Chukchi Peninsula.

Mayak (local Russian) A locality and inhabited place at the mouth of the Tigil River in Kamchatka.

Morda (Russian) A fish trap made of twigs.

Morskaya kapusta (Russian) (lit. "sea cabbage,") A seaweed which is used for food by coastal people.

Morskoy petushok (local Russian) Gray gurnard or sea horse (*morskoy konek*). An amulet made from the skin of a gray gurnard or sea horse. Also the likeness of the gurnard made of walrus ivory or wood. In the beliefs of the Eskimos such an amulet protected a hunter from various disasters during sea hunting or on protracted sea voyages.

Mukluks (Eskimo) The Eskimo *mukluks* (boots) are made with *oogruk* (bearded seal hide) soles, and uppers of wild deer, *nerpa* (ringed seal), or reindeer hides.

Muktuk (Eskimo) An Eskimo delicacy consisting of the outer skin layers of a whale. It is eaten fresh, frozen, cooked or pickled.

Nakolenniki (Russian, pl.) Knee-guards. Fur bands tied around the knees to protect the hunter from freezing and injury during hunting in the mountains or on ice.

Napakutak (Stolbovoye) A lake and inhabited place of Eskimos near the eastern coast of Kamchatka.

Narty (Russian, pl.) Sleds used throughout the Russian north for travel with harnessed dogs or deer.

National okrug (Russian) One of the territorial designations through which the autonomy of small nationalities is effected. In the 1920s and 1930s, national okrugs were established in krays and oblasts within the territory of the former Russian Soviet Federated Socialist Republic.

Naukan (Eskimo) A populated place on Cape Dezhnev in the Bering Strait. Until 1958 an ethnic group of Naukan Eskimos from ten communities lived there. After that year separate families of Naukans lived in the Chukchi settlements of Nunyama, Lorino, Uelen, and others.

Nepay (Itelmen, Koryak) A misfortune.

Nerpa (local Russian) A ringed seal (*Phoca hispida*). See *Akiba*.

Netelin (Chukchi) An inhabited place on the Chukchi Peninsula.

Neten (Chukchi) An inhabited place in Chukchi *rayon*. A Chukchi adaptation of the old Eskimo toponym *Natuk*.

Nunagmitsy (Eskimo) A clan in Nunak village.

Nunak (Eskimo) (lit. "village") A locality and inhabited place near Naukan (Cape Dezhnev, Russia).

Nyuvity (Koryak) Werewolves that played the role of malicious beings in Koryak folklore.

Oblast (Russian) An administrative district not containing an autonomous area. The 1977 constitution of the former USSR assigned the resolution of problems concerning *oblast* and *kray* administrative and territorial units to the governments of each former Soviet republic. Where an autonomous area peopled mainly by a national minority exists as an enclave within the district, the proper term is *kray* (q.v.). The governing body of an *oblast* was the *Oblast Soviet Deputies of the Working People*. (See also *autonomous oblast*).

Okrug (Russian) A tier of councils termed the *Okrug Soviet* in the early days of the Soviet Union. *Okrug* roughly corresponded to that of

the old *volost* or rural district in which both village soviets and city soviets were represented. (See also *national okrug*).

Olyutorka (local Russian) A small pouch containing a bead or bone amulet. It was worn by Eskimos around the neck to protect them from "evil spirits."

Oogruk (Eskimo) The bearded seal. Its prized hide is used in the making of *mukluk* soles. *Oogruk* oil is quite mild and the meat is dried for winter use. It is considered to be superior to that of other seal species.

Ostavka (Russian) Locality in which a killed animal is temporarily left.

Ostol (Russian) A stick or pole with a bone or iron point used in braking a sled to a stop.

Parka (Russian) Russian name for the outer fur garment adapted by Alaskan Eskimos. It is usually made of a heavy weight fabric shell lined with fur. The hood is lined with fur, usually wolverine, wolf, fox or polar bear, to keep the face warm in a cold wind.

Peegti (Chukchi) Stars in the *Aqua* constellation. With the appearance of the constellation, approximately in December, the Reindeer Chukchi celebrated the *Peegti* festival dedicated to the winter slaughter of reindeer.

Pesets (Russian) The arctic fox (*Alopex lagopus*) is found in treeless coastal areas of Chukotka and Alaska. Seasonally its fur color changes from blue to white.

Plashch (local Russian) The same as *dozhdevik* (q.v.).

Plavnik (Russian) Driftwood, which is extensively used by northern peoples for construction of dwellings, frames of boats, and firewood.

Podorozhniki (Russian) Fare of dried meat or fish prepared especially for journeys.

Podpolozki (Russian) Lining of sled runners made of bone or flat fillets of antler.

Poljg (local Russian) A sleeping platform inside a dwelling [a semi-subterranean house, a *yaranga*]. It consists of deer hides stretched over a wooden frame.

Poplavok (Russian) A floater among the coastal dwellers of Chukotka and Kamchatka. It consists of a tightly sewn and inflated stomach of a *nerpa* (ringed seal). It was tied to the harpoon with a long leather thong and kept the location of a harpooned sea mammal in sight of the pursuers.

Postel (Russian) [Bed, bedding]. The long-furred winter hide of a reindeer used by the natives of northern Siberia as bedding.

Pygpygh (Chukchi) A bag or floater made of seal skin (Igor Krupnik 1996, pers. com.).

Pyp (Chukchi) A complete fur-skin of a seal filled with rendered walrus blubber. The coastal dwellers of the Chukchi Peninsula prepared such *pyps* for their own future needs as well as for barter for reindeer products with the nomads of the interior.

Pyzhik (local Russian) The pelts of a young deer, a fawn with no antlers which has a soft, luxuriant fur and thin, delicate hide. *Pyzhik* is used in the very finest clothing and for children's coverings. At present, headgear is also made of such pelts.

Rayon (Russian) An administrative district of an *oblast* (q. v.). *Rayon* is an urban area, formed mainly on lines of economic production, comprising a number of adjacent villages and hamlets, together with such small cities and urban settlements as are found in the area. *Rayon* is normally smaller in size than *oblast'*, *kray* or *okrug*. The geographic size and population of the *rayon* differ according to local circumstances. It may thus comprise any number of villages with and without one or more urban settlements called *poselki* or small towns.

Red fox The red fox (*Vulpes vulpes*) is the subject of many stories, songs, fables, and parables. The red fox is a common species in most of northern Russia and North America.

Rekinniki (Koryak) A settlement on the West coast of Kamchatka.

Repalgyn (Chukchi) Walrus hide used by the coastal inhabitants of Chukotka for covering the wooden frames of their boats [umiaks] and the roofs of their dwellings. It is also used for making thongs attached to harpoons for sea-mammal hunting.

Rovduga (local Russian) Rawhide, suede or chamois made of deerskin.

Sanluk (Eskimo) A cliff and locality on the Asiatic shore of the Bering Strait.

Sapluk (Eskimo) A cliff and locality on the Chukchi Peninsula coast of the Bering Strait.

Saplyk (Eskimo) A small mountain stream entering the sea near the settlement of Sireniki.

Sarana (local Russian) Tubers of the red lily. In the past they were used by the peoples of Kamchatka as food. The tubers were eaten raw; when dried they were ground into flour.

Sayak (Eskimo) A ritual feast among Asiatic Eskimos.

Sedanka (local Russian) An inhabited locality in Kamchatka.

Selnitsa (local Russian) Among the Kamchadals a special, usually wooden, trough used for the preparation of *tolkusha* (q.v.). The form of the *selnitsa* was elongated and, earlier, round.

Shaman (Russian from Tungus) An anthropologist's name for a village spiritual leader or healer. According to the religious ideas of many northern peoples, the shaman was a person chosen by spirits and other supernatural creatures to fill the role of an intermediary between people and the other world.

Shisha (local Russian) A crowberry.

Siklúk (Eskimo) (lit. "meat pit," "meat storehouse"). Island and old settlement in the Strait of Senyavin. The people of this settlement were transferred to Unazik (Chaplino) in 1941.

Sireniki (Eskimo) An Eskimo settlement south of Providentiya Bay.

Snowshoes (Russian) Snowshoes were most often 60-70 cm. long and 15-25 cm. wide. They were used by settled coastal Chukchi and Eskimos during seal hunting to walk over the uneven ice surface. Reindeer Chukchi of the interior used them in driving reindeer herds when the snow was not particularly deep. In the literature snowshoes are known as "claws." Chukchi *velvyegyrn* means "raven claws" in literal translation. The Eskimo name for snowshoes is *u'alvyyag'yk*.

Stoybishche (local Russian) A temporary camp of nomadic reindeer herders.

Sushila (Russian) Drying racks. A sawhorse or trestle used for drying *baydaras* and also for drying of freshly removed pelts of animals.

Svistun (local Russian) In the folklore of the peoples of the Chukchi and Kamchatka Peninsulas, a werewolf that brings ill luck to people.

Tannit (Eskimo) A foreigner, newcomer, stranger, enemy [*tannity* pl.]. The term, in various phonetic variants, was widespread among the native peoples of the Chukchi and Kamchatka Peninsulas. The Asiatic Eskimos used the term to describe the bellicose bands of nomads, the Chukchi and Koryaks who came from the south of the Chukchi and Kamchatka Peninsulas with the goal of seizing reindeer from the nomads in the northern part of the Chukchi Peninsula. According to folklore, the peaceful settlements of the coastal dwellers, Eskimos and Chukchi, were subject to such raids. The *tannits* took the products of sea-mammal hunting, and sometimes also prisoners.

Tigil (local Russian) A river in Kamchatka.

Tigyt (Chukchi) Chukchi skis covered with deer *kamus*.

Tolkusha (Koryak, Itelmen) A meal prepared from chopped tubers and stalks of a number of edible plants mixed with fish, blubber, berries, and others.

Torbazy (local Russian, pl.) A footgear of seal skin or *kamus*. Winter *torbazy* were made of thick skins, usually from the lower part of reindeer legs, with the fur outside. Summer *torbazy* were made of the rawhide of seal throats.

Tukhtak (Eskimo) A strip of raw walrus meat sewn into a piece of walrus hide with blubber. *Tukhtak* was prepared by the Eskimos and stored for winter and early spring consumption.

Tungaki (Eskimo, pl.) Spirits, werewolves, who, according to Eskimo beliefs, brought various disasters to people – starvation, disease, death. In Chukchi folklore the *tungaki* are called *kele*; in Koryak, *kele* or *ninvity*; in Kerek, *kala*.

Tykygak (Eskimo) An old settlement in Alaska where journeys of Asiatic Eskimos and Coastal Chukchi ended. This place name is often mentioned in the folklore of the Asiatic Eskimos and Chukchi.

Tykyvak (Eskimo) An Eskimo word for the cracking of the earth caused by freezing.

Tynagyrgyn (Chukchi, lit. "dawn," "heavenly deities") In Chukchi beliefs, Tynagyrgyn managed the earthly doings of people and punished them for negligence and bad deeds. In legends, Tynagyrgyn is described as a simple hunter, head of household, married, with children, occupying a dwelling with household goods.

Tygagruk (Eskimo) A cliff in the vicinity of Naukan.

Uelen (Uvelen) A large Chukchi settlement on the Bering Strait in the vicinity of Cape Dezhnev.

Ukigaluk (Eskimo) A cliff near Cape Dezhnev in the Bering Strait.

Ukivok (Eskimo) A small island in the Bering Strait (King Island; belongs to the U.S.).

Uksik (Eskimo) Rocks in the vicinity of Sireniki.

Ulu (Eskimo) A traditional fan-shaped Eskimo women's knife used for cutting, chopping and scraping.

Umiak (Eskimo) An Eskimo skin-covered boat. It has a wooden frame covered with walrus hide. The *umiak* is much larger than a kayak and can carry many hunters to sea.

Umkuglyuk (Eskimo) A promontory in the Bering Strait.

Umuktak (Eskimo) An enclosure of snow built around an ice hole to protect the fisher from the winter wind.

Unazik (Chaplino) An Eskimo settlement on Cape Chaplino. Its inhabitants have been relocated to Tkachen Bay.

Uten A temporary seasonal camp of nomads near Mitkulin village, Chukotka.

Versta (Russian) Pre-Soviet system of measurement in Russia. One *versta* is equal to 3,500 English feet or 1,060 meters.

Vybivalka (local Russian) A beater or beating stick. A curved blade of reindeer antler used to remove snow from fur clothing and footgear.

Yanrakinot (local Russian) The Russian adaptation of the name of the Chukchi settlement of Yanrakynnot ("Stronghold") on the shore of Senyavin Strait.

Yaranga (Chukchi) A barrel-roofed dwelling in the form of a tent with a frame of poles covered with reindeer hides among the nomads or with walrus hides among the coastal dwellers. The *yarangas* of the coastal dwellers had a complex frame of beams, girders, and thin poles.

Yarar (Chukchi) A drum. The Chukchi did not have a specific drum for a shaman. The drum, *yarar* or *yaar*, was a family and household sacred object. Each family had a drum, and using it at the time of certain festivals was obligatory for all members of the household, men and women. To the Chukchi a *yarar* was only a musical instrument.

Yukola (local Russian) Split and sun-dried salmon. The fish were split lengthwise; the head and backbone were fed to dogs and the meat of the two sides joined by the tail was reserved for human consumption. The fish were dry-cured on a *yukolnik*. *Yukola* was prepared for winter consumption.

Zagon (Russian) A fenced area with one end open; it was used in hunting wild deer.

Zakol (Russian) The same as *zapor* (q.v.).

Zapor (Russian) A device for catching fish in rivers. It consists of a compact fence reaching across a river (or partly so). Fish traps were placed in the openings of the fence.

Zemlyanka (Russian) The semi-subterranean wooden dwellings of Eskimos, Coastal Chukchi, and Koryaks. The dwellings were made of driftwood, whale bones [ribs], turf, and stone.

Zhenskiy nozh (local Russian) [Woman's knife] A knife with a semi-oval blade inserted into a wooden holder that fits the palm of the hand, used by women in their domestic work. The same as the Eskimo *ulu* (q.v.).

Zhirnik (Russian) An oil lamp made of stone or, more rarely, of clay. It was used for light, heat or cooking. The wick was made of twisted fur. Fat of different animals was used as fuel for the *zhirnik*.

BIBLIOGRAPHY

Arron, W.

1957   Aspects of the Epic in Eskimo Folklore. In: *Anthropological Papers of the University of Alaska*, vol. 5, no. 2.

Arutyunov, S. A.

1988   Koryak and Itelmen: Dwellers of the Smoking Coast. In: *Crossroads of Continents: Cultures of Siberia and Alaska* by W. Fitzhugh and A. Crowell (eds.). Washington DC: Smithsonian Institution Press.

Baranikov, I.

1940   *Amamkhailymylo* (Koryak Tales about Ememkut). Edited and translated into Russian by S. N. Stebnitsky. Leningrad.

Belikov, L. V.

1956   *Osnovnye vidy ustnogo narodnogo tvorchestva chukchey.* (Primary Types of the Oral Traditions of the Chukchi.) Leningrad: AKD.

1960   *K kharacteristike ustnogo narodnogo tvorchestva chukchey* (The Characteristics of the Oral Traditions of the Chukchi). Leningrad: *UZ LGPI im. A. I. Gertsena*, vol. 167.

1961   *Lymnylte* (Lymnylte). Compiled by L. V. Belikov. (In the Chukchi language). Magadan.

1965   *Geroicheskiye skazaniya chukchey* (The Heroic Legends of the Chukchi). Leningrad: *UZ LGPI im. A. I. Gertsena*, vol. 269.

1967   *W. G. Bogoras kak sobiratel i issledovatel chukotskogo folklora* (W. G. Bogoras as a Collector and Investigator of Chukchi Folklore). Leningrad: *UZ LGPI im. A. I. Gertsena*, vol. 353.

Boas, Franz

1888 [1964]   *The Central Eskimo.* 6th Annual Report of the Bureau of American Ethnology for the Years 1884-1885, pp. 399-669. Washington, D.C.: U.S. Government Printing Office. Reprinted by the University of Nebraska Press, 1964, with an introduction by Henry B. Collins.

Bogoras, Waldemar

1900   *Materialy po izucheniyu chukotskogo yazyka i fol'klyora* (Materials for Studies of the Chukchi Language and Folklore). St. Petersburg.

1901   The Chukchi of Northeastern Asia. *American Anthropologist* 3: 80-108.

1902   Folklore of Northeastern Asia as Compared with that of Northwestern America. *American Anthropologist* 4: 577-683.

1909   The Chukchee. *The Jesup North Pacific Expedition 7*. Memoirs of the American Museum of Natural History. Leiden-New York (Reprinted 1975, New York: AMS Press).

1910   Chukchee Mythology. *The Jesup North Pacific Expedition* 8(1). Memoirs of the American Museum of Natural History. Leiden-New York (Reprinted 1975, New York: AMS Press).

1913   The Eskimo of Siberia. *The Jesup North Pacific Expedition* 8(3). Memoirs of the American Museum of Natural History. Leiden/New York (Reprinted 1975, New York: AMS Press).

1917   Koryak Texts. In: *PAES*, vol. 5.

1931   *Klassovoye rassloeniye u chukchey-olenovodov* (Class Divisions Among the Chukchi Reindeer Herders). *Sovetskaya etnografiya*, no. 12.

Carpenter, Edmund S.

1973   *Eskimo Realities*. New York: Holt, Rinehart and Winston.

Chaussonnet, Valerie (ed.)

1995   *Crossroads Alaska: Native Cultures of Alaska and Siberia*. Arctic Studies Center, National Museum of Natural History, Smithsonian Institution, Washington, D.C.

Dikov, N. N.

1969   *Drevniye kostry Kamchatki i Chukotki* (Ancient Fire Places [found] in Kamchatka and Chukotka). Magadan.

1971   *Naskalnye Zagadki Drevney Chukotki: Petroglify Pegtymelya* (Mysteries in the Rocks of Ancient Chukotka: Petroglyphs of Pegtymel). Moscow: Nauka.

1994   The Paleolithic of Kamchatka and Chukotka and the Problem of the Peopling of America. *Anthropology of the North Pacific Rim*. Edited by W. W. Fitzhugh and V. Chaussonnet. Washington, D.C. Smithsonian Institution Press. Pp. 87-96.

Dolitsky, Alexander B. and Henry N. Michael (eds.)

1997   *Fairy Tales and Myths of the Bering Strait Chukchi*. Juneau: Alaska-Siberia Research Center, Publication no. 9.

2000   *Tales and Legends of the Yupik Eskimos of Siberia*. Juneau: Alaska-Siberia Research Center, Publication no. 11.

Fitzhugh, William W. and Aaron Crowell (eds.)

1988   *Crossroads of Continents: Cultures of Siberia and Alaska*. Washington, D.C.: The Smithsonian Institution Press.

Fitzhugh, William W., and Valerie Chaussonnet (eds.)

1994   *Anthropology of the North Pacific Rim*. Washington D.C.: Smithsonian Institution Press.

Hughes, Charles

1984 Asiatic Eskimo: Introduction. *Handbook of North American Indians*. Volume 5 (Arctic). Edited by D. Damas. Washington, D.C.: Smithsonian Institution. Pp. 243-261.

Holtved, E.

1951 The Polar Eskimo; Language and Folklore. *Meddelelser om Grønland*, vol. 152, no. 1 and 2.

Ivanov, S. V.

1954 *Materialy po izobrazitel'nomu iskusstvu narodov Sibiri XIX–nachala XX vekov* (Components of the Graphic Arts of Siberian Peoples During the Nineteenth and Beginning of the Twentieth Century). Moscow-Leningrad.

Jochelson, Waldemar

1904 The Mythology of the Koryak. In: *American Anthropologist*, vol. 5, no. 4.

1908 The Koryak. *The Jesup North Pacific Expedition 6. Memoirs of the American Museum of Natural History*. Leiden and New York. Reprinted in 1975 by AMS Press, New York.

1915 *Obraztsy materialov po aleutskoy zhivoy starine* (The Patterns of the Components of the Living Past of the Aleutians). In: *Zhivaya Starina*, vol. 3, Petrograd.

Kerttula, Anna M.

2000 *Antler of the Sea*. Ithaca: Cornell University Press.

Krasheninnikov, Stephan P.

1755 *Opisaniye zemli Kamchatki* (The Description of Kamchatka), volumes I, II. St. Petersburg.

1972 *Exploration of Kamchatka*. Portland: Oregon Historical Society. (Translated with introduction and notes by E. A. P. Crownhart-Vaughan from *Opisaniye Zemli Kamchatki*, 1755).

Krupnik, Igor

1993 *Arctic Adaptations: Native Whalers and Reindeer Herders of Northern Eurasia*. Hanover and London: University Press of New England.

Levin, M. G. and L. P. Potapov

1964 *The Peoples of Siberia*. Translated by Scripta Technica, Inc. English translation edited by Stephen Dunn. Chicago and London: University of Chicago Press (Orig. Publ. as *Narody Sibiri*, 1956, Moscow: AN SSSR).

Historical-Ethnographic Atlas of Siberia, translated by Henry N. Michael. Editor of English edition is Igor Krupnik. Washington, D.C. To be published by the Smithsonian Institution Press (Orig. Publ. *Istoriko-ethnograficheskiy atlas Sibiri*, 1961, Moscow-Leningrad: AN SSSR). Unpublished manuscript.

Meletinsky, E. M.

1958   *Geroi volshebnoi skazki* (A Hero of the Magical Fairy Tale). Moscow: Nauka.

1963   *Proiskhozhdeniye geroicheskogo eposa* (The Origin of the Heroic Epos). Moscow: Nauka.

Menovshchikov, G. A.

1958   *Eskimosskiye skazki* (Eskimo Fairy Tales). Magadan.

1969   *Eskimosskiye skazki i legendy* (Eskimo Fairy Tales and Legends). Magadan.

1970   *Nekotoryye tipy yazykovykh kontaktov u aborigenov Krainego Severo-Vostoka Azii* (Some Types of Language Contacts Among the Aboriginal Population of the Northern Northeast Asia). Moscow: UP MSK.

1974   *Skazki i mify narodov Chukotki i Kamchatki* (Fairy Tales and Myths of the People of Chukotka and Kamchatka). Moscow: Nauka.

Mitlyanskaya T. and I. Karakhan

1987   *Novaya zhizn drevnikh legend Chukotki* (New Life of the Ancient Legends of Chukotka). Magadan.

Nungak Z. and E. Arima

1969   *Eskimo Stories—Unikkaatuat.* Ottawa.

Propp, Vladimir Ya.

1945   *Chukotskiy mif i gilyatskiy epos* (Chukchi Mythology and Giliak Epos). NBLTU.

Rubtsova, E. S.

1954   *Materialy po yazyku i folkloru eskimosov* (Reports on the Language and Folklore of the Eskimos). Moscow-Leningrad.

Sergeyev, D.

1955   *Nekapitalisticheskiy put razvitiya malykh narodov severa* (The Non-Capitalistic Development of the Small Peoples of the North). Moscow-Leningrad.

1970   *Motivy eskimosskogo fol'klora v drevneberingomorskoy skulpture* (Motives of the Eskimo Folklore in the Ancient Sculptures of the Bering Sea Region). *Folklor i etnografiya.* Leningrad.

Skorik, Peter Ya.

1957   *Ustnoye tvorchestvo narodov Severo-Vostoka Azii* (Oral Traditions of the Peoples of Northeast Asia). *Na Severe Dalnem.* Magadan.

1968   *Kerekskiy yazyk* (The Kerek Language), in *Yazyki narodov SSSR*, vol. V, Leningrad 1968, pp. 310-333.

Stebnitsky, S. N.

1938   *Lymnylo* (*Lymnylanskiye skazki*). Lymnylo (Lymnylan Tales) (In the Koryak language). Leningrad.

1941   *Koryakskiy istoricheskiy folklor i zarozhdayushchayasya koryakskaya literatura* (Koryak Historical Folklore and the Incipient Koryak Literature). Manuscript. In: IE AN SSSR, f. K-1, op. 1, no. 175.

Tynetegyn, F.

1940   *Skazki Chauchu* (Chauchu Fairy Tales). Leningrad.

Van Deusen, Kira

1999   *Raven and the Rock: Storytelling in Chukotka.* Seattle: University of Washington Press.

Vdovin, I. S.

1948   *Iz istorii obschestvennogo stroya chukchey i koryakov* (History of the Social Structure of the Chukchi and the Koryaks). *Sovetskaya Etnografia*, no. 3.

1965   *Ocherki istorii i etnografii chukchey* (History and Ethnography of the Chukchi). Moscow-Leningrad: Nauka.

Voblov, I. K.

1959   Eskimo Ceremonies (translated by Charles Hughes). *Anthropological Papers of the University of Alaska* 7(2): 71-90.

Volodin, A. P.

1995   *Itelmeny* (Itelmens). Prosveshcheniye, Sankt Petersburg.

Voskoboynikov, M and G. Menovshchikov (eds.)

1959   *Skazki narodov severa* (Tales of the People of the North). Moscow-Leningrad.

Worth, D.

1961   *Kamchadal Texts Collected by Jochelson.* Mouton.

Yatgyrgyn, V.

1963   *Lymnylte yegyskykyn* (Fairy Tales of the North). Magadan.